MILLER'S
Picture
PRICE GUIDE

WHAT'S IN ANTIQUES BULLETIN?

⋆ **The most comprehensive Auction Calendar**

⋆ **The only weekly Fairs Calendar**

⋆ **More news and prices than in any other antiques trade publication**

Plus ART PRICES INDEX
AUCTION PREVIEWS • BOOK
REVIEWS • AUCTION REPORTS
FAIRS NEWS • TALKING THE TRADE
EXHIBITIONS • IN FOCUS

Subscribe NOW and receive a **FREE** subscription to THE ANTIQUES FAIRS GUIDE ~ a publication that any serious fair goer cannot afford to miss!!

A year's subscription costs just £39.50 (46 issues + 2 free Fairs Guides) — Europe £60, USA/Canada £80, Australia £120.

Plus: Special offer for art collectors: subscribe to our monthly specialist art issue for only £14.00.
Other subscription deals available for furniture, silver & ceramics, and collectables.
Please phone for details.

MILLER'S
Picture
PRICE GUIDE

Consultants
Judith and Martin Miller

General Editor
Madeleine Marsh

1994
Volume II

MILLER'S PICTURE PRICE GUIDE 1994

Created and designed by
Millers
The Cellars, High Street,
Tenterden, Kent, TN30 6BN
Tel: 0580 766411

Consultants: Judith & Martin Miller

General Editor: Madeleine Marsh
Editorial and Production Co-ordinator: Sue Boyd
Editorial Assistants: Gail Jessel, Sue Montgomery, Marion Rickman, Jo Wood
Production Assistant: Gillian Charles
Advertising Executive: Elizabeth Smith
Advertising Assistants: Sally Marshall, Liz Warwick
Index compiled by: DD Editorial Services, Beccles
Design: Stephen Parry, Jody Taylor, Darren Manser

First published in Great Britain in 1993
by Millers, an imprint of
Reed Consumer Books Limited,
Michelin House, 81 Fulham Road,
London SW3 6RB
and Auckland, Melbourne, Singapore and Toronto

© 1993 Reed International Books Limited

A CIP catalogue record for this book is
available from the British Library

ISBN 1-85732-177-4

Bromide output by Final Word, Tonbridge, Kent
Illustrations by G.H. Graphics, St. Leonards-on-Sea
Colour origination by Scantrans, Singapore
Printed and bound in England by Bath Press, Avon

KEY TO ILLUSTRATIONS

Each illustration and descriptive caption is accompanied by a letter code. By reference to the following list of Auctioneers (denoted by *) and Dealers (•) the source of any item may be immediately determined. In no way does this constitute or imply a contract or binding offer on the part of any of our contributors to supply or sell the goods illustrated, or similar articles, at the prices stated. Advertisers in this year's directory are denoted by †.

A • Alma Gallery Ltd, 29 Alma Vale Road, Bristol.
Tel: 0272 237157

AdG • Adam Gallery, 13 John Street, Bath.

AG * Anderson & Garland (Auctioneers), Marlborough House, Marlborough Crescent, Newcastle-upon-Tyne.
Tel: 091 232 6278

AH * Andrew Hartley, Victoria Hall, Little Lane, Ilkley, W. Yorks.
Tel: 0943 816363

ALL * Allen & Harris, Bristol Auction Rooms, St John's Place, Apsley Road, Clifton, Bristol, Avon.
Tel: 0272 737201.

ALT • The Alton Gallery, 72 Church Road, Barnes, London SW13.
Tel: 081 748 0606

AMC • Anna-Mei Chadwick, 64 New Kings Road, London SW6.
Tel: 071 736 1928

ARE • Arenski, Stand 107, Gray's Antique Market, 58 Davies Street, London W1. Tel: 071 499 6824

BCG †• Betley Court Gallery, Betley, Nr. Crewe, Cheshire.
Tel: 0270 820652

Bea * Bearnes, Rainbow, Avenue Road, Torquay, Devon.
Tel: 0803 296277.

BLD †• Blond Fine Art, Unit 10, Canalside Studios, 2-4 Osman Road, London N1.
Tel: 071 739 4383.

Bne †• Bourne Gallery Ltd, 31/33 Lesbourne Road, Reigate, Surrey.
Tel: 0737 241614

Bon * Bonhams, Montpelier Galleries, Montpelier Street, London SW7.
Tel: 071 584 9161.

BOU/ †• Boundary Gallery, 98 Boundary Road,
Bou London NW8.
Tel: 071 624 1126

BRG †• Brandler Galleries, 1 Coptfold Road, Brentwood, Essex.
Tel: 0277 222269

BSG • Brian Sinfield Gallery, Grafton House, 128 High Street, Burford, Oxon.
Tel: 0993 82 2603

BuP • Burlington Fine Paintings Ltd., 12 Burlington Gardens, London, W1.
Tel: 071 734 9984

BW †• Betty Williams Gallery, The Gallery, Tyr Eglwys, Tredunnock, Usk, Gwent.
Tel: 063349 301

BWe * Biddle and Webb, Ladywood Middleway, Birmingham.
Tel: 021 455 8042

C * Christie, Manson & Woods Ltd., 8 King Street, St James's, London SW1.
Tel: 071-839 9060.

C(D) * Christie's Dublin, 52 Waterloo Road, Dublin 4.
Tel: 3531 6680 585

C(S) * Christie's Scotland Ltd., 164-166 Bath Street, Glasgow
Tel: 041 332 8134

Cae • Caelt Gallery, 182 Westbourne Grove, London W11.
Tel: 071 229 9309

C(Am) * Christie's Amsterdam, Cornelis Schuystraat 57, 107150 Amsterdam.
Tel: (3120) 57 55 255

CAS • Castle Gallery, 1 Thickthorn Mews, Kenilworth, Warwickshire.
Tel 0926 58727

CAT †• Catto Animation, 41 Heath Street, London NW3.
Tel: 071 431 2892

CBL • Chris Beetles Ltd, 8 & 10 Ryder Street, St James's, London SW1.
Tel: 071 839 7551

CCA • CCA Galleries, 8 Dover Street, London W1.
Tel: 071 499 6701

CE/Ce †• Century Gallery, 100/102 Fulham Road, London SW3.
Tel: 071 589 9468

CFA • Cooper Fine Arts, 768 Fulham Road, London SW6.
Tel: 071 731 3421

CG †• Coltsfoot Gallery, Hatfield, Leominster, Herefordshire.
Tel: 056882 277

CGa †• Cobham Galleries, 65 Portsmouth Road, Cobham, Surrey.
Tel: 0932 867909

Ch • Churzee Studio Gallery, 17 Bellevue Road, London SW17.
Tel: 081 767 8113

ChG • Charterhouse Gallery Ltd., 14 Birds Heath, Leighton Buzzard, Beds.
Tel: 0522 523 379

CLB • Cleveland Bridge Gallery, 8 Cleveland Place East, Bath, Avon.
Tel: 0225 447885

CNY * Christie, Manson & Woods International Inc, 502 Park Avenue, New York, NY 10022, USA.
Tel: (212) 546 1000 (including Christie's East)

CSG • Church Street Gallery, Stow-on-the-Wold, Glos.
Tel: 0451 831698

CSK * Christie's South Kensington Ltd, 85 Old Brompton Road, London SW7.
Tel: 071 581 7611

DA * Dee Atkinson & Harrison, The Exchange Saleroom, Driffield, East Yorks.
Tel: 0377 43141

DM • David Messum Fine Paintings Ltd, The Studio, Lords Wood, Marlow, Bucks.
Tel: 0628 486565

DN * Dreweatt Neate, Donnington Priory, Donnington, Newbury, Berks.
Tel: 0635 31234

Dr †• Driffold Gallery, 78 Birmingham Road, Sutton Coldfield, West Midlands.
Tel: 021 355 5433

E * Ewbank, Welbeck House, High Street, Guildford, Surrey.
Tel: 0483 232134

EAG • Equus Art Gallery, Sun Lane, Newmarket.
Tel: 0638 560445

EG †• Ealing Gallery, 78 St Mary's Road, London W5.
Tel: 081 840 7883

EW • East West, 8 Blenheim Crescent, London W11.
Tel: 071 229 7981

F †* Francis Fine Art Auctioneers, The Tristar Business Centre, Star Industrial Estate, Partridge Green, Horsham. Sussex.
Tel: 0403 710567

FAO • Fine Art of Oakham, 4/5 Crown Walk, Oakham, Leics.
Tel: 0572 755221

FdeL †• Fleur de Lys Gallery, 227A Westbourne Grove, London W11.
Tel: 071 727 8595

FI • Francis Iles, Rutland House, La Providence, High St, Rochester, Kent.
Tel: 0634 843081

FWA * F W Allen & Son, Central Salerooms, 15 Station Road, Cheadle Hulme, Cheshire.
Tel: 061 485 4121

G6 • Gallery 6, 6 Church Street, Broseley, Shrops.
Tel: 0952 882860

GAK †• G. A. Key, 8 Market Place, Aylsham, Norwich, Norfolk.
Tel: 0263 733195

Gan †• Gandolfi House, 211-213 Wells Road, Malvern Wells, Hereford & Worcs.
Tel: 0684 569747

GCP • Graham Clarke (Prints) Ltd, White Cottage, Green Lane, Boughton Monchelsea, Maidstone, Kent.
Tel: 0622 743938

GeC • Gerard Campbell, Maple House, Market Place, Lechlade-on-Thames, Glos.
Tel: 0367 52267

GL • George Large Gallery, 13-14 Margaret Place, Woburn, Beds.
Tel: 0525 290658

GOE • Gallery One Eleven, 111 High Street, Berkhamsted, Herts.
Tel: 0442 876333

GPS • Glasgow Print Studio, 22 King St, Glasgow.
Tel: 041 552 0704

HaG • The Hart Gallery, 23 Main street, Linby, Nottingham.
Tel: 0602 638707

HAR * William Hardie Ltd, 141 Regent Street, Glasgow.
Tel: 041-221 678

HCH * Hobbs & Chambers, Market Place, Cirencester, Glos.
Tel: 0285 4736

HFA †• Haynes Fine Art, The Bindery Gallery, 69 High Street, Broadway, Worcester
Tel: 0386 852649

HG • Holland Gallery, 129 Portland Road, London W11.
Tel: 071 727 7198

HI †• Hicks Gallery, 2 Leopold Road, Wimbledon, London SW19.
Tel: 081 944 7171

HN • Heather Newman Gallery, Milidduwa, Mill Lane, Cranham, Glos.
Tel: 0452 812230

Ho/HO • Angela Hone, The Garth, Mill Road, Marlow, Buckinghamshire.
Tel: 0628 484170

HOK * Hamilton, Osborne & King. 4 Main Street, Blackrock, Co. Dublin.
Tel: 010 3531 2885011

HOLL†* Holloways, 49 Parsons Street, Banbury, Oxon.
Tel: 0295 253197

Hou • Houldsworth Fine Art, 46 Bassett Road, London W10.
Tel: 081 969 8197

HSS * Henry Spencer and Sons, 20 The Square, Retford, Notts.
Tel: 0777 708633

JA • Jenny Asplund Fine Art.
Tel: 0372 469437

JAF †• John Adams Fine Art Ltd, 200 Ebury St, London SW1.
Tel: 071 730 8999

JAP • John A Pearson Antiques, Horton Lodge, Horton Rd, Horton, Nr Slough, Berks.
Tel: 0753 682136

JBA • John Bonham, Murray Feely Fine Art, 46 Porchester Road, London W2.
Tel: 071 221 7208

JD/JDG• John Denham Gallery, 50 Mill Lane, London NW6.
Tel: 071 794 2635

JGG • Jill George Gallery, 38 Lexington Street, London W1.
Tel: 071 439 7343

JMI • John Mitchell & Son, 160 New Bond St, London W1.
Tel: 071 493 7567

KG • Kilvert Gallery, Ashbrook House, Clyro, Hay-on-Wye, Hereford.
Tel: 0497 820831

KHG • Kentmere House Gallery, 53 Scarcroft Hill, York.
Tel: 0904 656507

L * Lawrence Fine Art Auctioneers, South Street, Crewkerne, Somerset.
Tel: 0460 73041

LA • Llewellyn Alexander (Fine Paintings) Ltd, 124-126 The Cut, Waterloo, London SE1.
Tel: 071 620 1322

LANG * Langlois, Westaway Chambers, Don Street, St Helier, Jersey.
Tel: 0534 22441

LAY * David Lay, ASVA, Auction House, Alverton, Penzance, Cornwall.
Tel: 0736 61414

LG • Lamont Gallery, 65 Roman Road, London E2.
Tel: 081 981 6332

LH †• Laurence Hallett.
Tel: 071 798 8977

LT * Louis Taylor Auctioneers & Valuers, Britannia House, 10 Town Road, Hanley, Stoke on Trent.
Tel: 0782 214111

LW * Lawrences Auctioneers, Norfolk House, 80 High Street, Bletchingley, Surrey.
Tel: 0883 743323

M * Morphets of Harrogate, 4-6 Albert Street, Harrogate, North Yorks.
Tel: 0423 502282.

MAA • Maak Gallery, Blackburn Rd, London NW6.
Tel: 071 372 4112

MAT * Christopher Matthews, 23 Mount Street, Harrogate, Yorks.
Tel: 0423 871756.

MBA 4 Miles Buildings Fine Art & Antiques, 4 Miles Buildings, (off George St), Bath.

McE • The McEwan Gallery, Glengarden, Ballater, Aberdeenshire.
Tel: 03397 55429

Mer • Merz Contemporary Art, 62 Kenway Rd, London SW5.
Tel: 071 244 6008

MJA • Marian & John Alway, Riverside Corner, Windsor Road, Datchet, Berks.
Tel: 0753 541163

MJW Mark J West, Cobb Antiques Ltd, 39a High Street, Wimbledon Village, London SW19.
Tel: 081 946 2811

Mon • Montpelier Studio, 4 Montpelier St, London SW7

MSW * Marilyn Swain, Westgate Hall, Westgate, Grantham.
Tel: 0476 68861

MT • Martin Tinney Gallery, 6 Windsor Place, Cardiff.
Tel: 0222 641411

NBO • Nicholas Bowlby, Owl House, Poundgate, Uckfield, East Sussex.
Tel: 0892 653722

NZ †• Nina Zborowska, Damsels Mill, Paradise, Painswick, Glos.
Tel: 0452 812460

OG • O'Shea Gallery, 89 Lower Sloane St, London SW1.
Tel: 071 730 0081

OLG †• On Line Gallery, 76 Bedford Place, Southampton, Hants.
Tel: 0703 330660

OM †• Omell Galleries Ascot, 55 High Street, Ascot, Berks,
Tel: 0344 873443

OSG • Oliver Swann Gallery, 170 Walton Street, London SW3.
Tel: 071 584 5684

P   * Phillips, Blenstock House, 101 New Bond Street, London W1.
Tel: 071 629 6602.

P(L) * Phillips Leeds, Hepper House, 17a East Parade, Leeds.
Tel: 0532 448011

P(S) * Phillips, 49 London Road, Sevenoaks, Kent.
Tel: 0732 740310.

P(Sc) * Phillips Scotland, 65 George Street, Edinburgh.
Tel: 031 225 2266, and
207 Bath Street, Glasgow.
Tel: 041 221 8377

PaHG • Paul Hayes Gallery, 71 High Street, Auchterarder, Perthshire.
Tel: 0764 62320

PCA • Peter Cardiff Fine Art.
Tel: 071 736 8998

PCh * Peter Cheney, Western Road Auction Rooms, Western Road, Littlehampton, Sussex.
Tel: 0903 722264/713418

**PHG/ †• Peter Hedley Gallery, 10 South Street,
PH**   Wareham, Dorset.
Tel: 0929 551777

PN †• Piano Nobile Fine Paintings, 26 Richmond Hill, Richmond upon Thames, Surrey.
Tel/fax: 081 940 2435

Pol • Polak Gallery, 21 King Street, St. James's, London SW1.
Tel: 071 839 2871

RB • Roger Billcliffe Fine Art, 134 Blythswood St, Glasgow.
Tel: 041 332 4027

RID * Riddetts of Bournemouth, 26 Richmond Hill, Bournemouth, Dorset.
Tel: 0202 555686.

RMG • Roy Miles Gallery, 29 Bruton Street, London W1.
Tel: 071 495 4747

S   * Sotheby's, 34-35 New Bond Street, London W1.
Tel: 071 493 8080.

S(NY) * Sotheby's, 1334 York Avenue, New York NY 10021, USA.
Tel: 212 606 7000

S(S) * Sotheby's Sussex, Summers Place, Billingshurst, Sussex.
Tel: 0403 783933

SAV †• The Saville Row Gallery, 1 Saville Row, Alfred Street, Bath.
Tel: 0225 334595

SBG • Stephen Bartley Gallery, 62 Old Church Street, London SW3.
Tel: 071 352 8686

SD • Sara Davenport (Fine Paintings), 206 Walton Street, London SW3.
Tel: 071 225 2223

SH • Sheila Hinde Fine Art, Idolsford House, Nr Billingshurst, Sussex.
Tel: 0403 77576

SWO * Sworders, G E Sworder & Sons, 15 Northgate End, Bishops Stortford, Herts.
Tel: 0279 51388

TAY * Taylors, Honiton Galleries, 205 High Street, Honiton, Devon.
Tel: 0404 42404

TBJ • T B & R Jordan (Fine Paintings), Aslak, Aislaby, Eaglescliffe, Stockton-on-Tees, Cleveland.
Tel: 0642 782599

TCG • The Catto Gallery, 100 Heath Street, Hampstead, London NW3.
Tel: 071 435 6660

TCHG • The Cedar House Gallery, Ripley, Surrey.
Tel: 0483 211221/224571

TES • Tesser Galleries, 106 Heath Street, Hampstead, London NW3.
Tel: 071 794 7971

TFA • Turtle Fine Art, 30 Suffolk Parade, Cheltenham, Glos.
Tel: 0242 241646

Tho • Thompson Gallery, 38 Albemarle Street, London W1.
Tel: 071 499 1314

TLG • The Loquens Gallery, The Minories, Rother Street, Stratford upon Avon, Warwickshire.
Tel: 0789 297706

ULG †• Upton Lodge Galleries, 6 Long Street, Tetbury, Glos.
Tel: 0666 53416. Also at Avening House, Avening, Tetbury.

VCG †• Vicarage Cottage Gallery, Preston Road, Northshields.
Tel: 091 257 0935

VDG †• Valentyne Dawes Gallery, Church St, Ludlow.
Tel: 0584 874160

Wa • Waterman Fine Art Ltd, 74a Jermyn Street, London SW1.
Tel: 071 839 5203

WBS * Welsh Bridge Salerooms, Welsh Bridge, Shrewsbury, Shropshire.
Tel: 0743 231212

WFA †• Wimbledon Fine Art, 41 Church Road, Wimbledon Village, London SW19.
Tel: 081 944 6593

WG • Walker Galleries, 6 Montpelier Gardens, Harrogate, Yorks.
Tel: 0423 567933

WILD • Wildenstein Gallery, 147 New Bond St, London W1.
Tel: 071 629 0602

WL * Wintertons Ltd, Lichfield Auction Centre, Wood End Lane, Fradley, Lichfield, Staffs.
Tel: 0543 263256

WO †• Wiseman Originals Ltd, 34 West Square, London SE11.
Tel: 071 587 0747

Wyk • Wykeham Gallery, 51 Church Road, London SW13.
Tel: 081 741 1277

CONTENTS

HOW TO USE THIS BOOK

Miller's Picture Price Guide provides a comprehensive pictorial survey of pictures available at auction and through dealers over the past year.

The Guide covers pictures of every style, medium and value, ranging from Old Master paintings worth millions of pounds to contemporary prints for less than £100.

For easy reference, pictures have been classified by subject matter. If all you know about your picture is that it portrays a ship, turn to the Marine section, where you can compare and contrast your work with the examples illustrated. Each section is arranged chronologically, so that you can see how a particular subject has been treated over the centuries, how styles have changed and how prices compare.

To find an artist by name, consult the index at the back of the book. This will refer you to the page or pages where the artist's work is illustrated.

Where possible, each individual entry includes the name, dates and nationality of the artist, the title, medium and measurements of the picture, the price range and finally, the source code, which refers to the auction house or gallery the picture came from. The full list of codes and sources (catalogued in alphabetical order) is to be found on page 5.

Price ranges have been carefully worked out to reflect the current state of the market place. While Miller's offers a carefully considered GUIDE to prices, no publication could attempt to provide a definitive price list. As with any other business, the art market changes and prices fluctuate depending on both internal and external factors. The generally high prices across the board in the 1980s have, in many instances, been replaced by considerably more modest ones in the recession-hit 1990s.

No two pictures are ever identical. Each work will have its own individual value depending on artist, subject, rarity, quality and condition. Other important considerations include whether a picture is fresh to the market, where it is being sold (a top London gallery and a country antiques shop will obviously have very different pricing systems), how many people want to buy it, and what they are prepared to spend.

In addition to details about individual pictures, Miller's provides reports on the state of the market place, information about specific artists and movements, and general advice about pictures for the dealer and collector. Many sections come complete with a helpful introduction and, in addition, information boxes are to be found throughout the guide.

The aim of all Miller's publications is to be as comprehensive as possible. With each edition of the Picture Price Guide, new sections are included and different areas covered. If you, the reader, have any information to add or suggestions for topics that we might use in future editions, please let us know. We rely on feedback from the people who use the Guide to help us to make it as useful and interesting as possible.

HOW TO RESEARCH YOUR PAINTING

Miller's Picture Price Guide provides a first step to finding out about your picture. By consulting the guide, you will learn generally about paintings, artists and all the most recent prices, but how can you take your investigations further?

Researching a picture is like any other piece of detective work. You begin with the evidence: the picture itself. Examine it closely for clues and try to compile the following information:

1. Title and/or subject matter: note down a short description of what the work portrays.
2. Medium: what material is it made from? Oil on canvas, watercolour, etc.
3. Measurements: measure the work in both inches and centimetres.
4. Signature, date marks and labels: is there a signature or any other written information on the front or back of the picture, or perhaps on the frame? Transcribe everything you find, including exhibition labels, lot numbers, and anything else that might be significant.

Having gathered as much information as you can from the object itself, it is time to look for circumstantial evidence. If the picture is inherited, are there any family stories associated with it? Write these down and collect together any related letters, bills or papers. If you purchased the object from a shop or at auction, see if you can discover who originally owned it or if it came from a house of any importance. The story of the people who owned a picture (known as the provenance) can in some instances be almost as important as that of the artist who painted it, and if a work belonged to a famous person or collection, its value can significantly increase. Once you have compiled all this information about your picture's known history, you can begin the serious business of investigation. There are many courses you can follow, many expert witnesses you can consult and, best of all, most of them are free.

Auction houses provide a free identification and valuation service if you take an object or a photograph along to their front desk and many dealers are happy to have a quick look at an object, free of charge.

Most museums will give opinions (but not valuations) on works brought in by the public. Some have weekly consultation days while with others you simply need to make an appointment. Try to pick the museum that best suits your picture: if you are researching a marine painting, perhaps the National Maritime Museum in Greenwich could assist with your enquiries; if you are looking into a portrait, try the National Portrait Gallery in London.

In addition to seeking expert advice, there are many libraries, archives and specialist resource centres open to the public, where you can investigate the history of your picture and its artist. Begin by contacting your local reference library to find out where your nearest art history library is, and take it from there.

12

PICTURE FRAMES

It is not only an Old Master picture that can be valuable, but also the old frame that surrounds it. However, it is only comparatively recently that picture frames have begun to be collectable items in their own right. In the 1950s, according to one London dealer, a man with a horse and cart would come round the West End galleries collecting old gilt picture frames to be burnt off for their gold and in the 1960s, when severe Scandinavian styles were in fashion, many wonderful 19thC frames were simply junked. Today, there are dealers who specialise in antique frames - Bonhams, Phillips, and Christie's (London) all hold sales devoted to frames, and in December 1989 a fine English frame made a record £33,000 at auction.

At picture sales, the catalogue will often mention if a painting is being offered in its original frame. Contemporary frames can provide an added insight into the picture and the culture that produced it. James Bruce-Gardyne, frame expert at Christie's, explained to Millers that 17thC Spanish pictures were often housed in poorly lit churches, but the solid frames with their brilliant high relief carving reflected the candlelight and enabled the pictures to be seen from a distance. In contrast, Dutch frames from the same period, simple, square and black, were designed for the home, as were more domestic pictorial subjects, their dark, restrained style mirroring the tastes of a Protestant nation.

Many of the finest craftsmen and cabinet makers (Adam, Chippendale, etc.) all produced designs for frames, although little is known about the frame makers themselves. Before the 19thC, frames were only rarely stamped, signed or labelled, making it very difficult to identify individual makers. A frame can, however, often be labelled or inscribed with valuable details about the history and provenance of a picture and should always be checked for information.

Only comparatively few Old Master pictures are likely to come up for auction in their original surround. Frames tended to follow the fashions of the day and would often be replaced when a picture changed hands or its owners redecorated their living room. Some of the best 18thC French frames in the National Gallery, for example, were specifically made for the Dutch 17thC pictures that they now surround.

Irrespective of the pictures they contain, frames can be wonderful examples of period craftmanship and carving and are often valuable in their own right. One of the most important factors in determining their worth is whether or not they maintain their original gilding. 'People have a habit of going over a frame with a damp rag and being amazed that the gold disappears,' one London frame dealer told Miller's sadly. Frames should never be washed, only dusted and if any restoration is required then always seek the advice of a gilder or a frame expert.

ACKNOWLEDGEMENTS

The publishers would like to acknowledge the great assistance given by our consultants:

Antiques Trade Gazette	17 Whitcomb Street, London, WC2.
Chris Beetles	8 & 10 Ryder Street, St James's, London SW1.
Bonhams	Montpelier Street, Knightsbridge, London SW7 1HH.
Nicholas Bowlby	Owl House, Poundgate, Uckfield, East Sussex.
John Brandler	Brandler Gallery, 1 Coptfield Road, Brentwood, Essex.
Simon Carter	Polak Gallery, 21 King Street, St. James's, London SW1.
Anna-Mei Chadwick	64 New King's Road, Parsons Green, London SW6.
Christie's	8 King Street, St James's, London SW1Y 6QT.
Vanessa Finn	Gagliardi Design & Contemporary Art, 507-509 King's Road, London SW10.
Martin Gallon	Sotheby's, 34-35 New Bond Street, London W1A 2AA.
David Gilbert	Driffold Gallery, The Smithy, 78 Birmingham Road, Sutton Coldfield, West Midlands.
Tony Haynes	Haynes Fine Art, The Bindery Gallery, 69 High Street, Broadway, Worcester.
Peter Hedley	10 South Street, Wareham, Dorset.
David Messum	The Studio, Lordswood, Marlow, Bucks.
Dr. Allan Smith	Fine Art of Oakham Ltd, 4 High Street, Oakham, Rutland.

LANDSCAPES

Many of the works included in the following sections devoted to landscape are in watercolour, a medium dear to the heart of the British, and appears in profusion throughout the current Guide.

When Secretary of State for National Heritage, Peter Brooke, himself a watercolour collector, opened the 'World of Drawings and Watercolours' Fair at the Park Lane Hotel, London, in January 1993, he described the year as an 'annus mirabilis' for the watercolour. He was right. Watercolour exhibitions and shows were held up and down the country, headed at the beginning of the year by 'The Great Age of British Watercolours 1750-1880' at The Royal Academy - which proved an enormous hit with the public and provided a unique opportunity to view some of the finest examples of the genre from private and public collections across the world.

The considerable media interest stimulated by this and other events certainly served to raise the profile of the watercolour, emphasising its importance as an art form in its own right, and not just as the poor relation of oil painting. But what of the watercolour market itself?

According to watercolour dealer and expert, Nicholas Bowlby: 'The watercolour market continues to be underpinned by knowledgeable and enthusiastic collectors, whilst at the same time attracting new buyers because of the medium's accessibility and affordability. I believe this market has survived the recession remarkably well,' he adds. 'Dedicated collectors might slow down when times are hard, but they will always buy, and in recent months the market has definitely improved.'

For Bowlby who, like many watercolour dealers, began his career as a private collector, the great appeal of the medium lies in its enormous range. 'The field offers immense variety, quality and quantity. With so many artists and so many subjects, you never feel that you have reached an end. It is a very good area for the new buyer and you can have enormous fun. Whereas with oils you have to spend hundreds of pounds before you can begin to get something good, you can buy a small pencil sketch for as little as £10 upwards. After that, the sky is the limit and there is something for every pocket and every taste.'

Watercolour collectors collect in many different ways; some specialise in a particular period, painter or group of artists, others might concentrate on a specific subject or geographical location. 'Inevitably, it's a medium that lends itself particularly well to landscape,' concludes Bowlby. 'Watercolours give you the freedom to work outside, paint quickly, and capture the scene on the spot. Watercolour is a natural art form for the landscape painter.'

15th-17th Century

Tobias Verhaecht (1561-1631)
Flemish
Mountainous River Landscape with Travellers
Oil on panel
20 x 27in (51.5 x 68cm)
£59,000-70,000 *S(NY)*

Pieter Brueghel the Younger (1564- after 1636)
Flemish
Winter Landscape with Skaters
Bears signature Brueghel
Oil on panel
11in (28cm) diam.
£36,000-40,000 *S*

Attributed to Pieter van Bloemen, called Standard (1657-1720)
Dutch
A Rocky Wooded Italianate Landscape with Muleteers at a Pool, a Fortified Bridge beyond
Oil on canvas
32 x 43½in (81 x 110.5cm)
£7,500-8,500 *CSK*

Esaias van de Velde
(1587-1630)
Dutch
A Horsedrawn Ferry with
Passengers on a Canal,
Inscribed E. Van de
Velde/1617 on the old
mount, two shades of
black chalk, brown ink
framing lines,
10 x 17in (24.5 x 43cm)
£35,000-40,000 *C(Am)*

**Miller's is a price
GUIDE not a price
LIST**

---

*Boudewijns was active as
a designer of wall
tapestries in Brussels.*

Frans Boudewijns (1673-1744)
Flemish
An Arcadian Landscape with a Temple by a Bridge over
a River Signed, dated, inscribed f Baudewijns inventor
et fecit 1706, pen and brown ink, grey wash, brown ink
framing lines, watermark arms of Amsterdam
8 x 12½in (20 x 32cm)
£1,100-1,500 *C(Am)*

Dutch School (late 17thC)
A View of Stolwijk, near Gouda
Inscribed Stolwijk buite Gouda, black lead,
grey wash, black ink framing lines
5½ x 8in (14 x 20cm)
£350-400 *C(Am)*

Jan van Call (1656-1703)
Dutch
A View of the Village of St Goar with the
Castle Rheinfels along the River Rhine
Inscribed roundel, black lead, pen and grey
ink, watercolour, black ink framing line
4½in (11cm) diam.
£3,700-4,200 *C(Am)*

Maerten de Cock (active 1620-46)
Dutch
Extensive Landscape with a Farmhouse and
Peasants with their Animals
Signed and dated, M. Cock fc. 1625, pen and
brown ink over traces of black chalk on
vellum   5½ x 8in (13.5 x 20cm)
£2,800-3,300 *S*

Follower of Cornelis Huysman
(1648-1727)   Flemish
A rocky Italianate Landscape with a
Traveller and Washerwoman on a Track, a
Peasant and Donkey Crossing a Fortified
Bridge Beyond
Oil on panel   10 x 9in (25.5 x 23.5cm)
£700-800 *CSK*

Allaert van Everdingen (1621-75)
Dutch
Travellers on a Road near a Village, in
Winter
Monogram AVE, black chalk, pen and brown
ink, brown wash, brown ink framing lines
5 x 6in (12 x 15cm)   **£10,000-11,000** *C(Am)*

Giovanni Francesco Grimaldi (1606-80)
Italian
Landscape with a Lake, Two Figures on the
Shore and a Group of Trees to the Right
Pen and brown ink
19 x 26½in (48 x 67.5cm)
£4,300-5,000 *S(NY)*

Jan van Goyen (1596-1656)
Dutch
Winter Landscape with Skaters
Signed and dated IV Goien/162 (?)
Panel
5 x 10in (13.5 x 26cm)
£165,000-175,000 *JMI*

**Giovanni Francesco Barbieri, Il
Guercino** (1591-1666)
Italian
An Extensive Hilly Landscape with a
Huntsman and other Figures near Isolated
Trees below a Castle on a Ridge
Pen and brown ink, watermark crossed arrows
10 x 16in (25.5 x 41cm)
£8,400-9,000 *C(NY)*

Claude de Jongh (d.1663)
Dutch
Figures in a Ferry Boat Crossing a Small
River
Signed and dated lower left Jong(h) 1634
Oil on panel
7 x 9in (18 x 23cm)
£7,600-8,400 *S(NY)*

Attributed to Hendrick Mommers
(1623-93) Dutch
Southern Landscape with a Shepherd and
Women by a Well
Oil on canvas
15 x 16in (38.5 x 41cm)
£2,300-2,800 *S(S)*

Follower of Pandolfo Reschi (1643-99)
Polish
A Rocky Italianate Landscape with Banditti
Oil on canvas laid down on panel
19 x 24in (48 x 60cm)
£3,400-4,000 *CSK*

Circle of Herman Saftleven (1609-85)
Dutch
A View Along the River Rhine at Oberwesel
with the Ruins of Castle Schönburg on a Cliff
at the right, Castle Gutenfels and the Pfalz
on the left, the Town of Kaub beyond
Inscribed verso, black lead, brown wash, grey
ink framing lines   7½ x 10in (19 x 25cm)
£1,100-1,500   *C(Am)*

Attributed to Philips Wouwermans
(1619-68)   Dutch
Hilly Landscape with Riders Halted Beside a
Pool near a Cottage
Oil on canvas, in a carved and giltwood frame
20½ x 26¾in (52 x 68cm)
And another landscape in the style of
Wouwermans
£20,000-25,000   *S*

Gaspar van Vittel, called Vanvitelli
(1653-1736)   Dutch
A View of the Badia Fiesolana, with the
River Mugnone in the foreground
Inscribed Occhiali and N.91 on the mount,
red chalk, pen and brown ink, grey wash
8½ x 16in (21.3 x 41cm)
£23,000-28,000   *C(NY)*

18th Century

John White Abbott (1763-1851)
British
The Warren
Inscribed with title on mount, pen and grey
ink and grey washes   7¼ x 10½in
(18.5 x 26.5cm)   **£850-1,000**   *S*

Attributed to Pieter von Bemmel
(1685- 1754)   German
Travellers Walking Upon a Hillside Path
Leading Out of a River Valley
Oil on canvas
10½ x 12½in (27 x 32cm)
£2,100-2,500   *P*

Pieter Pzn. Barbiers (1749-1842)
Dutch
A Watermill in a Wood
Signed, black chalk, watercolour, black ink
framing lines
16 x 14in (40.3 x 36cm)   **£850-1,000**   *C(Am)*

**Jan Frans van Bloemen, called
Orizzonte** (1662-1749)
Flemish
Classical Landscape with Two Figures
Conversing by a Pool, a Villa in the
Background
Oil on canvas, within a painted oval
29¼ x 24in (74.3 x 61cm)
£20,000-25,000 *S(NY)*

Carel Frederik Bendorp I (1736-1814)
Flemish
A View of the Hoogendijk near the Oostpoort,
Rotterdam
Signed, inscribed and dated 1774, pencil, pen
and brown ink, brown wash, watermark
Strasburg lily
10¼ x 13½in (25.8 x 34.8cm)   **£800-900**   *C(Am)*

Giovanni Battista Busiri
(1698-1757)   Italian
A Pair of Landscapes with Fishermen
by Waterfalls
Both gouache
13¼ x 8½in (34 x 21.6cm)
£5,600-6,200 *S(NY)*

John Robert Cozens (1752-97)
British
Between Lauterbrunn and Grindelwald
Pen and grey ink and watercolour over traces
of pencil, on laid paper formerly numbered
18, a fragment of the original label attached
to backboard
9¼ x 14in (23.5 x 35.5cm)
£11,100-12,100 *S*

*This watercolour dates from Cozens' first
journey to Italy in the company of Richard
Payne Knight in 1776 when they travelled
through Switzerland.*

Alexander Cozens (c1717-86)
British
An Extensive Rocky Landscape with a
Goatherd and Goats by a Hollow in the
foreground
Signed on original mount, inscribed below
and on reverse in a period hand Alex[r] Cozens
The Father
9 x 12¼in (22.9 x 31.2cm)
£2,000-2,500 *Bon*

*Early in the 1770s Cozens, the most famous
drawing master of his day, was known to
have been working on a formula for landscape
composition called 'The Various Species of
Landscapes and in Nature', illustrated by 16
etchings now in the British Museum
collection.*

Johann Christoph Dietzsch (1710-69)
German
A Winter Landscape with Skaters on a River
Gouache on vellum
6¾ x 9in (17 x 22.3cm)
£1,600-2,000 *S(NY)*

English School (c1750)
An extensive downland Landscape, with
cattle grazing by a pond, and countryfolk by a
hamlet in a wooded copse
53¼ x 63in (13.5 x 16cm)　　**£14,000-16,000** *C*

English School (late 18thC)
White River, St Mary's, Jamaica
Inscribed, watercolour with pen and black
ink
15¼ x 12¾in (39 x 32.5cm)
£800-900 *S*

Circle of Frans de Paula Ferg (1689-1740)
Austrian
Riders Gathered by a Roadside Stop with
Classical Ruins, Before an Extensive
Landscape
Oil on Canvas
11¾ x 14¼in (31 x 36cm)
And the companion
Travellers Gathered beside a Wall
surmounted by a Classical Urn, on a Hill
Overlooking a River Valley
£4,300-5,000 *P*

Thomas Gainsborough, R.A. (1727-88)
British
Wooded Landscape with Drover and
Packhorses
Stamped in gold with artist's monogram,
watercolour and bodycolour over pencil on
laid paper, with a gold embossed border
11¼ x 13½in (28.3 x 34.2cm)
£90,000-100,000 *S*

Jean Grandjean (1752-81)
French
A Watermill by a Gate with Travellers
Resting by a Road in a Mountainous
Landscape
Inscribed 'Grandjean 1777', recto, signed,
dated and inscribed 'D'après La Nature, a
Poppert,/J:Grandjean 1777', verso, pencil,
grey and brown wash, brown ink framing
lines, watermark Pro Patria
9¾ x 7¼in (24.5 x 18.8cm)
£2,000-2,500 *C(Am)*

Hackert and Linck (18thC)
German/Swiss
Vue du Mont Blanc et une partie de Genève,
Vue de Genève pris depuis Saconex en Savoie
Hand coloured engravings, a pair
13½ x 18in (34.3 x 45.7cm)
£3,200-3,800 *DN*

Edward Haytley (active 1740-61)
British
Figures in a Rural Landscape, Farm
Buildings Beyond
Watercolour with some bodycolour
11 x 14¾in (28 x 38cm)
£750-850 *S*

Thomas Horner (1745-1844)
British
Jolly Picnickers by the Bow Main
Overlooking the Vale of Neath
Pen and grey ink with brown and blue
washes
11¾ x 18¾in (29.5 x 47.5cm)
£1,300-1,600 *S*

Warnaar Horstink (1756-1815)
Dutch
Fishermen and Promenaders on the Beach at
Katwijk aan Zee
Signed, dated 1787, inscribed, pencil, pen and
brown ink, black and grey wash, grey ink
framing lines
8 x 11¾ in (20.4 x 30.4cm)
£1,200-1,600   *C(Am)*

Johannes Christiaan Janson (1763-1823)
Dutch
A Winter Landscape with Skaters on the Ice
by a Village at Night
Pen and brown ink, watercolour, black ink
framing lines
10¾ x 13in (27.7 x 33.8cm)
£2,400-2,800   *C(Am)*

Thomas Jones (1742-1803)
British
Part of the Rocks on which the Citadel of
Cumae Stood
Inscribed, pen and black ink
7¾ x 11½in (19.5 x 29cm)
£900-1,000   *S*

*Cumae, near Naples, was the earliest Greek
settlement in Italy, famous for the
inaccessibility of its citadel. Jones visited
there on 14th November, 1778, together with
John 'Warwick' Smith and two other
Englishmen, Storace and Cobley.*

Julius Caesar Ibbetson R.A. (1759-1817)
British
Country Folk Resting with Cattle in a
Wooded, Hilly Landscape, with Calgarth Hall
and Lake Windermere Beyond
Signed and dated Julius Ibbetson pinx 1803
27 x 36in (68.6 x 91.5cm)
£21,000-26,000   *C*

Johannes Janson (1729-84)
Dutch
A Winter landscape with Skaters on a Canal,
and Drovers on the Towpath
Signed and dated J. Janson f 1783
Oil on panel
16½ x 22in (41.7 x 55.8cm)
£7,000-8,000   *S*

Circle of George Lambert (1700-63)
British
Figures and Cattle in a Classical Landscape
with Buildings beyond
Oil on canvas
40¼ x 50½in (102.3 x 128.3cm)
£7,500-8,500   *C(S)*

Follower of Andrea Loccatelli (1693-1741)
Italian
Goatherds resting by a Rocky Gorge
Oil on canvas
18 x 25in (47 x 63.5cm)
£3,000-4,000 *CSK*

Bernard Lens III (1682-1740)
British
The Spring Head Under Ochie Hole,
Somerset
Inscribed, pen and grey ink and grey washes
9¾ x 14in (24.5 x 35.5cm)
£380-450 *S*

Hendrik de Meijer (1737-93)
Dutch
A River Landscape with Fishermen, a Ruined
Castle and a Mill in the distance
Signed and dated 1771, pen and black ink,
Watercolour
9¾ x 13¼in (24.5 x 34cm)
£600-700 *C*

Manner of Isaac de Moucheron
(1667-1744)
Dutch
An Italianate Landscape with Figures on a
Garden Terrace overlooking a Town
Oil on canvas
39½ x 38½in (100.3 x 97.8cm)
£2,500-2,800 *CSK*

Circle of Alexander Nasmyth (1758-1840)
British
A Highland River Landscape with Figures on
a Track by a Footbridge
Oil on canvas
15 x 20in (38.2 x 50.8cm)   **£1,100-1,500** *CSK*

**Christian George Schutz
the Younger**   (1758-1823)
German
An Extensive Rhineland View with
Figures on a Path in the Foreground
Oil on canvas
24 x 40in (61 x 101.5cm)
£3,500-4,000 *P*

Paul Sandby, R.A.
(1725-1809)
British
Borrowdale
Pencil and watercolour
8½ x 11in (21.6 x 28cm)
£1,000-1,500 *C*

Roman School
(1st Quarter 18thC)
Landscape with Hunters
Oil on canvas
23 x 62in (58 x 157.8cm)
£9,500-10,500 *S(NY)*

William Taverner (1703-72)
British
Landscape with Figures, a
Temple in the
Distance
Watercolour with pencil
9 x 18¾in (23 x 48cm)
£2,000-2,500 *S*

*Taverner was an important figure in the
development of 18thC watercolour painting,
specialising in romantic and poetical
landscapes under the influence of Marco
Ricci. This watercolour demonstrates a
compositional device which Taverner often
used, of a road or river in the centre of the
picture leading the eye to a distant
architectural incident, usually a temple or
Italianate building.*

Charles Henry Schwanfelder (1774-1837)
British
An Extensive Mountainous River Landscape
with Anglers
33 x 44in (83.8 x 111.9cm)
£7,000-8,000 *C*

Patrick Nasmyth (1787-1831)
British
A Wooded Mountainous Landscape with
Figures on a Bridge
Oil on Board
17½ x 24in (44.8 x 61cm)
£11,600-12,600 *C*

**Attributed to Maximilian Joseph
Schinnagl** (1697-1792)
German
An Extensive Landscape with a Farmstead
by a Wooden Bridge
Oil on canvas
14 x 18in (35.6 x 45.7cm)
£2,100-2,500 *CSK*

Joseph Mallord William Turner R.A.
(1775-1851)
British
Landscape, c1795
Watercolour
6 x 7in (15 x 18cm)
£2,550-2,750 *NBO*

Francis Towne (1740-1816)
British
The Vale of St John, Cumberland
Signed F. Towne/delt 1786 No. 32, pen and
grey ink and watercolour
6 x 9½in (15.5 x 23.5cm)
£20,000-25,000 *S*

Willem Uppink (1767-1849)
Dutch
A pair of landscapes with a Peasant Family
Resting on a Country Road and a Sleeping
Rustic and his Dog Beneath a Tree by a
Stream, Other Country Folk Beyond
Oil on canvas   113½ x 69¾in (288.3 x 177.2cm)
£25,000-30,000 *S(NY)*

Hendrik Voogd (1768-1839)
Dutch
A River in a Ravine near Civita Castellana
Signed, dated and inscribed verso, pencil,
watercolour, black ink framing lines,
watermark Strasburg lily and D & C Blauw
23 x 18¼in (59 x 46.8cm)
£3,900-4,900 *C(Am)*

*Civita Castellana is situated by the famous
waterfalls at Terni, which was a favourite
subject of German artists of the period. Voogd
is also known to have painted the same
subject as a proof of his skill as an artist to
obtain a 3 year's grant from Holland to stay
in Italy.*

School of the Veneto (18thC)
Italian
Extensive Landscape with Travellers Along a
Path by Stream: A Triptych
Oil on canvas, laid down on board
48½ x 65in (123.2 x 164.6cm)
£11,500-12,500 *S(NY)*

Joseph Wright of Derby (1734-97)
British
The Bowder Stone, Borrowdale, Cumberland
Inscribed, Bowder Stone Borrowdale,
Watercolour over pencil
15½ x 21½in (39 x 55cm)
£5,600-6,600 *S*

19th Century

Over the past year it has sometimes seemed that the British Art Market has been principally sustained by the presence of Continental and foreign dealers in the salerooms. British buyers, however, have been showing a renewed interest in the decorative, traditional landscapes of the 19thC, but this interest tends to be extremely discerning. 'Such works usually have to have everything going for them,' comments the *Antiques Trade Gazette*, 'freshness to the market, unrestored condition, good subject, good size, and (above all) a good name to fetch a really substantial price.' In a reduced market, when fewer purchasers are buying less pictures, those prepared to spend want quality for their money, and as we have noticed when compiling this edition, considerably fewer landscapes appear to have sold at auction than when we were collating material for the 1993 edition.

Circle of John Absolon (1815-95)
British
Bringing in the Harvest
Watercolour
17 x 30in (43.2 x 76.2cm)
£700-800 *Bon*

Helen Allingham, R.W.S. (1848-1926)
British
A Harvest Field near Westerham, Kent
Signed and title inscribed on a contemporary label, pencil and watercolour with scratching out   9¾ x 7¼in (24.7 x 18.4cm)
£8,000-9,000 *C*

John White Abbott (1763-1851)
British
Ashton
Inscribed and dated on the reverse Ashton Sep.ᵗ 25 1819
Pen and brown ink, grey wash
7¼ x 10½in (18.4 x 26.7cm)
And a drawing titled 'From Cowick'
£800-1,000 *C*

Agostino Aglio (1777-1857)   Italian
La Vendemmia ai Colli Romani
Signed and dated 1827
Oil on canvas
28¾ x 42¾in (73 x 108.6cm)
£7,800-9,000 *C*

Rudolf von Alt (1812-1905)
Austrian
A View of Reichenau and Mount Ghans, Lower Austria
Signed and dated, Reichenau 8 Juni '876, Watercolour
8½ x 12¼in (21.5 x 31.5cm)
£27,000-35,000 *S*

Alt executed several views of Reichenau, which he visited on the way to the sanitorium at Treplitz. There he was to receive medical treatment for gout and arthritis, the latter brought on by sitting in cold churches and castles - an unfortunate but perhaps unavoidable penalty for an artist who specialised in architectural subjects as well as landscape.

American School (19thC)
A Hudson River View with Paddle Wheeler
and Sail Boats: A Sandpaper Picture
Charcoal and chalk on sandpaper
20½ x 25½in (52 x 64.8cm)
£550-650 *S(NY)*

American School (19thC)
Rural Landscape with Mountains, Broad
Meadows and Trees
A pair of paintings
Oil on canvas
20½ x 30¼in (52 x 76.8cm)
£1,300-1,600 *S(NY)*

Edward Arden (active 1881-89)
British
Durham Cathedral from the River
Signed
10¾ x 14¾in (27 x 37.5cm)
£200-300 *AG*

W. D. Barker (active 1870-80)
British
The Conway Valley
Signed, inscribed on a label on the
backboard, watercolour over traces of pencil
23½ x 35¼in (59.5 x 89.5cm)
£850-1,000 *S(S)*

John James Bannatyne, R.S.W.
(1836-1911)
British
On the Sands Near Culzean Castle, A
Fishing Village
A pair, both signed, one with title inscribed
on a label on the stretcher, oil on canvas
24¼ x 36¼in (61.5 x 92cm)
£2,000-2,500 *S*

Wilfred Williams Ball (1853-1917)
British
Windmills and Reeds
Signed and dated 1910, watercolour
9½ x 15in (24 x 38cm)
£500-580 *LH*

Edouard François Bertin (1797-1871)
French
Figures in a Classical Landscape
Signed and dated 1823 on the stretcher, oil
on canvas
8 x 12in (20.5 x 30.5cm)
£4,100-5,000 *S*

Gustav Barbarini (1840-1909)
Austrian
An Extensive Wooded Lake Landscape with a
Drover and Goats on a Track
Signed and dated 1885, oil on canvas
30½ x 40½in (77.5 x 102.8cm)
£1,700-2,300 *CSK*

William James Blacklock (1816-58)
British
A Miller's Homestead, Cumberland -
Westmorland, Lake District
Signed and dated 1854, inscribed on the
stretcher
15½ x 28½in (39.5 x 72.5cm)
£7,800-9,000 *Bea*

Circle of George Price Boyce, R.W.S.
(1826-97)
British
A Windmill on an Old Town Wall,
probably in Sussex
Watercolour
12½ x 9¼in (32 x 23.5cm)
£350-450 *S*

Arthur Blackburn (active late 19thC)
British
Harvest Time
Oil on canvas
20½ x 30in (52 x 76cm)
£7,000-8,000 *M*

Samuel C. Bird (d1893)
British
Love On The Rocks
Signed and dated 1879, oil on canvas
24 x 36¼in (61 x 92cm)
£1,400-1,800 *C*

John Blair (active 1885-1920)
Scottish
Rain it Raineth
Signed, watercolour
14¼ x 21¼in (36 x 54cm)
£950-1,050 *CGa*

Attributed to Walter Borridge
(19th/20thC)
American
Long's Peak and Mount Meeker, Estes Park,
Colorado, and View of Estes Park Colorado
A pair, signed with initials, dated 78, oil on
canvas
36 x 48in (91.5 x 122cm)
£3,300-5,000 *S(NY)*

Alfred de Breanski, Snr. (1852-1928)
British
The River Dee at Dusk
Signed, inscribed, oil on canvas
30 x 50in (76.5 x 127cm)
£14,000-15,000 *C*

*Amongst the many landscapes received for
inclusion in this guide, there were more
examples by Alfred de Breanski than any
other artist. As the examples illustrated
show, his pictures might vary in size, quality
and price, their basic theme remains the
same: Highland lochs, Welsh and Scottish
mountains - portrayed in an unashamedly
dramatic and romantic style, with rolling
clouds, roseate sunsets and theatrical
lighting. De Breanski established a
successful pictorial formula, and as saleroom
results demonstrate, his pictures are as much
in demand today as they were during the
artist's own lifetime.*

William Joseph Julius Caesar Bond
(1833-1928)
British
A Lily Pond
Signed, oil on board
12 x 18½in (30.5 x 47cm)
£1,200-1,600 *S*

Alfred de Breanski, Snr. (1852-1928)
British
Glencoe After a Storm
Signed, signed and inscribed with title on
reverse, oil on canvas
20 x 30in (51 x 76cm)
£7,000-8,000 *S*

Alfred de Breanski, Snr. (1852-1928)
British
The River Dee
Oil on canvas
8 x 12in (20 x 30.5cm)
£1,700-2,000 *SWO*

John Brett (1830-1902)
British
On the Foreshore
Signed and dated 1883, oil on canvas
15 x 30¼in (38 x 76.8cm)
£8,700-9,000 *C*

R** Bridgehouse (19thC)
British
Lakeland Landscape with Figures and Sheep
Signed and dated 1853, oil on canvas
10 x 14in (25.4 x 35.5cm)
£550-700 *DN*

Walter Wallor Caffyn (active late 19thC)
British
Old Lane, Minster, near Ramsgate
Signed and dated 1899, signed and inscribed
on reverse, oil on canvas
24¼ x 16in (61.5 x 41cm)
£2,500-3,000 *S*

William Callow (1812-1908)
British
A Figure on a Lane Before a Lake, in a Hilly
Landscape
Signed, colour washes
6¾ x 10½in (17 x 26cm)
£720-900 *P(L)*

*According to contemporary reports, William
Callow was an impressive physical specimen.
Tall, strong and handsome, he walked 5 miles
or more every day of his life, lived till the age
of 96, and held his final exhibition at 95. He
began his career early, too. At the age of only
11, he was employed by the artist and
engraver Theodore Fielding to colour prints
and by the time he was 20 he had moved to
Paris. There he shared a studio with Thomas
Shotter Boys and established a drawing class
whose highborn pupils included the family of
King Louis Philippe. Callow travelled
throughout Europe on walking/sketching
holidays, and during one ten-week trip to the
South of France he tramped 1,700 miles.
Returning to London in 1841, he became an
active member of the Old Water Colour
Society, exhibiting there every year until his
death, showing a total of over 1,500 works.*

John Mulcaster Carrick (active 1854-78)
British
Twickenham From the Ferry; and Hampton-
on-Thames
A pair, signed and dated J. M. Carrick 1886,
inscribed on reverse, oil on board
8 x 12in (20 x 30.2cm)
£4,900-5,900 *C*

Eugène Ciceri (1813-90)
French
Figures in a River Landscape
Signed and dated '48, oil on panel
9½ x 18¼in (24 x 46cm)
£3,800-4,500 *C(NY)*

Hugo Charlemont (b1850)
Austrian
Peasants on a Woodland Path
Signed and dated 1900, oil on canvas
32 x 26in (81 x 66cm)
£3,400-4,000 *S*

Charles Collins, R.B.A. (1851-1921)
British
Near Bude, Cornwall
Signed and dated 1895, oil on canvas
16 x 30in (40.6 x 76.2cm)
£850-1,200 *DN*

      John Sell Cotman (1782-1842)
      British
      A Cottage in Wales
      Pencil and watercolour
      6½ x 12¼in (16.6 x 31cm)
      £950-1,200 *C*

Edward William Cooke, R.A. (1811-80)
British
Cactus Opuntia on the Walls, Monaco
Signed and dated 1845, oil on paper laid on
board
9½ x 13½in (24.4 x 34.5cm)
£500-600 *S*

Salomon Corrodi (1810-92) Swiss
An Alpine Lake Scene
Signed and dated 1875, watercolour
17½ x 25in (44.5 x 64cm)
£2,600-3,000 *S*

David Cox, Jnr. (1809-85) British
Pen-y-Gwryd
Signed and dated 1858, pencil, watercolour
and gum arabic with scratching out
24¼ x 34¼in (61.6 x 87cm)
£2,100-2,800 *C*

Thomas Creswick (1811-69) British
Landscape with Cattle and Farm
Signed, watercolour
7 x 10½in (18 x 27cm)
£600-660 *LH*

David Cox, Snr. (1783-1859)
British
A Windy Day
Signed and dated 1855
10¾ x 14¾in (27 x 37cm)
£3,500-4,000 *HOLL*

Johann-Mongels Culverhouse (1820-92)
Dutch
A Winter Landscape with Figures by a
Farmstead
Indistinctly signed and dated JM
Culverhouse 1855, oil on canvas
16 x 21in (40.7 x 53.3cm)
£3,400-4,000 *CSK*

Dr William Crotch (1775-1847)
British
Clear Water Pond, Heathfield, Sussex
Signed and dated 1806 verso, watercolour
over pencil heightened with bodycolour
12 x 18¼in (30.5 x 46.6cm)
£380-450 *S*

Circle of Francis Danby, A.R.A.
(1793-1861) British
Evening Landscape with a Shepherd and his
Flock
Oil on canvas
17 x 13¼in (43 x 34cm)
£950-1,200 *S*

Danish School (mid-19thC)
An Extensive River Landscape with Figures
in the Foreground, a Castle Beyond
Oil on canvas
29 x 36¾in (74 x 93cm)
£3,500-4,000 *Bon*

Hippolyte Camille Delpy (1842-1910)
French
A Punt in a River Landscape
Oil on panel
9 x 15¾in (22.9 x 40cm)
£4,600-5,600 *C(NY)*

Eckenbrecher (19thC)
German
An Extensive Mediterranean Coastal Scene
with Figures upon a Terrace in the
foreground
Signed
30 x 22in (75 x 55cm)
£500-600 *HSS*

Johannes Bartholomäus Duntze
(1823-95)
German
A Winter Landscape with Figures Skating on
a Frozen River
Signed and dated J. Duntze 1860, oil on
canvas
31 x 44¾in (78.7 x 113.7cm)
£17,500-20,000 *C*

Seth Eastman (1808-75)
American
View in Texas - Miles North of San Antonio
Signed, inscribed and dated 1849
Watercolour and ink on paper
5 x 7¾in (12.7 x 19.7cm)
£3,800-4,500 *S(NY)*

*Seth Eastman was born in Brunswick, Maine
and was educated at the United States
Military Academy at West Point from 1824-
28. While there, he studied topographical
drawing - the accurate sketching of terrain so
fundamental to warfare as it was then fought.
Eastman specialised in landscape views and
Indian subject matter. Assigned to Texas, he
painted the Commanche Territory, producing
some of his best known works. Following
this, he began a project to illustrate a series of
books authorised by Congress, recording all of
the Indian tribes in the United States.
Eastman retired as a general and in 1867
became the first American artist
commissioned by Congress to paint Indian
and fort scenes to hang in the Capitol
Building.*

English Provincial School (early 19thC)
A View of St John's Church and The Crown
Inn, Groombridge, with Groombridge Place
Beyond
Oil on canvas
23½ x 35½in (59.5 x 90cm)
£3,600-4,500 *S*

Rasmussen Eilerson (1827-1912)
Danish
A Wooded River Landscape
Signed and dated 1886, oil on canvas
42½ x 56¼in (108 x 143cm)
£3,600-4,500 *S*

English School (c1830)
A Wooded River Landscape with a Man on a
Footbridge
Oil on panel
18 x 19½in (45.7 x 49.6cm)
£450-550 *CSK*

David Farquharson (1840-1907)
British
The Millionaire's Pool, River Don
Signed and dated 1897, oil on canvas
18 x 30in (46 x 76cm)
£2,700-3,500 *S*

Amelia Long, Lady Farnborough
(1772-1837)
British
Cattle Watering
Oil on board
17 x 13in (43.5 x 34cm)
£700-800 *S*

Joseph Farquharson, R.A. (1846-1935)
British
A Winter's Lane
Signed, oil on canvas
12 x 18in (30.5 x 46cm)
£6,200-8,200 *S*

*The Scottish landscape painter Farquharson
was renowned for his winter subjects,
snowstorms, snowy landscapes and winter
woods. Amongst his many admirers was the
painter and writer Walter Sickert. In an
article in the Daily Telegraph dated 7th April
1926, entitled 'Snow Piece and Palette Knife',
Sickert compared the artist favourably to
Courbet, commending his truth to nature and
commitment to telling a story. 'The subject is
the very raison d'être of the picture,' wrote
Sickert, describing one painting of a hunting
fox. 'Bloomsbury will perhaps tell you that it
is wrong to paint a live fox,' he added
sarcastically. 'Fortunately, the writ of
Bloomsbury does not run in the North of
Scotland.'*

John Faulkner (c1830-1888)
Irish
An Irish River Landscape with Figures and a
Goat in the Foreground
Signed and dated 1876, watercolour
heightened with touches of bodycolour
17 x 28¾in (45 x 73cm)
£1,500-2,000 *S(S)*

Myles Birket Foster, R.W.S. (1825-99)
British
San Giovanni, Lake Como
Signed with monogram, watercolour
heightened with white over traces of pencil
4¾ x 7in (12 x 18cm)
£3,300-4,000 *S*

Myles Birket Foster, R.W.S. (1825-99)
British
Bellagio, Lake Como
Signed with monogram, inscribed, pencil and
watercolour heightened with bodycolour
13¼ x 28in (33.2 x 71cm)
£28,000-35,000 *C*

*This watercolour was the first Continental
subject exhibited by Birket Foster at the Royal
Watercolour Society in 1867.*

Robert Fowler (1853-1926)
British
Thurstaston
A pair, signed, oil on canvas
12 x 16in (30 x 40cm)
£900-1,000 *BCG*

BETLEY COURT GALLERY

BETLEY, CREWE, CHESHIRE CW3 9BH
(nr M6)
Phone & Fax: (0270) 820652

*Quality oils & watercolours at
reasonable prices*

Historic Betley Court - setting of Godfrey Brown's *This Old House*

Ettore Roesler Franz (1845-1907)
Italian
A View of the Roman Campagna
Signed and inscribed Roma, watercolour
12 x 29in (30.5 x 74cm)
£4,700-5,700 *S*

Angelos Giallina (1857-1939)
Greek
On a Sunlit Country Path
Signed, watercolour
15 x 27¾in (38 x 70.5cm)
£3,000-3,500 *S*

Robert Gallon (1845-1925)
British
Evening
Signed, oil on canvas
20 x 30in (51 x 76cm)
£2,800-3,500 *S*

Arthur Anderson Fraser (1861-1904)
British
Fenland River in Flood
Signed with initials, dated 1888, watercolour
10¾ x 14¾in (27.2 x 37.5cm)
£450-550 *Bon*

William Alfred Gibson (1866-1931)
British
Les Laveuses Sur Le Loire
Oil
15½ x 19½in (39 x 49.5cm)
£6,000-6,500 *McE*

Giuseppe Giardiello (19th/20thC)
Italian
Italian Women Picking Flowers on the
Italian Coast
Signed, oil on canvas laid down on board
11 x 16in (28 x 41cm)
£1,500-2,000 *S*

Alfred Augustus Glendening
(active 1861-1903)
British
Sheep Grazing by a Loch
Signed with initials and dated '66, oil on
canvas
11½ x 26in (29 x 66cm)
£1,500-2,000 *S*

Circle of John Glover, O. W.S. (1767-1849)
British
An Italianate Wooded River Landscape with
Goats and Sheep Grazing on a Hilltop
Watercolour on paper laid down on canvas
29 x 43in (73.7 x 109cm)
£2,600-3,000 *C(S)*

Alfred Augustus Glendening
(active 1861-1903)
British
Harvesters by a River Bank on a Summer
Afternoon
Signed with initials and dated A.A.G. 90, oil
on canvas
18 x 32in (46 x 81.6cm)
£7,500-8,500 *C*

*Similar to de Breanski in style, subject matter
and feeling, Glendening is another popular
favourite whose works regularly appear in the
salerooms. Glendening worked as a railway
clerk before becoming a landscape painter,
and concentrated on views of Wales, Scotland
and the River Thames, producing decorative
if unchallenging works.*

Alfred Augustus Glendening
(active 1861-1903)
British
Iffley
Signed, oil on canvas
17½ x 12½in (44.5 x 32cm)
£2,500-3,000 *S*

John Glover (1767-1849)
British
An Alpine Landscape
Watercolour over traces of pencil
16¼ x 24in (41.5 x 61cm)
£3,600-4,400 *S*

Subsequent critics have been less than kind to this prolific, self-taught artist, son of a farmer and born with two club feet, who was a founder member, and later President, of the Old Watercolour Society. Ellis Waterhouse (see Bibliography) called him 'one of the most ... pedestrian painters of landscape both in oils and watercolours,' who produced a vast number of paintings until 'he mercifully emigrated to Tasmania in 1831,' while according to watercolour historian Colonel Grant: 'Technically Glover is one of the least distinguished painters that our School has produced.' In spite of this, Glover had a number of pupils and his style spawned many imitators both amateur and professional.

Johan Conrad Greive, Jnr. (1837-91)
Dutch
Punting on the Canal at Oudewater
Signed and dated 1867, watercolour
8¾ x 12in (22 x 31cm)
£900-1,000 *CSK*

Charles Harrington (1865-1943)
British
Horses Watering in a Meadow Below the Downs
Signed, watercolour over pencil
13 x 18½in (32 x 46cm)
£1,200-1,600 *S*

Edward Hargitt (1835-95)
British
Gathering Peat
Signed and dated 1872, watercolour
15½ x 23½in (39.4 x 59.7cm)
£1,200-1,800 *Bon*

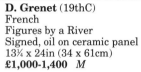

Thomas Hart (19thC)
British
The Lizard, Coastal Scene
Signed, watercolour
21½ x 14in (54.5 x 36cm)
£270-330 *BWe*

D. Grenet (19thC)
French
Figures by a River
Signed, oil on ceramic panel
13¼ x 24in (34 x 61cm)
£1,000-1,400 *M*

William Gosling (1824-83)
British
A Harvest Field
Signed, signed and inscribed on reverse, oil
on canvas
13 x 24in (33 x 61cm)
£1,900-2,400 *Bon*

Karl Heffner (1849-1925)
German
A Barge on a Stream
Signed, oil on panel
10 x 13in (25 x 33cm)
£2,300-2,800 *S*

Joseph Morris Henderson (1863-1936)
British
Children Picnicking by a Farmstead
Signed, oil on canvas
17½ x 23½in (45 x 60cm)
£4,000-4,500 *Bon*

Claude Hayes (1852-1922)
British
Haystack and Cart, Mortimer, Berkshire
Signed, watercolour
9½ x 13¾in (24 x 35cm)
£500-600 *S*

*Son of the marine painter Edwin Hayes,
Claude Hayes ran away to sea when his
parents tried to force him to become a
businessman. On his return home, his father
relented and Claude entered the Royal
Academy School, and also studied painting in
Antwerp. Beginning as a portrait painter, he
then turned to landscape and moved from oils
to watercolours. A very rapid worker, he was
fond of wide stretches of moorland dominated
by the sky, capturing his subject in a fresh
and open air style.*

Karl Adam Heinisch (1847-1923)
German
A Rural Scene
Signed and dated München 1881, oil on panel
5 x 9½in (13 x 24cm)
£4,900-5,500 *S*

James Watterston Herald (1859-1914)
British
A Village Roup
Signed, watercolour heightened with
bodycolour
13½ x 17½in (34.2 x 43.5cm)
£1,900-2,400 *C(S)*

William Hoggatt (19thC)
British
A Viaduct
Signed, oil on canvas
36¾ x 44in (93 x 112cm)
£2,900-3,400 *S*

Richard H. Hilder (active 1836-51)
British
Milking Time
Oil on panel
11¾ x 16in (29.7 x 40.6cm)
£3,000-3,500 *C*

Abraham Hulk, Jnr. (1851-1921)
British
By the Stile
Signed, oil on canvas
35½ x 27½in (90.5 x 70cm)
£750-850 *Bea*

Peter Richard Hoare (1772-1849)
British
A Villa at Corbyn Head, Torquay, Devon
Inscribed Torquay, pen and grey ink and
brown washes
7½ x 21in (19 x 53.5cm)
£550-750 *S*

William Samuel Jay (1843-1933)
British
In the Beechwood
Signed, oil
38 x 54in (96.5 x 137cm)
£3,700-4,000 *Bne*

Jessie Joy (active 1843-69)
British
Richmond, Yorkshire from the River Swale
Signed and dated 1853, pencil and
watercolour with touches of white
heightening
18½ x 26¾in (47 x 68cm)
£1,100-1,400 *C*

J. M. Hilson (19thC)
British
Elizabeth Castle with Horse and Cart in
foreground
Signed, watercolour
7 x 10½in (18 x 27cm)
£220-260 *LANG*

Impressionist School (c1900)
Seascape
Oil on canvas
22 x 16in (56 x 41cm)
£850-950 *JBA*

Johan Barthold Jongkind (1819-1891)
Dutch
La Côte de St André
Signed, inscribed, and dated 30 Oct 1878,
watercolour over pencil heightened with
white on squared paper
5¼ x 10¼in (13.3 x 26cm)
£2,700-3,200 *CNY*

Henry John Kinnaird (active 1880-1908)
British
A Farm at Burpham
Signed, watercolour heightened with white
20¼ x 14¾in (51.4 x 37.5cm)
£1,700-2,200 *C*

Willem de Klerk (1800-76)
Dutch
A Cart on a Woodland Path
Signed, oil on panel
13¾ x 15¾in (35 x 55cm)
£4,700-5,700 *S*

John Knox (1778-1845)
British
Lismore Castle, Ireland
Bears another signature and date, oil on
canvas
25 x 35in (63.5 x 89cm)
£6,000-7,000 *S*

Hermanus Koekkoek (1815-82)
Dutch
An Estuary Scene with Figures
Signed and dated 1834, oil on canvas
20 x 25in (50.9 x 63.6cm)
£17,500-22,000 *C*

David Law (1831-1902)
British
The Thames near Goring
Signed and dated '74, watercolour
13 x 19¾in (33.3 x 50.2cm)
£600-700 *DN*

Karl-Josef Kuwasseg (1802-77)
French
Etretat
Signed and dated 1886, inscribed Falais à
Etretat - Normandie on reverse, oil on canvas
25½ x 21¼in (65 x 54cm)
£1,800-2,400 *CSK*

Frederik Marianus Kruseman (1817-82)
Dutch
A Winter Landscape with Figures Skating on
a Frozen River by a House
Signed and dated 1868, inscribed on reverse,
oil on canvas
27¾ x 39½in (70.5 x100.7cm)
£110,000-150,000 *C*

*Good quality Dutch pictures have been
enjoying consistent success in the salerooms.
Offered by Christie's, King Street, in March
1993, Kruseman's attractive winter landscape
came complete with the artist's own
declaration of authenticity on a label on the
back, from an anonymous but apparently
'noble' source. The work inspired fierce
bidding, resulting in an auction record for the
artist when it was finally knocked down to a
London dealer.*

Benjamin Williams Leader, R.A.
(1831-1923)
British
A Summer Meadow
Signed and dated 1883, oil on canvas
24 x 36¼in (61 x 92cm)
£10,600-11,600 *S*

Edward Lear (1812-88)
British
Yepagos, the Ionian Isles ... an Extensive
Mountainous Landscape
Inscribed and dated April 1863, pen and
sepia ink with colour washes
2¾ x 8in (7 x 19.5cm)
£1,300-1,600 *P(L)*

Edward Lear (1812-88)
British
The Dead Sea
Signed, inscribed and dated 'The Dead
Sea/south end. west side/1858. Edward Lear
del' and inscribed on reverse of the mount
'Miss Baring. Stratton Hall. Micheldever.
Hants', pencil and watercolour
6½ x 10¼in (16.5 x 26cm)
£5,300-6,300 *C*

Charles Henri Joseph Leickert
(1818-1907)
Belgian
Figures on a Frozen Lake
Signed and dated '63, oil on panel
9¾ x 12in (24.5 x 30.5cm)
£7,500-8,500 *S*

Charles Henri Joseph Leickert
(1818-1907)
Belgian
The Ferry
Signed, oil on panel
25 x 37½in (63.5 x 95cm)
£81,000-100,000 *C*

Edward Lear (1812-88)
British
Montenegro
Signed with monogram, signed again and
inscribed on reverse 'Montenegro/A Drawing
made by me in 1870-72/from sketches made
on the spot in 1866/Edward Lear/Purchased
by Thomas Baring, Esq. MP'; pencil,
watercolour and bodycolour on Whatman
paper
29½ x 47½in (75 x 121cm)
£65,000-80,000 *C*

*Edward Lear visited Montenegro late in April
1866, during a tour of the Dalmatian coast,
and this large watercolour seems to be the
work referred to by the artist in a number of
letters of the 1870s and 1880s. Lear wrote to
Lady Wyatt in December 1870, 'I am at work
on a large watercolour picture of Montenegro;
the Montenegro is a cold and gloomy scene -
as it is intended to be, for it is so in reality:
and I have done one bit of rock so well you
sprain your ankles directly you look at it. In
the foreground I had taken a gt. deal of pain
in a large figure of a Montenegrine, & he was
really like life. But some days back as I went
into the next room I heard an odd trumpetty
noise, and coming back, he had put out his
hand, & had taken my pocket-handkerchief
off the table, and was blowing his nose
violently! I instantly had to sponge out the
whole man, for I thought, if he can take up a
handkf, he may take up spoons or money. So
I killed him, and I wonder where his better
part has gone to.'*

Frederick Richard Lee, R.A. (1798-1879)
British
An Extensive Landscape with Figures
Herding Sheep on a Country Road in the
Foreground
Indistinctly signed and dated 1841?, oil on
board
14½ x 19¾in (36.5 x 50cm)
£1,900-2,500 *S(S)*

W. L. Leitch (1804-83)
British
The Bas Rock
Signed and dated 1867, watercolour
heightened with bodycolour
18½ x 32½in (47 x 82.5cm)
£300-400 *PCh*

James Liston (active 1846-48)
British
An Extensive River Landscape with Classical
Ruins and Cattle Watering
Oil on canvas
29in (74cm) diam.
£2,700-3,500 *P(S)*

William Linnell (1826-1906)
British
Vale of Avoe
Indistinctly signed and dated 1880, oil on
canvas
36 x 50¼in (91.5 x 127.5cm)
£6,900-7,500 *CNY*

Emile van Marcke de Lummen (1827-90)
French
A Figure in a Wooded Landscape
Signed, oil on canvas
26 x 39in (66 x 99cm)
£8,000-9,000 *S*

Andrew McCallum (1821-1902)
British
Burnham Beeches
Signed and dated 1862, oil on canvas
27½ x 36½in (69.8 x 92.6cm)
£3,900-4,900 *C(S)*

Kenneth Mackenzie (active 1884-1899)
British
A Landscape with a Shepherdess and Sheep
in the Foreground
Signed, oil on canvas
23½ x 35½in (59.5 x 90cm)
£450-550 *S(S)*

Thomas Mackay (active 1893-1912)
British
Children Watching The River and
Haymaking
Signed and dated 1899
11½ x 17½in (29 x 44cm)
£3,300-4,000 *HAR*

John Blake McDonald, R.S.A. (1829-1901)
British
St Monance, Fife
Signed, oil on canvas
48 x 78in (121.9 x 198.2cm)
£5,000-6,000 *C*

William Manners (active 1885-c1910)
British
Harvest Scene with Figures Resting in the
Foreground, a Summer Sky Above
Signed and dated 1897, on board
8 x 14in (19 x 23cm)
£600-700 *HSS*

William Henry Mander (active 1880-1922)
On The Eden Above Tyn-y-Groes; and Near
Festiniog, a pair
Both signed and dated 96 and 01, inscribed
with title and dated on the reverse
19½ x 29¾in (49.5 x 75.5cm)
£3,300-3,800 *S(S)*

George Marks (active 1876-1922)
British
When Orchard Boughs are Full
Signed, watercolour
13¾ x 9½in (35 x 24.5cm)
£1,100-1,400 *S*

Henry Martin (1835-1908)
British
Driving Geese
Signed, inscribed on reverse, oil on panel
5 x 8in (12.5 x 20cm)
£350-400 *LAY*

William Mellor (1851-1931)
British
On the Wharfe, Yorkshire
Signed, oil on canvas
24 x 35¾in (61 x 91cm)
£5,000-6,000 *S*

Thomas Rose Miles
(active 1869-88)
British
Ballanahinch, Connemara
Signed and inscribed with title on reverse, oil
on canvas
29 x 21½in (73.5 x 54.5cm)
£850-950 *S*

Robert Angelo Kittermaster Marshall
(1849-c1923)
British
Near Warbleton, Sussex
Signed, watercolour
13¼ x 23in (34 x 59cm)
£3,550-3,750 *CGa*

Circle of Arthur Meadows (19thC)
British
Figures Beside a Boat in an Extensive River
Signed, oil on canvas
16¼ x 26in (41.2 x 66cm)
£650-750 *CSK*

Edward Metzger (b1807)
German
A Greek Landscape
Signed, oil on canvas
15¾ x 25¼in (40 x 64cm)
£4,000-5,000 *S*

J. Miller Marshall
(active 1885-c1925)
British
An Old Marsh Mill, Norfolk
Signed and dated 1886, oil on canvas
44 x 70in (112 x 178cm)
£4,300-5,000 *S*

Thomas Moran (1837-1926)
American
Castle Butte, Green River, Wyoming
Signed with monogrammed signature
TMoran N.A., dated 1900, watercolour on
paper
19¾ x 15½in (50.2 x 39.4cm)
£182,000-200,000 *S(NY)*

*Castle Butte was the first spectacular view of
the legendary Wyoming landscape for
travellers going west on the railroad and
made an indelible and lasting impact on
Moran. It was the first view he ever executed
of the west and he continued to paint it many
times over the next 40 years. The Butte had a
mixture of monumentality and notoriety. It
had once been the source of a diamond hoax,
and was a favourite view with those back east
anxious to share in western lore and heritage.
'I have always held that the grandest most
beautiful, or wonderful in nature, would, in
capable hands, make the grandest, most
beautiful or wonderful pictures,' claimed
Moran, 'and the business of the great painter
should be the representation of great scenes of
nature.'*

Paul Jacob Naftel, R.W.S. (1817-91)
British
Vazon Bay, Guernsey
Signed with monogram, dated 1864,
watercolour heightened with bodycolour
4¾ x 14in (12 x 35.5cm)
£3,700-4,500 *S(S)*

*This Guernsey scene by a Guernsey painter
went five times above its estimate when
knocked down at Sotheby's Sussex in January
1993 to a Channel Islands dealer,
emphasising the fact that landscapes often
sell best to those living in the location
portrayed.*

Henry Moore, R.A., R.W.S. (1831-95)
Summer
Signed and dated 1856, oil on canvas
11 x 15in (28 x 38cm)
£5,000-6,000 *S*

George Washington Nicholson
(1832-1912)
American
Bahamian Scene
Signed, watercolour and gouache on paper
11 x 15¼in (27.9 x 38.7cm)
£1,900-2,400 *S(NY)*

Adelsteen Normann (1848-1918)
Norwegian
A Summer Day on a Norwegian Fjord
Signed
27¾ x 37⅛in (70.5 x 94.5cm)
£9,700-10,700 *S(S)*

Harry Sutton Palmer (1854-1933)
British
On the Dart
Signed and dated 1878, watercolour
13 x 18in (33 x 45.5cm)
£2,300-2,600 *HO*

*One of the leading members of the Royal
Institute, Palmer specialised in gentle and
idyllic portrayals of the countryside - Surrey
providing the subject matter for many of his
pictures. As Martin Hardie (see
Bibliography) points out, beneath the simple
appeal of Palmer's rural landscapes, lies a
deliberate and careful artistry: 'It is a
pleasing but conscious and sophisticated art,'
he notes, 'depending upon recipe and very
skilful technique.'*

Norwich School (early 19thC)
Rural Setting with Cottage, Figures and
Sheep
Oil on canvas
16½ x 20½in (42 x 51cm)
£850-950 *RID*

James Arthur O'Connor (1792-1841)
Irish
Figures on a Path in County Wicklow
Oil on canvas
11½ x 15½in (29 x 39.5cm)
£1,400-1,800 *S*

Henry H. Parker (1858-1930)
British
Across the Stream
Signed, oil on canvas
23½ x 35½in (60 x 90cm)
£4,000-5,000 *S*

Ernest Parton (1845-1933)
American
A River Bank
Signed and inscribed 'To Mrs Summer with
the compliments of Ernest Parton', dated
London 1887 on reverse, oil on canvas
24 x 16¾in (61 x 42.5cm)
£750-850 *S*

James Peel (1811-1906)
British
The Coast Road
Signed, oil on canvas
30¾ x 46½in (78 x 118cm)
£2,500-3,000 *S*

Circle of Sidney Richard Percy (1821-86)
British
A Quiet Stream on the Avon
Bears a monogram and dated, oil on canvas
18 x 30in (46 x 76cm)
£1,500-2,000 *S*

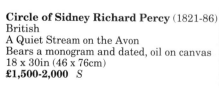

Sidney Richard Percy (1821-86)
British
Pleasant Pasturage
Signed and dated 1858, inscribed on reverse
No. 2 Pleasant Pasturage/Sidney R
Percy/Florence Villa, Wimbledon Park,
Surrey, oil on canvas
20 x 35¼in (50.8 x 90.2cm)
£10,000-12,000 *C*

Arthur Perigal, R.S.A., R.S.W. (1816-84)
British
Cattle Grazing on the Banks of the River Tay
with a View of Dunkeld in the Distance
Signed and dated 1864, framed lunette, oil on
canvas
16 x 23¾in (40.6 x 60.5cm)
£1,700-2,200 *C(S)*

Charles H. Passey (active 1870-85)
British
Harvest Time
Signed, oil on canvas
27½ x 35¼in (69.5 x 89.5cm)
£700-800 *S(S)*

Albert Pollitt (active 1889-1920)
British
Caemes Bay, Anglesea
Signed and dated 1907, pencil and colour
washes
14 x 21in (36 x 53cm)
£850-950 *P(L)*

Sidney Richard Percy (1821-86)
British
Borrowdale, Lake District
Signed and dated 1876, oil on canvas
24 x 38in (62 x 96.5cm)
£45,000-50,000 *FAO*

The Rev. George Poole (active 1827-43)
British
Aston Church, Birmingham, with Elegant
Figures by a Stream
Signed and inscribed on label, oil on canvas,
in original frame (re-gilded)
12 x 16in (30.5 x 40.5cm)
£1,450-1,650 *CGa*

Emilios Prosalentis (1859-96)
Greek
A Coastal Landscape
Signed in Greek, watercolour on paper laid
down on board
12¼ x 31⅛in (31 x 79.4cm)
£3,500-4,000 *C*

Edward John Poynter (1836-1919)
British
A Rocky Cove with a Sketching Party Below
a Hut
Signed, inscribed and dated 1884
15½ x 23½in (39.3 x 59.7cm)
£1,300-1,600 *Bon*

Archibald David Reid, A.R.S.A., R.S.W.
(1844-1908)
British
Arran From Kintyre
Signed, inscribed on label, oil on canvas
24 x 48in (61 x 122cm)
£600-700 *S*

Pierre-Auguste Renoir (1841-1919)
French
Paysage dans les Environs de Cagnes
Watercolour, c1880-86
5½ x 7¼in (14.4 x 18.5cm)
£19,000-23,000 *S*

William Trost Richards (1833-1905)
American
Fisherman on the Shore, Trebarwith Strand,
Cornwall
Signed, dated 1879, watercolour and gouache
on paper
23 x 37in (58.4 x 94cm)
£20,000-25,000 *S(NY)*

Ramsay Richard Reinagle (1775-1862)
British
A View on the River Thames with Barges and
Cattle; and a View on the River Thames with
Figures on a Path and Children Fishing
A pair, the former signed and dated
20¾ x 36in (55.3 x 91.5cm)
£8,700-10,000 *C*

**Thomas Miles Richardson, Jnr., R.S.A.,
R.S.W.** (1813-90)
British
Cuchullin Hills from the Bay at Portree, Isle
of Skye
Signed and dated 1876, watercolour
heightened with white
22¾ x 44in (57.5 x 112cm)
£6,400-7,400 *S*

*Richardson was known for his landscape
portrayals of Scotland, Italy and Switzerland.
He favoured panoramic effects (using long
narrow sheets of paper), bright colours and
powerful perspective. John Ruskin, although
he admired the manual dexterity of
Richardson's landscapes, was less than
convinced about their aesthetic merit,
complaining that 'the rich medley' of his
Highland views appeared to have been
conceived 'under the cheering influence of
champagne'. Yet while critics might have
disapproved of his mannered style and
brilliant tones, Richardson's works enjoyed
considerable success with the buying public,
his landscapes fetching over £300 a piece in
the salerooms during the artist's own lifetime.*

Thomas Sewell Robins (1814-80)
British
A Coastal Scene at Evening with Fishermen
Bringing a Boat Ashore; and Fisherfolk on
the Shore at Evening, a pair
Signed with initials and dated '69,
watercolour
7¼ x 13¾in (18.4 x 35cm)
£900-1,200 *Bon*

**Thomas Miles Richardson, Jnr., R.S.A.,
R.S.W.** (1813-90)
British
Taormina, Sicily
Signed and dated 1861, watercolour
8 x 19in (20 x 48cm)
£1,550-1,650 *PCA*

Theodore Rousseau (1812-67)
French
A Country Road
Signed, oil on board
6¼ x 8¼in (15.8 x 21cm)
£900-1,200 *CSK*

Léon Richet (1847-1907)
French
Figure Beside a Pond in a Wooded Landscape
with a Church Beyond
Signed, oil on panel
18 x 21½in (45.5 x 54.5cm)
£3,800-4,500 *CNY*

James Scott (exh. 1809-75),
after **Paulus Potter** (1625-54)
British
Milking Time
Line stipple and aquatint engraving printed
in colours, published 1814
11 x 14in (28 x 35cm)
£300-325 *CG*

Tom Scott, R.S.A., R.S.W. (1854-1927)
British
Returning Home
Signed, watercolour heightened with
scratching out
17¾ x 23¼in(45 x 59cm)
£1,000-1,400 *S*

Daniel Sherrin
(active 1895-1915)
British
Evening Landscape
Oil
24 x 16in (61 x 40.5cm)
£950-1,250 *SAV*

Locate the Source
The source of each illustration in Miller's can be found by checking the code letters below each caption with the list of contributors.

William Joseph Shayer, Jnr.
(active 1829-85)
British
Figures Resting at Netley Abbey Ruins
Signed, oil on panel
11½ x 9½in (29 x 24cm)
£2,200-2,400 *CGa*

Sir Frank Short, R.A. (1857-1945)
British
A Roman Canal
Signed, mezzotint
6 x 14½in (15 x 36.5cm)
£200-225 *CG*

Attributed to William Shayer (1787-1879)
British
A Drover's Rest
Bears a signature and date, oil on canvas
17¾ x 24in (45 x 61cm)
£1,900-2,400 *S*

Fred Slocombe (1847-1920)
British
Winter Landscape
Etching
13 x 20in (32.8 x 50.5cm)
£85-95 *CG*

Francis Hopkinson Smith (1838-1915)
American
River View
Signed, c1905, watercolour, charcoal and
gouache on paper laid down on board
18¼ x 26¾in (46.4 x 68cm)
£5,300-6,300 *S(NY)*

Jan Jacob Spohler (1811-66)
Dutch
Figures Skating on a Frozen Lake
Signed, oil on canvas
16 x 25in (41 x 63cm)
£8,700-10,000 *S*

Thomas James Soper (active 1836-90)
British
Sheep and Cattle in a Meadow
Signed with monogram, watercolour
7 x 19¾in (17.5 x 50cm)
£350-450 *Bea*

Jan Jacob Spohler (1811-66)
Dutch
Figures Skating by a Windmill
Signed, oil on canvas
13¾ x 20½in (35 x 52cm)
£4,200-5,200 *S*

After George Clarkson Stanfield
(1828-78)
British
The Castle of Ischia
Oil on canvas
17 x 24in (43.2 x 61cm)
£950-1,200 *CSK*

Attributed to Clarkson Stanfield R.A.
(1793-1867)
British
On the Coast at Guernsey, St Peterport
Beyond
Signed, pencil and watercolour heightened
with white
10 x 13in (25 x 33cm)
£750-850 *CSK*

A. Stanley (active 1847-77)
British
A View of the Old House at Humewood from
the Lake with Figures and Dogs
Signed and dated 1857
13¾ x 21in (35 x 53cm)
£950-1,200 *HOK*

Anthony Carey Stannus (active 1862-1903)
British
The Salmon Pool
Signed, watercolour heightened with white
19¼ x 34⅜in (49 x 80.5cm)
£1,500-2,000 *S*

A Victorian album of masked watercolour
drawings of a journey in Europe, Switzerland
and the Tyrol, c1850 (bookplate Sir Oswald
Moseley, 5 bart.)
£300-350 *WL*

An album of aquatints, lithographs and
engravings, including approx. 48 small
coloured aquatints part printed in colours
illustrating Swiss towns and landscapes
published by Keller et Fussli, Zurich, 4
coloured tinted lithographs of Mont Blanc by
A. Cuvillier, 3 coloured aquatints part
printed in colours of Berne; L'Hospice du
Grimsel; and Cascade Inferieurs du
Richenbach, published by Birman & Fils, and
a number of aquatints illustrating Swiss
regional costume.
£2,300-4,000 *CSK*

Stiglmaier (19thC)
German ?
A Wooded Landscape with Figures on a
Track by a Pool
Signed and dated 1872, oil on canvas
22 x 38in (55.8 x 96.5cm)
£1,000-1,500 *CSK*

James Stark (1794-1859)
British
Wooded Landscape with Figures in Centre
Foreground, a Windmill and Farmstead
Beyond a Clearing
Oil on canvas
17¾ x 24⅜in (45 x 63cm)
£3,200-3,800 *HOLL*

Willie Stephenson
(active late 19thC, d1938)
British
Women, Child and Bushes
Signed, watercolour
10½ x 14in (27 x 36cm)
£600-650 *LH*

Friedrich Salomon Fussli, Publisher
Views of Switzerland
24 plates, coloured aquatints part printed in
colours, touches of gum arabic, with full
margins
6¾ x 8in (17 x 20.5cm)
£3,900-5,000 *CSK*

August Strindberg (1849-1912)
Swedish
Fackelblomster
Signed, inscribed and dated 1892, oil on
canvas
10¼ x 13¼in (26 x 34cm)
£56,000-75,000 *S*

Edward Train (19thC)
British
A Sunny Winter's Day
Signed
11½ x 17¼in (29.5 x 44cm)
£2,000-2,400 *AG*

Paul Désiré Trouillebert (1829-1900)
French
Fisherman on the Bank of a River
Signed, oil on canvas laid down on panel
25½ x 32in (64.8 x 81.3cm)
£17,000-20,000 *CNY*

Constant Troyon (1810-65)
French
In the Woods at Meudon Above Sèvres
Signed, oil on canvas
28½ x 41in (71.4 x 104.2cm)
£13,500-15,000 *C(S)*

George Turner (1843-1910)
British
Fishing From a Bridge
Signed and dated 1897, oil on canvas
16 x 24in (40.5 x 61cm)
£1,800-2,500 *S*

William Turner of Oxford (1789-1862)
British
A Scene in Bagley Wood near Oxford
Inscribed and numbered 4 on
reverse, water and bodycolour with
scratching out
14½ x 20½in (37.2 x 52.3cm)
£1,000-1,500 *Bon*

*Called 'Turner of Oxford' to distinguish him
from J.M.W. Turner, William Turner's talent
was so pronounced that he was elected an
associate of the Old Watercolour Society when
he was only 18. He studied under John
Varley, and his early works bear comparison
with those of both his master and John
Cotman, but as Hardie comments: 'After this
magnificent beginning, the youthful ardour,
promise and innocence were to be spoiled by
experience and sophistication.' (See
Bibliography).*

John Varley (1778-1842) British
Figure Near a Ruined Abbey at Sunset; and
an Italianate Landscape with Trees
Both signed, framed together, watercolour
laid on paper
3½ x 5in (8.9 x 12.7cm)
£1,000-1,400 *Bon*

Eugène Verboeckhoven (1798-1881)
Henry Campotosto (d1910)
Belgian
Sheep and Cows by the River
Signed by both artists, dated 1877, oil on
canvas
24 x 39in (61 x 99cm)
£7,200-8,200 *S*

Louis Pierre Verwee (1807-77)
Eugène Verboeckhoven (1798-1881)
Belgian
Shepherdess in a Pastoral Landscape
Signed, inscribed and dated Louis Verwee f.
1858/figures par Eugène Verboeckhoven, oil
on canvas
31½ x 45¼in (80 x102cm)
£11,500-12,500 *CNY*

Alfred Vickers Snr. (1786-1868)
British
A River Landscape with Figures, Cattle and
Sheep
Signed
21 x 29½in (53 x 75cm)
£2,500-3,000 *S(S)*

Ernest Walbourn (active 1897-1904)
British
A Riverside Path
Signed and dated 1900, oil on canvas
24 x 42in (61 x 107cm)
£5,500-6,500 *S*

George Augustus Wallis (1770-1847)
British
An Extensive Arcadian Landscape with
Telemachus Bathing and Nymphs in the
foreground
Signed and dated Wallis/184...
67½ x 42¾in (171.5 x 108.5cm)
£5,800-7,800 *C*

Edward Arthur Walton P.R.S.W., R.S.A.
(1860-1922)
British
A Pastoral
Signed, watercolour heightened with
scratching out
13¼ x 20¼in (33.6 x 51.4cm)
£1,800-2,200 *C(S)*

George Weatherill (1810-90)
British
Runswick
Colour washes
6¾ x 10in (17 x 25cm)
£650-750 *P(L)*

William Page Atkinson Wells (1872-1923)
British
Field Work
Signed, oil on canvas
10¼ x 14¼in (26 x 36cm)
£2,000-2,500 *S*

Frederick John Widgery (1861-1942)
British
Castle Rock, Lynton; A Coastal View, a pair
Both signed, one inscribed with title, gouache
14 x 21in (35.5 x 53cm)
£750-850 *S(S)*

John White R.I. (1851-1933)
British
The Morning Light, Coverack, Cornwall
Inscribed and dated on reverse
12 x 16in (31 x 41cm)
£1,800-2,500 *TAY*

Edward Williams (1782-1855)
British
Rustic Views, c1825, a pair
Oil on panel
9½ x 13½in (24 x 34cm)
£3,000-4,000 *AdG*

Edward Charles Williams (1807-81)
British
The Approaching Storm
Oil on panel
15 x 20in (38.2 x 50.8cm)
£900-1,000 *CSK*

Penry Williams (1798-1885)
British
Figures in a River Landscape at Sunset
Oil on canvas
23¾ x 36in (61 x 91.5cm)
£3,800-4,500 *CNY*

Warren Williams (1863-1918)
British
God's Acre Church, Bettyscoed (sic); and 'The
River Conway at Talycan'
Signed, inscribed verso, watercolours
11¾ x 18¼in (29.8 x 46.3cm)
£1,600-2,000 *Bon*

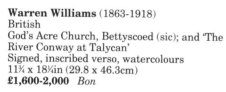

Peter de Wint, O.W.S. (1784-1849)
British
In Wales Between Bangor and Capel Curig
Inscribed as title on reverse by Harriet de
Wint, and lot number from artist's sale '342'
Pencil and watercolour
14¼ x 20⅜in (36.2 x 52.8cm)
£14,000-16,000 *C*

*Peter de Wint first visited North Wales in
1829 or 1830, returning on several occasions
up to 1835. He married Harriet Hilton on
16th June 1810. She was the sister of the
painter William Hilton and wrote a short
memoir of her husband, published privately
after his death.*

Peter de Wint, O.W.S. (1784-1849)
British
On the Thames near Cookham, Berkshire
Watercolour, with added strip
4½ x 8½in (11.5 x 21.5cm)
£2,700-3,200 *S*

**Giovanni Lutero, called Dosso
Dossi** (active 1517-48)
Italian
Landscape with Figures on a Country
Road, a View of a Town Beyond
Oil on canvas
32 x 52½in (81.3 x 133.4cm)
£140,000-170,000 *S(NY)*

Govaert Flinck (1615-60)
Dutch
Landscape with a Tower
Oil on panel
16 x 22½in (40.6 x 57.2cm)
£78,000-90,000 *S(NY)*

Jan Josefsz. van Goyen
(1596-1656)
Dutch
A River Landscape with a Manor
House, Rowing Boats and Smalschips
Signed and dated 'VGO.EN 1.45'
Oil on panel
27¼ x 36in (69.3 x 92cm)
£125,000-150,000 *C*

Philips de Koninck (1619-88)
Dutch
A Panoramic River Landscape
Signed and dated, oil on canvas
33 x 47½in (84 x 121cm)
£1,000,000-1,250,000 *S*

Jan Apeldoorn (1765-1838)
Dutch
Herdsmen on the Fringes of a Wood
Pencil, watercolour, black ink framing lines,
inscribed 'In Randenbroek' verso
16¼ x 22in (42 x 56cm)
£4,000-5,000 *C(Am)*

Flemish School (18thC)
Extensive Landscape with Figures
near a Flemish Castle
Oil on canvas
28 x 35in (71 x 89cm)
£10,500-12,500 *S(NY)*

Johann Christian Vollerdt (1708-69)
German
Extensive Hilly Landscape wtih Figures and Animals,
a Waterfall in the Foreground
Signed and dated 1759, oil on canvas
23¾ x 29in (60.3 x 74cm)
£17,000-20,000 *S(NY)*

Jan Griffier the Younger (d circa 1750)
Dutch
Extensive Mountainous River Landscape
with Figures Travelling in Boats
Signed, oil on canvas
17¼ x 23¼in (43.8 x 59cm)
£17,500-20,000 *S(NY)*

Johann Jacob Hoch (1750-1829)
German
A Forest with Deer, Rabbits and
Egrets by a Pool
Signed and dated 1774, gouache
9¾ x 10¼in (24.6 x 26cm)
£6,400-7,400 *S(NY)*

Alexander Nasmyth (1758-1840)
British
A View of Loch Trool, at the head of Glentrool, Galloway
33½ x 51in (85 x 130cm)
£12,500-15,000 *C*

Pietro Barucci (1845-1917)
Italian
Fisherfolk on an Italian Lake
Signed and inscribed Roma, oil on
canvas
31¾ x 56½in (80.5 x 144cm)
£9,000-10,000 *S*

Eugène Boudin (1824-98)
French
Etude de Ciel
Stamped with initials (Lugt
828), executed c1860, pastel
on blue paper
5½ x 8in (13.5 x 20.5cm)
£7,200-8,500 *S*

Alfred de Breanski Snr. (1852-1928)
British
Snowdon, N. Wales
Signed, oil on canvas
24 x 36in (62 x 92cm)
£17,000-18,000 *FAO*

**Sir David Young Cameron, R.A.,
R.W.S.** (1865-1945)
British
The Eagle's Crags
Signed, oil on canvas
37½ x 42¾in (95.5 x 108.5cm)
£9,000-10,000 *S*

Hans Andreas Dahl (1881-1919)
Norwegian
A Young Goatgirl by a Fjord
Signed, oil on canvas
31¼ x 46¾in (80 x 118.5cm)
£10,500-12,000 *S*

Hans Andreas Dahl was Hans Dahl's son.

Charles Collins (active 1867-1903)
British
The Wayside Rest
Signed, oil on canvas
21 x 32in (53 x 81cm)
£6,000-6,500 *HFA*

Hippolyte Camille Delpy
(1842-1910)
French
A View of a Country Village
Signed and dated '90, oil on panel
20 x 32in (51 x 81cm)
£14,500-17,500 *S*

Gustave Courbet (1819-77)
French
Paysage aux Environs d'Ornans
Signed, oil on canvas
Executed 1876
25 x 19in (63 x 48cm)
£17,500-20,000 *S*

Eastern European School (19thC)
A Fête Day in a Mountainous Landscape
Oil on canvas
72 x 103¼in (183 x 262cm)
£10,000-11,000 *S*

*This painting possibly depicts a place in the
Carpathians, and possibly includes a self-
portrait of the artist in the lower left of the
painting.*

Henry Farrer (1843-1903)
American
Evening Sail
Signed and dated 1900, watercolour on paper
18¼ x 25¼in (46.4 x 64cm)
£5,700-6,700 *S(NY)*

Robert Gallon (1845-1925)
British
Angler in Wooded River Landscape
Signed, oil on canvas
20 x 30in (51 x 76cm)
£2,500-3,000 *FdeL*

Henry John Kinnaird (1861-1929)
British
A Sussex Lane
Signed and inscribed, watercolour
13½ x 21in (34 x 53cm)
£3,600-4,000 *MJA*

Edouard Kasparides (1858-1926)
Austrian
A Lady by a Lake
Oil on canvas
36¼ x 46¼in (92 x 117.5cm)
£5,000-6,000 *S*

John William Hill (1812-79)
British
River Landscape with Boy Fishing
Signed and dated '61, watercolour on paper
9 x 13½in (23 x 34.3cm)
£11,500-12,500 *S(NY)*

Giacinto Gigante (1806-76)
Italian
Figures on a Path by a Monastery in
Southern Italy
Signed and dated 'nap 1834', watercolour
8 x 10in (20 x 26cm)
£8,000-9,000 *S*

John Knox (1778-1845)
British
On the Banks of Loch Katrine
Oil on canvas
25¼ x 43¾in (64 x 111cm)
£3,700-5,000 *S*

James Thomas Linnell (1826-1905)
British
Harvest Time
Signed and dated 1865, oil on canvas
30½ x 40¼ in (77.8 x 102.2cm)
£14,500-16,500 *C*

Charles Henri Joseph Leickert
(1818-1907)
Dutch
Near Voorburg; A Winter Landscape
with Figures Skating on a Frozen River
Signed and dated 'Ch. Leickert f.70', oil
on canvas
25 x 39½in (64 x 100cm)
£25,500-35,500 *C*

Edward Lear (1812-88)
British
Mount Athos and the Monastery
of Stavroniketes
Indistinctly signed and dated
'Edward Lear 1862', pencil and
watercolour heightened with
bodycolour and gum arabic
6½ x 10in (16.5 x 25.5cm)
£6,000-7,500 *C*

Benjamin Williams Leader (1831-1923)
British
Capel Curig
Signed and dated 1888, oil on canvas
20 x 30in (51 x 76cm)
£10,000-11,000 *HFA*

William Mellor (1851-1931)
British
A pair, Posforth Gill, Bolton Woods,
Yorkshire and On the Wharfe, Bolton
Abbey, Yorkshire
Oil on canvas
12 x 18in (31 x 46cm)
£4,000-4,500 *HFA*

Peder Mønsted (1859-1941)
Danish
The Return Home
Signed and dated 1898, oil on canvas
35½ x 59in (90 x 150cm)
£12,000-14,000 *C*

William Mellor (1851-1931)
British
One of the pair, see above

**Georg Anton
Rasmussen** (1842-
1914)
Norwegian
A Norwegian Fjord
Signed, oil on canvas
30 x 49¼in (76 x
125cm)
£15,500-16,500 *Pol*

Henry H. Parker
(1858-1930)
British
A Coastal Cornfield
Signed, oil on canvas
24 x 36in (61 x 92cm)
£17,000-18,000 *HFA*

Sidney Richard Percy (1821-86)
British
The Mawddarm, near Dolgelly,
N. Wales
Signed and dated 1876, oil on
canvas
24 x 38in (61 x 96.5cm)
£30,000-35,000 *FAO*

Jan Jacob Spohler (1811-66)
Dutch
Figures Skating on a Frozen River by Windmills
Signed, oil on canvas
24¾ x 33in (63 x 83.5cm)
£12,000-14,000 *S*

Karl Christian Sparmann (1805-64)
German
A View of the Rhine Valley
Signed and dated 1837, oil on canvas
30½ x 41in (78 x 104cm)
£5,800-7,000 *S*

Edmund George Warren (1834-1909)
British
The Harvesters' Rest, a View of Helsby Hill
from Frodsham, Cheshire
Signed and dated 1874, watercolour
19½ x 30in (49 x 76cm)
£8,500-9,000 *Pol*

Frederick Judd Waugh (1861-1940)
American
Looking West, St Ives
Signed, executed circa 1896
Watercolour on paper mounted on board
14½ x 20½in (36.8 x 52cm)
£5,500-6,500 *S(NY)*

George Wolfe (1834-90)
British
A Castle on the Coast by Moonlight
Signed, pencil and watercolour heightened with
white
22 x 41½in (56 x 105.4cm)
£4,000-5,000 *C*

Nick Andrew
(20thC)
British
Waves 1
Acrylic on paper
18½in (47cm)
square
£600-650 *OLG*

Diana Armfield, A.R.A., R.W.S. (b1920)
British
The White Gate from Llwynhir
Oil on board
12¾in (33cm) square
£2,000-4,000 *BSG*

Peter Bishop (b1953)
British
Cader Idris 3
Mixed media on canvas
30 x 42in (76 x 106.5cm)
£900-1,000 *KG*

André Bourrié (b1936)
French
The House on the Port
Original zinc plate lithograph
7 x 9in (18 x 22.8cm)
£225-250 *TES*

Robert Craig-Wallace (active 1929-40)
British
Fishing
Signed, oil on canvas
12 x 15in (31 x 38cm)
£2,500-2,800 *NZ*

Brian Graham (20thC)
British
Egmont Bight
Acrylic on board
9½ x 12½in (24 x 32cm)
£250-275 *OLG*

Maggie Hambling (20thC)
British
Sunrise, Hadleigh, Suffolk
Signed, watercolour
23 x 26in (58.5 x 66cm)
£800-880 *OLG*

Ivan Dmitriev (b1958), Russian
The Orchard, signed in Cyrillic script, 1992
Oil on canvas, 23 x 27in (59 x 69cm)
£900-950 *Ch*

John Hope-Falkner (b1942)
British
The Gorge
Signed and dated, oil on canvas
30 x 18in (76 x 46cm)
£650-750 *SBG*

Jean Dupas (1884-1964)
French
Woman with Gazelles in Landscape
Signed and dated 1924, oil on canvas, in original
frame
29½ x 37in (75 x 94cm)
£22,000-26,000 *S(NY)*

Jack Hellewell (20thC)
British
Moon Contours
Acrylic on paper
22 x 28in (56 x 71.5cm)
£350-400 *KHG*

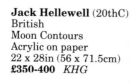

Moïse Kisling (1891-1953)
French
Les Sablettes
Signed, titled and dated 1937, oil on canvas
18 x 21½in (46 x 55cm)
£24,500-30,000 *S*

George Luks (1867-1933)
American
Autumn Landscape
Signed, executed c1930, watercolour on paper
14 x 20in (35.6 x 50.8cm)
£5,500-6,500 *S(NY)*

Hayley Lever (1876-1958)
American
Gloucester Hills
Signed, watercolour on paper
11 x 15½in (28 x 39.4cm)
£6,600-7,000 *S(NY)*

Mervyn Knight (b1956)
British
Winding Lane, Dorset
Signed, oil on canvas
30 x 30in (76 x 76cm)
£800-875 *AMC*

John MacLauchlan Milne
(1886-1957)
British
Harvest Time on Arran
Signed, oil on canvas
19¼ x 23½in (48 x 60cm)
£11,000-12,000 *McE*

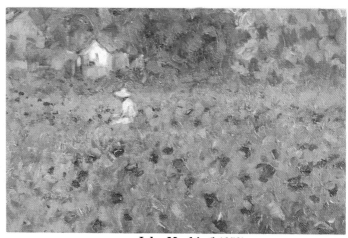

John Mackie (b1953)
Scottish
Poppy Field, near St. Tropez
Oil on canvas
23½ x 28in (60 x 71cm)
£1,200-1,400 *WG*

Arthur Maderson
(b1942)
British
Morning Floods
Oil on canvas
34 x 46in
(86 x 116.5cm)
£3,000-3,500 *A*

Algernon Newton, R.A. (1880-1968)
British
Trees in a Landscape
Signed with monogram , oil on canvas
20 x 32in (51 x 81cm)
£2,700-3,500 *C*

Sir Thomas Monnington (1902-76)
British
Trees at Leyswood
Oil on canvas
13½ x 19in (34 x 48cm)
£1,400-1,500 *NBO*

David Mynett (b1942)
British
Majorcan Farmhouse
Pastel
11 x 14in (28 x 35.5cm)
£450-500 *A*

Alush Shima (b1942)
My Village
Oil on canvas, executed 1991
32 x 28in (81 x 71cm)
£3,500-4,000 *RMG*

Tony Paul (20thC)
British
February Mist
Egg tempera
15½ x 22in (39 x 56cm)
£800-900 *PHG*

James McIntosh Patrick (b1907)
British
Woods above Dundee
Signed and dated '37, oil on canvas
30 x 20in (76.2 x 50.8cm)
£3,000-4,000 *C(S)*

Mark Spain (b1962)
British
Shades of Summer
Etching, 10 colours
12¾ x 18in (32.4 x 45cm)
£100-125 *CCA*

Simon Palmer (20thC)
British
The Sisters Went Their Separate Ways
Silkscreen, 26 colours
16 x 21¾in (40.5 x 55cm)
£125-150 *CCA*

Ludovico Tommasi (1866-1941)
Landscape with Figures
Signed, oil on panel
17¾ x 12¾in (45 x 32.5cm)
£3,500-4,500 *S*

George Arnald, A.R.A. (1753-1806)
British
The Menai Bridge, North Wales
Signed, oil on canvas
38½ x 50½in (98 x 128cm)
£13,500-15,500 *S*

William Williams (active 1758-89)
British
The Iron Bridge, Coalbrookdale
Signed and dated 1786, oil on canvas
30 x 32⅓in (76.2 x 82cm)
£22,000-30,000 *DN*

John Wilson Carmichael
(1800-68)
British
Victoria Bridge over the River Wear
Oil on canvas
24 x 37½ in (61 x 95cm)
£12,000-15,000 *DN*

Frederick Waters Watts (1800-62)
British
A River Landscape with Countryfolk
and Cattle at a Ford, Travellers with a
Covered Wagon Crossing a Bridge
25 x 30in (63.5 x 76.2cm)
£9,000-10,000 *C*

Henry John Yeend King (1855-1924)
British
Fishing in the Mill Stream
Signed, oil on canvas
45 x 33in (114 x 84cm)
£12,000-12,500 *HFA*

Sir Charles D'Oyly (1781-1845) British
The Rock at Jahangira on the Ganges
Oil on canvas, 8 x 11in (20.5 x 28cm)
£7,250-8,500 *S*

Mary Jackson (20thC)
British
The Cataract, Aswan
Oil on canvas
20 x 24in (51 x 61.5cm)
£1,200-2,500 *BSG*

Claude Muncaster (1903-74) British
Dhows off Bombay
Signed, oil on board, 24 x 36in (61 x 92cm)
£850-950 *Cae*

Edwin Lord Weeks (1849-1903)
British/American
Indian Scene
Signed, oil on canvas
21¾ x 17½in (55 x 44.5cm)
£23,000-28,000 *CNY*

Lieutenant Harris, H.M. 24th Foot
(active 1816)
British
The Taking of Harihapur, Nepal, 1st of
March 1816
Signed and inscribed
16 x 22in (40.7 x 56cm)
£2,300-3,300 *C*

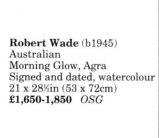

Robert Wade (b1945)
Australian
Morning Glow, Agra
Signed and dated, watercolour
21 x 28½in (53 x 72cm)
£1,650-1,850 *OSG*

Henri Duvieux (19thC)
French
View of Constantinople
Signed, oil on canvas
16 x 25½in (41 x 65cm)
£5,500-6,000 *CNY*

Hermann Corrodi (1844-1905)
Italian
Prayers by the Nile at Sunset
Signed and dated Kairo 1879, oil on canvas
33¾ x 25½in (85.5 x 65cm)
£9,500-11,000 *S*

Michel-François Préaulx
(early 19thC)
French
The Besiktas Heights with
the Selimiye Barracks in the
Distance
Pencil, pen and black ink
and watercolour
13 x 22½in (33 x 57.2cm)
£5,800-7,000 *C*

Amadeo, Count Preziosi
(1816-82) Italian
Ladies on the Bosphorous
with Rumeli Hisar beyond
Signed and dated 1873,
pencil and watercolour on
paper
11½ x 18¼in (29.2 x 46.4cm)
£8,000-9,000 *C*

Alberto Pasini (1826-99)
Italian
Shehzade Baçi, near the
Beyazit Mosque,
Constantinople
Signed and dated 1872, oil on
canvas
9¾ x 16in (24.7 x 41cm)
£42,000-50,000 *C*

20th Century

The contemporary market, in landscape as in other subjects, remains difficult at present. 'Times are hard,' one Bath dealer admitted. 'Our area has been very badly hit by the recession and there is not much disposable income around. People are looking for bargains, special offers and reduced prices, just as in every other area of shopping.' Peter Hedley, gallery owner in Dorset, thinks the market is more variable. 'Last year, in spite of the recession, we had a record turnover: this year things have been slow but we have just had a very successful show and I am sure things are going to get better.'

Prices are low at the moment and the contemporary field can be a very exciting area for the collector, providing original works by living artists, often at a fraction of the price of 'older' pictures. If you buy pictures from a young painter, part of the fun can be watching how his career progresses over the years. There is always the chance that you might have selected someone who will subsequently be considered a master of his period, though it is almost impossible to predict future values of a painting and this should be a consideration when buying a contemporary work. 'I know it's a terrible old cliché,' says Peter Hedley, 'but it cannot be stressed too often: always buy what you like, never buy for investment. If you like something, you will never be disappointed in it.'

Gerald Ackermann (1876-1960)
British
Blakeney, Norfolk
Signed, watercolour
10 x 14in (25 x 36cm)
£1,550-1,750 *NBO*

American School (early 20thC)
An Indian Camp Site by a Lake in Moonlight
Oil on canvas
30 x 46in (76.2 x 116.8cm)
£1,900-2,500 *S(NY)*

John Arthur Malcolm Aldridge, R.A.
(1905-84)
British
A Cottage in a Country Landscape
Inscribed verso 'North Essex March 1938
John Aldridge', oil on board
14 x 18in (36.5 x 46.6cm)
£650-800 *Bon*

Diana Armfield (1920-)
British
The Washing Line
Signed, oil on panel
7 x 12in (17.5 x 30.5cm)
£1,000-1,200 *BRG*

Adrian Paul Allinson (1890-1959)
British
Mallorcan Brook, c1936
Signed, inscribed verso, oil on canvas
26 x 32in (66 x 81.2cm)
£1,100-1,500 *Bon*

Gaston Balande (1880-1970)
French
L'Eglise du Village
Signed G. Balande, oil on canvas
18 x 21½in (45.7 x 54.7cm)
£1,400-1,800 *CSK*

Brian Bennett (20thC)
British
Grasses and Sow Thistle
Oil
16 x 12in (40.5 x 30.5cm)
£300-350 *GOE*

Oscar E. Berninghaus
(1874-1952)
American
Hills of Taxco, c1940
Signed O.E., inscribed, watercolour on paper
14½ x 20in (36.8 x 50.8cm)
£6,500-7,500 *S(NY)*

Camille Bombois (b1883)
French
Summer Landscape
Signed, oil on canvas
5½ x 8¾in (14 x 22.2cm)
£4,000-5,000 *S(NY)*

Owen Bowen (1873-1967)
British
Cows Grazing in a Meadow
Before Haystacks
Signed, oil on panel
11 x 15in (28 x 38cm)
£2,000-2,200 *WG*

Samuel John Lamorna Birch (1869-1955)
British
A Woodland Pool
Signed, oil on canvas
29¼ x 36in (74.3 x 91.5cm)
£2,000-2,500 *Bon*

James Brown (1863-1943)
British
Four Poplars
Oil on board
24 x 36in (61 x 91.5cm)
£850-950 *BRG*

William Bowyer (b1926)
British
Sunset, Walberswick
Oil on panel
16 x 15in (40.5 x 38cm)
£1,800-2,000 *BRG*

William Brymner (19th/20thC)
Canadian
An Indian School
Signed, oil on canvas
10 x 17in (25.5 x 42.5cm)
£1,900-2,500 *P*

Edward Bruce (1879-1943)
American
Landscape with Corral and Barn
Signed, oil on canvas
24 x 29in (61 x 73.3cm)
£2,300-3,000 *S(NY)*

David Burliuk (1882-1966)
Russian
Winter in Ural Mountain Town, late 1930s
Signed and indistinctly titled, oil on masonite
10¾ x 16¼in (27.3 x 41.3cm)
£1,000-1,500 *S(NY)*

Joy Brand (20thC)
British
Summer River
Lithograph
14 x 21½in (35 x 54cm)
£85-95 *CCA*

*Clarence K. Chatterton was born in
Newburgh, New York and studied under
William Merritt Chase and Robert Henri at
the Art Student's League. He was to remain
in New York for the remainder of his career,
never to go west of the state or to Europe.
Chatterton painted small towns and pastoral
scenes in the tradition of the Hudson River
School and was particularly interested in the
changing conditions of light and of the
seasons. He worked out of doors; his style was
realistic and became recognised as one of the
most respected of this tradition at a time when
abstraction was of significance in the art world.*

Clarence K. Chatterton (1880-1973)
American
Snake Hill
Signed and dated '06, gouache and pencil on
paper laid down on board
12¾ x 18½in (32.4 x 47cm)
£2,300-2,800 *S(NY)*

Henry Charles Clifford, R.B.A.
(1861-1947)
British
Sunshine In The Woods
Signed, inscribed on reverse, oil on canvas
24 x 30in (61.5 x 76.5cm)
£550-650 *LAY*

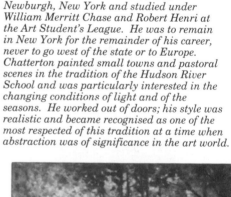

Mario Carreño (20thC)   Cuban
Paisaje
Signed and dated 43
Oil on canvas
41 x 31in (104.1 x 78.7cm)
£150,000-200,000 *S(NY)*

*Returning to Cuba at the end of 1941, after
five years of living in Europe and then New
York, Mario Carreño began one of the most
productive periods of his long career. Leaving
behind the subdued colour schemes and
classical and surrealist inspired nudes and
still lifes shown with great success in his first
solo show in New York, at the Perls Galleries
in the spring of 1941, Carreño now embarked
on a rediscovery of his homeland.*

*A great deal of the joyful boldness of Paisaje
may be credited to Carreño's return, like the
small boat in the painting, to the safe haven
of Cuba, where the war was very far away.
Also, his marriage to Maria Luisa Gómez
Mena, an important patron of the arts, and
his new role as one of the leaders of the Cuban
avant garde, contributed to his maturing into
the artist he became in this period. Protected
by the twin deities of the Caribbean sky, the
sun and the royal palm, the snug hamlet of
Paisaje celebrates love, security, and the
human and natural landscape of Cuba.*

Alan Cotton (20thC)
British
Gnarled Apple Tree - Provence
20 x 16in (51 x 41cm)
£1,450-1,650 *DM*

Othon Coubine (1883-1959)
Czechoslovakian
Summer Landscape with Hills and Olive
Trees
Signed, oil on canvas
19¾ x 24in (50.2 x 61cm)
£2,000-2,500 *S(NY)*

Fred Cuming
(20thC)
British
Winter Tree
Oil on board
24in (61.5cm) square.
£4,000-4,250 *BRG*

Locate the Source

*The source of each
illustration in Miller's
can be found by checking
the code letters below
each caption with the
list of contributors.*

Gabriel Deschamps (20thC)
French
Provençal Landscape
Signed
18 x 21¾in (45.6 x 55cm)
£800-900 *CSK*

Alan Cotton (20thC)
British
Farm In The Spring Near Rustrel
36 x 40in (92 x 101.5cm)
£5,500-6,000 *DM*

*Cotton's work is dominated by the subject of
Provence, which he first visited as a student
and which has remained his principle source
of inspiration ever since. As well as the
landscapes, mountains and hillside towns of
Southern France, another theme that he
returns to repeatedly is trees and orchards.*

*'I think an orchard in full blossom, where you
can see light coming through blossoms
against a blue sky or the patterns of deep
shadows cast by the trees is something very
timeless and visually is one of the most
arresting things that you can see,' claims
Cotton. 'Of course there are traps in painting
it. You could end up with something
amazingly twee and rather sentimental, or
you can try in a very fundamental way,
almost like a child, to convey the sense of joy
and wonder at this stunning visual feast.'*

**Ronald Ossory Dunlop, R.A., R.B.A.,
N.E.A.C.** (1894-1973)
British
Hampton Court
Signed, oil on canvas
20 x 24in (50.7 x 61cm)
£850-1,000 *Bon*

Marcel Dyf (1899-1985)
French
Figures Picnicking in an Orchard
Signed, oil on canvas
18 x 21¾in (45.7 x 55.3cm)
£6,100-7,000 *C(S)*

Graham Evernden (20thC)
British
Tall Cow Parsley
Etching, 12 colours.
8 x 5in (20 x 13cm)
£65-75 *CCA*

Miles Fairhurst (20thC)
British
Suffolk Farmhouse
Oil
16½ x 20in (42 x 51cm)
£750-850 *Wyk*

Richard Eurich (20thC)
British
The Rainbow
Oil on canvas
20 x 24in (50.5 x 61cm)
£3,250-3,450 *BRG*

Mary Fedden (b1915)
British
Esch-sur-Sure
Signed, inscribed on reverse twice, dated
1934
Oil on panel
£3,000-5,000 *BRG*

John Duncan Fergusson, R.B.A.
(1874-1961)
British
Near St Tonge, Royan
Charcoal, black ink and watercolour, c1910
7 x 8¼in (17.8 x 21cm)
£1,900-2,500 *C(S)*

Frederick R. Fitzgerald
(late 19th/early 20thC)
British
Balholm (?) Norway
Signed and dated 1911, watercolour and
gouache over pencil
21¼ x 30½in (54 x 77cm)
£550-650 *S(S)*

Donald Hamilton Fraser (b1929)
British
Lindisfarne
Silkscreen, 26 colours
16 x 21in (40.5 x 53cm)
£200-225 *CCA*

Henry Charles Fox (1860-?)
British
Carting Hay at Sway, Hants
Signed and dated 1922, watercolour
14½ x 21¾in (37.3 x 55cm)
£1,650-1,850 *CG*

Mervyn Goode (b1948)
British
The River Bank in June
Oil
32 x 42in (81 x 106.5cm)
£2,600-2,800 *Bne*

*A self-taught painter, Goode's works celebrate
the English landscape, concentrating
particularly on the scenery and views of East
Hampshire and West Sussex. Many of his
paintings have been reproduced by The
Medici Society as greetings cards, a true
barometer of an artist's popular appeal with
the general public.*

Albert Goodwin (1845-1932)
British
Beachy Head
Signed and dated 1914, watercolour
10 x 16in (25 x 40.5cm)
£900-1,000 *RID*

Jean-Baptiste-Armand Guillaumin
(1841-1927) French
La Roche de L'Echo
Signed, oil on canvas
18 x 25¼in (48 x 64cm)
£20,000-25,000 *S*

Peter Graham (b1959)
British
Grey Day, Iona
Oil
12 x 16 in (31 x 40.5cm)
£650-750 *Bne*

Alan Gwynne-Jones, R.A. (1892-1982)
British
Spring Evening
Original etching
12 x 14⅓in (30.2 x 36.7cm)
£200-240 *CG*

Victor Higgins (1884-1949)
American
Adobe and Windmill
Signed, watercolour on paper,
c1920
15 x 21in (38 x 53.3cm)
£10,500-12,000 *S(NY)*

Rowland Hill (1919-79)
British
Irish Cottages, Connemara
Signed, inscribed on reverse,
oil on canvas board
12 x 17in (31 x 43cm)
£700-800 *LAY*

Hillier had a turbulent childhood. Born in Peking, where his father was manager of the Hong Kong and Shanghai Bank, his mother was an invalid who died of cancer when he was 12. His father went blind at the age of 30 and planned to shoot himself until a friend suggested he 'became a Roman Catholic instead'. This he did, sending his son to Downside. In his late teens, Hillier himself considered becoming a monk, spending some time at a trappist monastery in Mongolia. Their rigorous programme firmly extinguished all sense of vocation and he went to Cambridge University, subsequently joining a firm of chartered accountants. This unpromising situation provided him with the impetus to become an artist. Every morning a fresh sheet of blotting paper would be placed on his desk and the bored young man would cover it with drawings and doodles. According to Hillier's own report, one day an old company cashier confided that he had kept all these drawings and given them to his wife. You'll never make a chartered accountant,' he assured Hillier, '...you ain't got no 'eart for it. I says to my missus last night, ' 'e's an artist, that's what 'e is ... You go off and have some paintin' lessons, and one day you might be paintin' the Lord Mayor of London.' Hillier took his unlikely mentor's advice, and remembered him throughout his career as a painter.

Tristram Hillier, R.A. (1905-83)
British
December Sunset
Signed, inscribed with title, dated 1946 on reverse, oil on panel
7 x 10in (18 x 25.5cm)
£3,900-4,500 *S*

France Hilon (20thC)
French
Méditerranée
etching, 6 colours
19 x 15in (47.5 x 37.5cm)
£100-125 *CCA*

David Hockney, R.A. (b1937)
British
Glyndebourne
Signed print
£7,000-7,500 *BRG*

Thomas Swift Hutton (c1875-1935)
British
St Mary's Island; and Table Rocks, Whitley Bay
A pair, signed and dated 1924, watercolour
6½ x 12¼in (17 x 31cm)
£900-1,200 *AG*

James Dickson Innes (1887-1914)
British
Near Arenig, North Wales
Oil on paper, 1912
£2,900-3,500 *S*

François d'Izarny (20thC)
French
Brittany Coastline
Lithograph, 10 colours
22 x 29¾in (56 x 75.5cm)
£125-150 *CCA*

Andrew King (20thC)
British
Figures on the Beach
Watercolour
7 x 10in (18 x 25cm)
£200-230 *Wyk*

Elmyr de Hory (1905-78)
French
Fauve Landscape
Oil on canvas
25 x 31in (63.5 x 79cm)
£1,000-1,350 *BRG*

Ernst Lang (20thC)
German
A Chalet in the Alps
Signed and dated Ernst Lang München 22
Oil on canvas
16 x 24in (40.7 x 60.9cm)
£850-950 *CSK*

Louis Aston Knight (1873-1948)
British
A Farmhouse Along The River's Edge
Signed and inscribed Paris, oil on canvas
18½ x 21¾in (47 x 55.2cm)
£1,400-1,800 *S(NY)*

Kathleen Sylvester Le Clerc Fowle
(1903-92)
British
Storm over Malta
Signed and inscribed on reverse
28 x 36in (71 x 91.4cm)
£80-100 *CSK*

Peter Lanyon (1918-64)
British
Ilfracome Pier (sic)
Signed, inscribed and dated 1957 on reverse,
charcoal and wash
19½ x 16in (49.5 x 40.5cm)
£580-680 *CSK*

William Lee-Hankey, R.W.S. (1869-1952)
British
Afternoon Gossip
Signed, oil on panel
8 x 10½ in (20.5 x 27cm)
£1,700-2,000 *S*

Neville Lewis (20thC)
British
The Spanish Coast
Signed
18 x 25in (45.6 x 63.5cm)
£420-500 *CSK*

Donald McIntyre (20thC)
British
Highland Cottages by a Lane
Oil on hardboard
24 x 40in (61 x 101.5cm)
£800-1,200 *BRG*

Sidney M. Litten (1887-1949)
British
The Farmstead
Original etching
8 x 11⅖in (19.4 x 29cm)
£100-120 *CG*

Arthur Maderson (b1942)
British
Winter Sunshine, Co. Waterford
Oil
36 x 26in (92 x 66cm)
£2,000-2,500 *A*

Nicolas Lytras (1883-1927)
Greek
A Coastal Landscape
Signed in Greek, oil on canvas
21 x 17¾in (53.7 x 45cm)
£26,000-36,000 *C*

John Maclauchlan Milne, R.S.A.
(1885-1957)
British
Corrie, Arran
Bears title on a label attached to backboard
Oil on canvas
28¼ x 35¼in (72 x 89.5cm)
£9,500-10,500 S

Frank McKelvey, R.H.A. (1895-1974)
British
The Lagan Valley
Signed, oil on canvas
15 x 20in (38 x 51cm)
£8,000-9,000 S

Sir William MacTaggart, P.R.S.A., R.S.W.
(1903-81)
British
Lasswade Road and Stooks
Signed, oil on board
20 x 24in (51 x 61cm)
£3,800-4,500 S

Paul Mascart (1874-)
French
The Canal of Mons
Signed, oil on canvas
15 x 21½in (38 x 54.6cm)
£450-550 S(NY)

Peder Mønsted (1859-1941)
Danish
A Deciduous Forest in Winter
Signed and dated 1916, oil on canvas
44 x 67in (112 x 170cm)
£17,000-20,000 *S*

A. J. Meyer (20thC)
The Green, Cowes, Isle of Wight
Signed, watercolour
9 x 13in (23 x 33cm)
£1,250-1,450 *Ho*

Sidney Dennant Moss (20thC)
British
Irish Landscape
Oil on canvas
30 x 50in (76 x 127cm)
£850-950 *BRG*

John Miller (20thC)
British
Burnt Earth and Olive Trees
28 x 24in (71.5 x 61.5cm)
£2,650-2,850 *DM*

*Following the opening of John Miller's most
recent exhibition, David Messum reported a
75% sell-out of Miller's works at the private
view alone. 'I think the market is very alive a
the moment,' says Messum, encouragingly.
'In the contemporary field there is a growing
demand for good, traditional, romantic
paintings such as those by Miller. British
20thC art is very exciting and very under-
rated in price compared to works by Europea
and American painters. It's a marvellous and
often comparatively unexploited area for the
collector.'*

Derek Menery (20thC)
British
Towards Lyonesse
Acrylic
14 x 24in (36 x 61cm) **£400-475** *OLG*

Laslo Neogrady (1900-?)
Hungarian
A Valley in Spring
Signed Neogrady Laslo, oil on canvas
24 x 31½in (61 x 80cm)
£720-820 *CSK*

John Nash, R.A. (1893-1977)
British
Hills Near Kintail, Scotland
Signed, watercolour over traces of pencil
18 x 13¼in (46 x 34cm)
£900-1,000 *S*

*For his biographer and friend, John
Rothenstein, what distinguished Nash's work
from that of his contemporaries, including his
famous brother Paul Nash, is the artist's total
commitment to landscape itself. 'John Nash
lives in the country; he is an impassioned
gardener and botanist and a life-long and
single-minded lover of landscape,' wrote
Rothenstein in 1956. 'The landscapes of John
Nash are uncommon in that they are the work
of a countryman. His brother Paul also loved
landscape, but he brought to his
interpretations of it a town-sharpened and
inately literary intelligence and town-forged
weapons, but John is a countryman by life-
long residence and in all his interests. Where
Paul would write a manifesto or form a
group, John transplants some roses; where
Paul would cherish the words of Thomas
Browne or Blake, John consults a seed
catalogue.'*

**Christopher Richard Wynne Nevinson,
A.R.A.** (1889-1946)
British
St Ouen - Women Gardening
Signed, oil on panel
15¾ x 20in (40 x 51cm)
£5,600-6,600 *S*

Charles Oppenheimer, R.S.A., R.S.W.
(1875-1961)
British
Spring
Signed, oil on canvas
22½ x 29¼in (57 x 74cm)
£6,700-7,700 *S*

John Anthony Park (1880-1962)
British
The Life Ring
Oil on canvas laid on card
12 x 16in (31 x 41cm)
£3,000-3,250 *Mon*

Bror Julius Olsson Nordfeldt
(1878-1955)
Swedish, active in U.S.A.
Trees and Sunlight
Signed, watercolour on paper
15 x 22in (38 x 56cm)
£3,600-4,500 *S(NY)*

Simon Palmer (20thC)
British
The Small Farmer and
The Large Farm
Worker
Silkscreen, 26 colours
22 x 15¼in (56 x 39cm)
£125-150 *CCA*

James Paterson (1854-1932)
British
A Breton Harbour
Signed, oil on canvas
23½ x 28¼in (59.7 x 71.7cm)
£2,200-2,600 *Bon*

Lord Holroyd Pearce (1901-90)
British
Snow Scene near Wengen
Signed, oil
10 x 14in (25 x 36cm)
£240-280 *NBO*

James McIntosh Patrick, R.S.A. (b1907)
British
Littleton Den
Signed, oil on canvas
24 x 20in (61 x 51cm)
£4,000-5,000 *S*

Samuel John Peploe, R.S.A. (1871-1935)
British
A Perthshire Landscape
Signed, oil on canvas
15½ x 17¼in (39.5 x 44cm)
£17,000-20,000 *S*

Paulemile Pissarro (1884-1972)
French
La Saulée du Roule
Signed, oil on canvas
21¼ x 25½in (54 x 64.8cm)
£3,200-4,000 *S(NY)*

Jane Peterson (1876-1965)
American
The Trade Winds
Oil on canvas
24in (61cm) square.
£1,400-1,800 *S(NY)*

Philip C. Priestley (20thC)
British
Mullion Cove
Inscribed on reverse, oil on canvas
13 x 14in (33 x 35.5cm)
£170-250 *CSK*

Ernest Procter (1886-1935)
British
Boat on a River
Signed, oil on canvas
14 x 16in (36 x 41cm)
£680-750 *LAY*

Carlos Orozco Romero (20thC)
Latin-American
Valle de Mexico
Signed and dated 1944, oil on canvas
18 x 24in (46 x 61cm)
£18,500-22,500 *S(NY)*

Herbert Davis Richter (1874-1955)
British
Winter Rest
20 x 24in (51 x 61cm)
£1,000-1,500 *CSK*

Herbert Royle (1870-1958)
British
Haymaking
Signed, oil
19¾ x 23¾in (50 x 60cm)
£1,500-2,000 *AH*

Gaston Sebire (20thC)
French
Printemps Normand
Signed, oil on canvas
38 x 57½in (96.5 x 146cm)
£2,000-2,500 *S(NY)*

Charles Simpson (1885-1971)
British
The Prince of Wales' Covert, Quorn Country
Signed, gouache
15 x 21in (37.5 x 53.5cm)
£1,600-2,000 *S*

*During the 1920s, the artist frequently stayed
at Baggrave Hall in Leicestershire with the
Master of the Quorn, Major A. E. Burnaby.
The Fine Art Society's label records that this
work shows 'the Oak Tree planted by the late
King Edward in 1871'.*

Tony Brummell Smith (20thC)
British
Cows on the Banks of the River Nidd
Signed, pastel
24 x 28in (61 x 71cm)
£660-760 *WG*

Peggy Somerville (1918-75)
British
Spring at Newbourne
Signed on reverse, dated 1958, pastel
12 x 17½in (31 x 45cm)
£2,000-2,250 *DM*

Mark Spain (20thC)
British
The Temperate House, Kew
Etching, 6 colours
13 x 17½in (32.5 x 44.5cm)
£100-125 *CCA*

Leonard Russell Squirrell (1893-1979)
British
Golden Evening, Dovedale
Signed and inscribed 1944
12 x 19¼in (30 x 49cm)
£450-650 *AG*

Henry John Sylvester Stannard
(1870-1951)
British
Little Gleaners
Signed Sylvester Stannard RBA, pencil
and watercolour
10 x 14in (25.4 x 35.6cm)
£2,500-3,000 *C*

Philip Sutton (b1928) British
Snape Village
Signed and inscribed on reverse, dated 1957
Oil on canvas
10 x 14in (25 x 36cm)
£1,000-1,200 *BRG*

Graham Sutherland (1903-80)
British
Hangar Hill
Etching, 1929, signed in pencil, No. 52/77
5½ x 5in (14 x 13cm)
£700-900 *P*

Frank Taylor (20thC)
British
Oyster Fishermen's Huts, Arcachon
Acrylic
21in (53cm) square.
£850-950 *PHG*

Ludovico Tommasi (1866-1941)
Italian
Landscape
Signed, oil on paper laid down on paper
17¾ x 12¾in (45 x 32.5cm)
£3,100-3,500 *S*

Epaminondas Thomopoulos (1878-1974)
Greek
Returning Home
Signed in Greek, oil on canvas
32 x 25½in (81.3 x 65cm)
£11,600-12,600 *C*

Charles Frederick Tunnicliffe, R.A.
(1901-79)
British
Terns Mobbing a Heron
Signed, watercolour heightened with
scratching out
17½ x 26in (44.5 x 66cm)
£3,600-4,500 *S*

Allen Tucker (1866-1939)
American
Maple Trees
Signed, titled and dated 1930, watercolour
and charcoal on paper
20 x 14in (50.8 x 35.6cm)
£800-1,000 *S(NY)*

José Antonio Velasquez (20thC)
Active in Honduras
San Antonio de Orient
Signed and dated H.C.A. 1951, oil on canvas
20½ x 28½in (51 x 72.4cm)
£2,300-3,000 *S(NY)*

Alfons Walde (1891-1958)
Austrian
Spät Winter
Signed, oil on board, 1932
19 x 27½in (48 x 70cm)
£39,000-50,000 *S*

Frederick John Widgery (1861-1942)
British
Moorland View With Pool and Reeds
Signed, watercolour
10½ x 14in (27 x 36cm)
£500-580 *LH*

Jack Butler Yeats, R.H.A. (1871-1957)
Irish
Winter in Galway
Signed, oil on board
9 x 14in (23 x 35.5cm)
£9,500-10,000 *S*

Painted from Lady Gregory's house at Coole Park.

Andrew Wyeth (b1917) American
Rough Pasture
Signed, watercolour on paper laid down on board, 1939
21¾ x 29⅜in (55.2 x 75.6cm)
£45,000-60,000 *S(NY)*

Carel Weight, R.A. (b1908)
British
He's Seen The Demon Rider
Signed, oil on canvas
18 x 20in (46 x 51cm)
£2,500-3,000 *S*

Bridges

Bridges have always been a favourite subject
with the landscape and topographical artist,
and for this year's Guide we have isolated a
selection of works portraying them. The topic
serves as a bridge in itself between the
sections of the book devoted to rural
landscapes and urban views. Pictures include
small country stone bridges, railway bridges
and viaducts, the great engineering triumphs
of the 19thC, and urban bridges, instantly
recognisable landmarks of the great towns
and cities of the world. (See also Cities,
Towns and Street Scenes).

George Barret, R.A. (1732-84)
British
Classical River Landscape with a Figure
Crossing a Bridge and Figures Resting in the
Foreground
Oil on canvas, in a carved wood frame
13¼ x 18¼in (33.5 x 46.5cm)
£1,700-2,200 *S*

George Smith of Chichester (1714-76)
British
An Extensive River Landscape with
Fishermen, by a Bridge and Cottages Beyond
Signed and dated 1769
31½ x 39½in (80 x 100.4cm)
£10,500-12,000 *C*

Antonietta Brandeis (b1849)
Austrian
A View of the Ponte Vecchio, Florence
Signed, oil on panel
6½ x 9in (16.5 x 23cm)
£7,200-8,200 *S*

John T. Bowen (1801-56)
American
Natural Bridge, Virginia
Watercolour on paper
9¾ x 7¼in (24.8 x 18.4cm)
£2,300-2,800 *S(NY)*

Consalvo Carelli (1818-1900)
Italian
Figures Before a Shrine in an Extensive
Italianate Landscape
Signed and dated 1846, oil on canvas
41 x 34in (104.5 x 86.5cm)
£9,600-10,600 *P*

George Vicat Cole, R.A. (1833-93)
British
The River Crossing
Signed and dated 1868, oil on canvas
30 x 48in (76.2 x 122cm)
£7,000-8,000 *C*

William Fraser Garden (1856-1921)
British
St Neot's Bridge, St Ives
Signed and dated '95, watercolour
18¼ x 22¾in (46.5 x 57.5cm)
£8,300-9,300 *S*

Jasper Francis Cropsey (1823-1900)
American
Starrucca Viaduct, Susquehanna County,
Pennsylvania
Signed and dated 1896, oil on canvas
37 x 59in (94 x 150.2cm)
£54,000-60,000 *CNY*

*The Starrucca Viaduct, considered an
engineering triumph of the day as well as a
popular landmark, first captured Cropsey's
imagination on an excursion to the
Susquehanna Valley in 1853. The bold stone
viaduct, built by the Erie-Lackawanna
Railroad near Lanesboro, Pennsylvania, in
1848, inspired the artist with its dramatic
contrast to the 'green and delightful ...
meadows, the luxuriant and beautiful ... trees'
of the flourishing countryside. He painted
several versions of the bridge, which proved
an extremely popular subject with his
patrons.*

George Henry (1859-1943)
British
The Bridge
Signed, oil
20 x 24in (51 x 61cm)
£5,000-5,500 *Dr*

Engish School
Wharncliffe Viaduct, Hanwell, Middlesex
Pencil and watercolour
18 x 30½in (46 x 78cm)
£1,400-1,800 *CSK*

*The Viaduct, named after Lord Wharncliffe,
was designed by Isambard Kingdom Brunel
and was built in 1838 to cross the River
Brent. The view is taken from what is now
the Uxbridge Road.*

Maurice Lévis (1860-1940)
French
Le Vieux Pont à Mende
Signed, oil on canvas
16½ x 23¾in (42 x 60cm)
£3,300-4,000 *S*

John William North (1842-1924)
British
The Return from the Harvest Field
Signed and dated 1880, pencil and
watercolour heightened with bodycolour and
scratching out
11½ x 17¼in (29.2 x 43.8cm)
£8,000-9,000 *C*

William Mellor (1851-1931)
British
Ponty Aberglaslyn, N. Wales
Signed, oil on board
14½ x 8½in (37 x 21.5cm)
£750-850 *AH*

Eugène Joseph McSwiney, A.R.W.S.,
(b1866) British
Watching the Ducks
Signed, oil on canvas
16 x 24in (40.5 x 61cm)
£2,500-3,000 *S*

James Peel (1811-1906)
British
Pont y Garth, Capel Curig
Bears a signature and dated, oil on canvas
12½ x 20in (32 x 51cm)
£900-1,000 *S*

Charles Oppenheimer,R.S.A., R.S.W.,
(1875-1961) British
On the River Dee, Galloway
Signed, oil on canvas
28 x 36in (71.2 x 91.4cm)
£6,000-7,000 *C(S)*

David Roberts, R.A. (1796-1864)
British
The Bridge at Cordoba, Spain
Dated 1832, pencil and watercolour
heightened with white
10½ x 15in (27 x 38cm)
£5,600-6,600 *C*

Joseph Mallord William Turner, R.A.
(1775-1851) British
Abergavenny Bridge, Monmouthshire:
Clearing Up After a Showery Day
Signed 'Turner', signed again and inscribed
with title on reverse, pencil and watercolour
20 x 28¼in (51 x 71.8cm)
£72,000-85,000 *C*

*According to Turner's biographer, Walter
Thornbury, (Life of J. M. W. Turner, 1862),
Turner was extremely secretive about how he
painted his watercolours: 'he generally
painted with his door locked if he was at a
stranger's house; and if anyone approached
him or idlers tried to overlook him, he covered
his drawing. He had no special secrets to
hide; for Turner's colours were of little use to
men who had not Turner's brain. But he had
been accustomed as a boy to paint up in his
bedroom, and he could not change his solitary
habits. He did not like imitators, and he did
not wish absurd stories spread of his
mechanical artifices.'*

Joseph Thors (active 1863-1900)
British
Fishing Near The Bridge
Signed, oil on canvas
20 x 24in (51 x 61cm)
£5,500-6,000 *HFA*

Edward Charles Williams (1807-81)
British
A Towpath on the Thames
Signed with initials, oil on canvas
30¼ x 50½in (77x 128.3cm)
£3,700-4,500 *C*

**Samuel John Lamorna Birch, R.A.,
R.W.S.** (1869-1955)
British
River Dee at Lochnagar
Signed and dated 1952, oil on canvas
16 x 20in (41 x 51cm)
£1,000-1,400 *S*

Joseph Pennell (1860-1916)
American
Brooklyn Bridge, Lighting Up
Signed with monogram, c1900, inscribed on
reverse
10½ x 12½in (26.7 x 31.8cm)
£4,400-5,500 *S(NY)*

*Pennell had become a successful illustrator
and one of the few American artists working
in the painter/etcher tradition. He was a
founder member of the Society of Etchers in
Philadelphia and a member of the New York
Etching Club. He also produced watercolours
which have great charm and show Whistler's
influence on the artist.*

Max Beckmann (1884-1950)
British
Grosse Brücke
Drypoint, 1922, on thick wove paper, signed
in pencil, from an edition of about 50
16½ x 10in (42.7 x 25.5cm)
£27,000-35,000 *C*

Wat Miller (20thC)
British
November on Jamaica Bridge
Signed, oil on board
9¾ x 14in (25 x 35.5cm)
£850-1,000 *S*

Ed Smith (20thC)
British
New York Bridge
Watercolour on paper
22 x 36in (56 x 92cm)
£600-650 *JDG*

Joseph Southall (1861-1944)
British
A June Morning At Cahors
Signed with monogram, dated 1936,
Watercolour over pencil
12 x 18¾in (30.5 x 47.5cm)
£2,700-3,200 *S*

Jacqueline Rizui, R.W.S., N.E.A.C.
(b1944)
British
The White Drawbridge, St. Katherine's Dock
Signed, watercolour and gouache
24 x 28in (61 x 71cm)
£7,000-7,500 *Dr*

Valerie Thornton (20thC)
British
The Loire at Vendôme
Etching, 4 colours
9¼ x 14¼in (23.5 x 36.5cm)
£100-125 *CCA*

India

Thomas Daniell (1747-1840)
British
A Fort In India
Oil on canvas
27 x 38½in (68.5 x 97.8cm)
£2,900-3,500 *DN*

William Daniell, R.A. (1769-1837)
British
The Fortress of Chinnar on the Ganges
Watercolour over pencil
4 x 5½in (10 x 14cm)
£1,300-1,800 *S*

Andrew Nicholl, R.H.A.
(1804-86) British
A View of Colombo from
Mutwal Signed, watercolour
over pencil with scratching
out
18½ x 28¾in (47 x 73cm)
£3,600-4,600 *S*

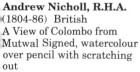

Thomas Colman Dibdin (1810-93)
British
Vihara Cave, India
Signed and dated 1844, watercolour over
pencil, heightened with bodycolour and gum
arabic
9¼ x 14½in (23.5 x 37cm)
£950-1,200 *S*

Sir Charles d'Oyly, Bt. (1781-1845)
British
The Road from Calcutta to Patna, with an
Elephant and a Camel
Oil on canvas
8½ x 11in (21.5 x 28cm)
£6,700-7,700 *S*

*D'Oyly was a talented amateur painter who
entered the service of the East India Company
in 1798 and held several government posts.
Whilst in Dacca he met George Chinnery and
went on painting expeditions with the
celebrated artist with whom he became a close
friend. One of the most productive periods
was during his time in Patna from 1821 until
1831, during which he was Opium Agent and
the Commercial Resident, when he produced
numerous topographical paintings and
sketches. '... he is the best gentleman artist I
have ever met with,' wrote his acquaintance,
Bishop Heber. 'He says India is a
beautiful and picturesque country, if people
would but stir a little from the banks of the
Ganges, and his own drawings and paintings
certainly make good his assertion.'*

F. Slate (19thC)
British
An Indian Village in a Wooded River
Landscape; and Sailing Boats and Indian
Shipping in an Extensive River Landscape
A pair, one signed and dated 1855
16 x 24in (41 x 61cm)
£2,900-3,500 *C*

Sir Charles d'Oyly, Bt. (1781-1845)
British
A View on the Ganges with Dhows
Oil on canvas
8 x 10½in (20.5 x 27cm)
£2,900-4,000 *S*

Albert Goodwin, R.W.S. (1845-1932)
British
The Taj Mahal, Agra
Signed, inscribed and dated 1917, pencil and
watercolour heightened with white on grey
paper
10 x 14in (25.5 x 36cm)
£2,600-3,000 *C*

William Walcot (1874-1943)
British
Perspective View of the South Elevation of
the Viceroy's House, New Delhi
Signed by Lutyens, dated 1914, watercolour
and bodycolour
18½ x 43½in (47 x 110.5cm)
£14,000-18,000 *S*

*Walcot was perhaps the greatest architectural
perspectivist of the early part of this century.
Born in Russia, he studied architecture in St.
Petersburg and practised in Moscow from
1897-1905. Leaving Russia for England in
1906 following the death of his wife from
tuberculosis, he found little architectural
work, but was soon in great demand by other
architects as a perspectivist, including
Lutyens who commissioned perspectives of his
buildings for New Delhi.*

*The announcement of this new capital for
India, replacing Calcutta in the winter
months and Simla in the summer, was made
by King George V at the Coronation Durbar at
Delhi in December 1911. Early in 1912,
Edwin Lutyens was asked to serve on the
three-man Commission set up to advise the
Government of India on the siting and layout
of the new capital. The Viceroy Lord
Hardinge wanted an Indian style city, but
Lutyens was able to persuade him that a
fusion of Eastern and Western styles would be
more appropriate and wrote: 'In giving India
some new sense of architectural construction,
adapted to her crafts, lies the great chance of
creating what may become a new and
inspiring period in the history of her art.'*

*The new Viceroy's House, larger than
Versailles, was regarded as a triumphant
synthesis of East and West, and is now
considered as Lutyen's masterpiece.*

Oriental Views

Gustav Bauernfeind (1848-1904)
Austrian
A View of Beirut from Brumana
Signed and dated Aug 1900, oil on board
9 x 12in (23 x 30.4cm)
£3,100-3,800 *C*

Robert Wade (b1945)
Australian
The Blue Gate, Fez
Signed and dated, watercolour
14 x 21in (36 x 53cm)
£1,000-1,250 *OSG*

Michel-François Préaulx (early 19thC)
French
The Golden Horn and the Marmara Sea
from the Uskudar Heights
Pencil and watercolour
10 x 17in (25.5 x 43.5cm)
£5,800-6,800 *C*

George Sheffield (1839-92) British
Oriental Fantasy
Watercolour
9½ x 13⅓in (24 x 34cm)
£1,400-1,500 *BCG*

Frederick R Fitzgerald** (exb. 1897-1938)
British
Malta Harbour, Constantinople
A pair, signed, watercolours
10¾ x 17½in (27.3 x 44.5cm)
£1,800-2,400 *DN*

Louis Claude Mouchot (b1830)
French
A Cairo Street
Signed and dated 1862, oil on canvas
28 x 18in (71.2 x 45.8cm)
£1,300-1,600 *CSK*

Lt. Col. Evelyn L. Engleheart
(exh. 1906-21)
British
The Gate to The Desert, Eikautaro, Algeria
Signed and dated '07, watercolour
13¼ x 9¼in (34 x 23.5cm)
£500-580 *CGa*

Harry Sutton Palmer (1854-1933)
British
Cairo
Signed, watercolour heightened with white
12½ x 18¼in (31.5 x 46.5cm)
£1,500-2,000 *S*

Attributed to Louis Tesson (19thC)
French
Beyond the City Walls
Bears initials LT, oil on canvas
24⅕ x 30in (62.3 x 76.2cm)
£1,900-2,400 *CSK*

CITIES, TOWNS AND STREET SCENES

The Oxford English Dictionary defines topography as 'the accurate and detailed delineation and description of any locality', or, as artist Henri Fuseli called it, the 'tame delineation of a given spot'. Many of the accurate and detailed views of townscapes and street scenes in the following pages were provided for tourists. 18thC view painters created innumerable pictorial souvenirs for the wealthy patrons visiting Italy on their Grand Tour; the expansion of the railways in the 19thC opened up Britain and the Continent to artists and tourists alike. In the days before the postcard, amateur painters travelled with paints and sketchbook in hand, while many people relied on the services of a professional artist or watercolour painter to provide a memento of their holiday or favourite view. According to Henry Wemyss of Sotheby's Watercolour Department, certain towns and sights can be guaranteed to appear at every sale: Italian, French and Spanish scenes; Middle Eastern and Greek views. Some subjects will have a general appeal, while more esoteric locations are more likely to sell to those with a specific interest. 'You can sell a Venetian picture to anyone,'

explains Wemyss, 'while a Greek view will, more often than not, end up with a Greek collector.'

In Britain, London and Thameside views are perenially popular themes and the City itself has been an inspiration to artists throughout the centuries. Portrayals of spa and seaside towns will abound from the period when they were patronised by Royalty or became desirable holiday spots, and certain places come into fashion with artists and visitors and then drop out again. The towns of the Yorkshire coast (e.g. Whitby and Scarborough) would no doubt find their place in a 'top ten' of British seaside towns portrayed in 19thC watercolours, giving way towards the end of the century to the towns and coastal sights of Cornwall. Cathedral cities and picturesque views of the great British towns are all commonplace and desirable subjects. Equally, however, less frequently portrayed locations such as the Channel Islands, in particular Jersey and Guernsey, often fetch good prices precisely because of their rarity. These are obviously particularly in demand with local dealers and residents.

Towns - General

Jacques Carabain (1834-92)
Belgian
Return From Market
Signed, oil on canvas
22½ x 16½in (57 x 42cm)
£4,600-5,600   *P*

Joseph Mallord William Turner, R.A.
(1775-1851)
British
Luxembourg From The North
Pen and red ink and watercolour heightened with bodycolour on blue paper
5¾ x 7¾in (13.7 x 18.7cm)
£67,000-80,000   *S*

This previously unrecorded watercolour is one of a group of views of Luxembourg which Turner seems to have completed in connection with the 'Rivers of Europe' project. Luxembourg is seen from the north looking towards the Rocher du Bock in the centre of the composition with the Rham towers visible beyond and the Pont du Château and the fortifications clearly delineated. A mist is seen rising from the river Alzette. This watercolour conveys vividly the height and impregnability of what was often referred to in Turner's day as the strongest fortress in Europe.

Rudolf von Alt (1812-1905)
Austrian
The Palace of Schönbrunn seen from the Ehrenhof, Vienna
Signed, watercolour heightened with white bodycolour on brown paper
10¼ x 18¼in (26.5 x 46.5cm)
£34,000-44,000   *S*

Anton Doll (1826-87)
German
Figures in a Town Square
Signed and inscribed München, oil on canvas
22¾ x 29½in (58 x 75cm)
£6,000-7,000 *P*

English School (c1840)
A Continental Town on a River
Watercolour
23 x 32in (58.5 x 81.2cm)
£1,300-1,800 *C*

Johann Nepomuk Geller (1860-1954)
Austrian
The Market Square, Misfrau
Signed, oil on canvas laid down on board
22½ x 30in (57 x 76cm)
£13,700-15,000 *CNY*

Angelo Garino (b1860)
Italian
A View of a Mediterranean Port
Signed and dated 1908, oil on panel
19 x 25¼in (48.5 x 64.5cm)
£3,500-4,000 *S*

Paul Marny (1829-1914)
French, active in Britain
A Continental Town Scene
Watercolour
9¼ x 6½in (24 x 17cm)
£600-680 *PCA*

G. Marney (19thC)
British
Continental Street Scenes
A pair, signed watercolours
12½ x 10in (32 x 25cm)
£480-580 *LH*

Arcadio Mas y Fondevila (1852-1934)
Spanish
The Flower Market
Signed and inscribed Rome, oil on panel
12½ x 8in (32 x 20.5cm)
£3,100-3,800 *P*

Charles Euphrasie Kuwasseg (1838-1904)
French
Townscape
Oil on canvas
7½ x 12in (19 x 31cm)
£2,800-3,300 *LT*

Jean François Raffaëlli (1850-1924)
French
Village Street Scene
Signed, oil on panel
7 x 5½in (17.5 x 14cm)
£4,500-5,500 *CNY*

Ivo Ambros Vermersch (1810-52)
Flemish
View of Nurembourg
Signed and dated 1850, oil on canvas
21 x 28in (53 x 71cm)
£35,000-37,000 *HFA*

Ivo Ambros Vermersch, born in Maldeghan on 9 January 1810, was a painter of town views - an illusive limner of bright sunlight on stunning architecture, as topographical as Springer but even more detailed and equally masterful in his composition. He painted the old buildings, squares and canals of his country cleverly and unemotionally, in a manner that is always reminiscent of his forefathers. He was a pupil at The Academy of Ghent, and later settled in Munich, from where he visited Italy.

Frederick William Booty
(late 19th/early 20thC)
British
Continental Street Market with Figures
Signed and dated 1916
30½ x 22in (78 x 56cm)
£650-750 *AH*

Eugeni Sinyov (b1952)
Russian
Warm Winter (Moscow)
Oil on canvas
23 x 31in (59 x 79cm)
£650-750 *SAV*

American Towns

Allan R. Crite (b1910)
American
Boston Street Scene
Signed and dated 1939, oil on canvas board
20 x 16in (50.8 x 40.6cm)
£700-800 *S(NY)*

Allan Crite did a series of neighbourhood paintings in the late 1930s and early 40s.

Charles Demuth (1883-1935)
American
Welcome To Our City
Signed and dated 1921, oil on canvas
25 x 20in (63.5 x 50.8cm)
£570,000-650,000 *S(NY)*

Charles Demuth's pioneering oils and temperas of 1920-21, architectural and industrial scenes of his native Lancaster, Pennsylvania, are few in number. These innovative works paved the way during the 1920's for a style and wide ranging artistic vocabulary that would become identified with the modern industrial reality of the day and which came to be labelled Precisionism.

Harry Shokler (b1896)
American
New York 9th Avenue and 17th to 19th
Signed and dated 1936, oil on canvas
24 x 40in (61 x 101.6cm)
£1,600-2,000 *S(NY)*

Guy Wiggins (1883-1962)
American
City Snow Storms
Signed and dated 1934 on reverse, oil on canvas
16 x 20in (40.6 x 50.8cm)
£6,000-6,500 *S(NY)*

Albert-François Fleury (1848-1925)
French
Michigan Avenue, Chicago
Signed and dated 1901, oil on board
12 x 18½in (31 x 47cm)
£8,000-8,500 *CE*

British & Irish Towns

Attributed to John Claude Nattes
(c1765-1822) British
North Parade, Bath
Inscribed on reverse, pen and grey ink, grey
wash, watermark Fleur-de-Lys
10½ x 14½in (26.7 x 36.5cm)
£1,000-1,500 *C*

*There is, perhaps, no better literary account of
Bath in the late 18thC and early 19thC than
in the novels and letters of Jane Austen.
While the smart set of London had moved on
to Regency Brighton, the country gentry still
repaired to Bath for relaxation and
amusement, hence the proliferation of pictures
and prints of Bath from this period. In
'Northanger Abbey', Jane Austen conjures up
a vivid picture of fashionable daily life in the
holiday town, when her young heroine,
Catherine Morland, pays her first visit there.
'Every morning brought its regular duties -
shops were to be visited, some new part of the
town to be looked at, and the Pump Room to
be attended, where they paraded up and down
for an hour looking at everybody and
speaking to no-one.' Night times were equally
busy, entailing theatre and concert parties
and balls in the Assembly Rooms. With
precise geographical descriptions and exact
street names, Austen describes the roads filled
with gigs and curricles, the pavements packed
with parties of ladies 'in quest of pastry,
millinery - or even ... young men,' and the
bustle of a town 'where everybody goes to see
and be seen.'*

*Austen's writings provide a revealing and
often amusing insight into the varied social
standing of British towns of the period: 'One
has no great hopes of Birmingham. I always
say there is something direful in the sound,'
advises Mrs Elton in 'Emma'.*

Henry Edridge, A.R.A., (1769-1841)
British
Taunton
Pencil, pen and brown ink, grey wash
12½ x 9¾in (31.5 x 24.7cm)
£900-1,300 *C*

*Although Edridge specialised in painting
small full-length portraits, he also painted
landscapes and topographical subjects.*

William James Boddy (1832-1911)
British
York From The New Walk
Signed with initials, inscribed and dated
1864, colour washes heightened with white
£4,200-5,200 *P(L)*

William Joseph Julius Caesar Bond
(1833-1928)
British
Whitby
Signed and dated '89, oil on canvas
14 x 21in (35.5 x 53.5cm)
£1,900-2,400 *S*

Frederick William Booty (19th/20thC) British
Whitby, Yorkshire
Signed and dated 1911
19½ x 29¼in (49 x 74cm)
£1,000-1,500 *AH*

Frank Thomas Carter (1853-1934)
British
Durham City
Signed
15 x 25in (39 x 64cm)
£350-450   *AG*

Alfred de Breanski (1852-1928)
British
The Fishermen's Quarter, Hastings
Signed, inscribed and dated 1882, oil on
board
17½ x 13½in (44.5 x 34.2cm)
£1,700-2,300   *C*

After Brocas (19thC)
Irish
Post Office, Sackville Street, Dublin
Coloured aquatint
24½ x 32¼in (62 x 82cm)
£4,200-5,200   *C(S)*

Frederick E. J. Goff (1855-1931) British
Norwich
Signed and inscribed with title, watercolour
heightened with bodycolour
6 x 4½in (15 x 11.5cm)
£1,000-1,200   *S*

Noel Harry Leaver (c1889-1951)
British
Bootham Bar, York
Signed
10¼ x 14in (26 x 36cm)
£1,000-1,400   *AG*

Alfred Leyman (1856-1933)
British
The Buttermarket, Dartmouth
Signed and dated 1893, watercolour
21½ x 15in (54.6 x 38cm)
£600-700   *Bon*

Charles Oppenheimer, R.S.A., R.S.W.
(1875-1961)
British
Signed and inscribed, oil on canvas
25 x 36in (63.5 x 91.5cm)
£2,500-3,000 *S*

W. Stuart Lloyd (active 1875-1929)
British
Chichester; Gloucester
A pair, both signed, inscribed with title, oil
on canvas
24 x 20in (61 x 51cm)
£1,800-2,200 *S*

Louise Rayner (1832-1924)
British
The Blue Bell, Northgate Street, Chester
Signed, watercolour
11½ x 18½in (29 x 47cm)
£14,000-14,500 *Pol*

*'Louise Rayner is always very popular with
our clients,' claims Simon Carter of the Polak
Gallery in London. 'In my opinion there is
not another watercolour artist of the period
who records architecture in such a human
fashion.' Louise Rayner was the daughter of
the architectural painter Samuel Rayner
(active 1821-72). Born in Derby, she was one
of five daughters, who all became artists of
some repute. Although her father had a great
influence on her work, he limited his subjects
to abbeys and churches. Louise portrayed the
towns and cities of Britain concentrating not
only on picturesque buildings and
architectural landmarks, but capturing the
hustle and bustle of city life. In her pictures,
carts clatter by, chimneys smoke and people
stop to gossip in the streets. According to the
Polak Gallery, her brother, Richard, also an
artist, might well have helped with gathering
material for her work since 'it probably
would not have been seemly for a lady to be
sketching at street corners at that time.'*

*A fine watercolour artist and the most gifted
member of a talented family, Louise Rayner
exhibited at the Royal Academy, the New
Watercolour Society and the British
Institution.*

J. W. Walshaw (d1906)
British
Lower Bridge Street, Chester, and another
Signed with initials, watercolour
5 x 7in (12.5 x 17.5cm)
£500-540 *DCG*

Thomas Miles Richardson, Snr.
(1784-1848)
British
The Foot of The Side, Newcastle-upon-Tyne,
1816
22½ x 17¼in (57 x 44cm)
£1,700-2,300 *AG*

James Isherwood (1917-91)
British
The High, Oxford
Signed and inscribed on reverse
Oil on canvas
18 x 24in (46 x 61cm)
£1,000-1,200 *BRG*

Fred Stead (1863-1940) British
Robin Hood's Bay, Woman Hanging Out The
Washing
Signed
19¾ x 15¾in (48 x 40cm)
£1,250-1,500 *AH*

John Syer (1815-85)
British
View of Nottingham from the River Trent
Signed and dated 1838
11½ x 17¼in (29.5 x 44cm)
£3,000-3,500 *MSW*

Frank H. Mason (1876-1963)
British
Robin Hood's Bay
Signed
12½ x 18in (32 x 46cm)
£750-1,000 *AH*

London

Attributed to Thomas van Wyck (1616-70)
Dutch
A View of Old Horse Guards Parade from St
James's Park with Tiltyard Stairs, the Old
Tennis Court, the Banqueting House and
Holbein Gate beyond
45½ x 72in (113 x 183cm)
£10,000-12,000 *C*

Robert Martin (19thC)
British
Martin's View of London Bridge, and another
Lithograph, published R. Martin, 124 High
Holborn, London 1832, part 1, A View of
London Bridge in the Year 1647, from an
engraving by Hollar.
£700-800 *CSK*

Edward Dayes (1763-1804)
British
View of St Paul's and Blackfriars Bridge from
The Thames
Signed on mount E. Dayes, dated 1791,
inscribed on reverse, watercolour over pencil
on original washline mount
5½ x 8½in (14 x 21.5cm)
£5,800-6,800 *S*

*If 19thC accounts are to be believed, Dayes,
though a fine draughtsman and an
influential teacher, was not a likeable figure.
According to W. Tornbury (see Biblio): 'Dayes
was a conceited, jealous man who eventually
got embarrassed and committed suicide, it
was supposed from envy at the progress of his
contemporaries - Turner and his old pupil
(Thomas Girtin).' So jealous was he of
Girtin's obvious talents that he confined his
apprentice to simply colouring in prints for
months on end, and when Girtin finally
refused to do any more of this menial work,
Dayes committed him to Bridewell Prison as
a 'contumacious apprentice'. There Girtin
amused himself by covering the white walls of
his cell with chalk landscapes. The Earl of
Essex came to see his sketches and was so
impressed that he purchased Girtin's
indentures from Dayes, obtained the artist's
release and remained one of Girtin's kindest
friends and patrons throughout the artist's
life.*

English School (c1780)
A View of St Paul's from the Thames, London
Bridge, the Monument and the City
Churches beyond
30 x 50in (76.3 x 127cm)
£7,000-8,000 *C*

Thomas Priest (active mid-18thC) British
View of Lambeth Palace from the Thames
Oil on canvas
21¼ x 31in (54 x 78.5cm)
£1,800-2,300 *S*

James Miller (active 1773-91)
British
A Sketchbook of Drawings of London and the
Upper Thames
42 leaves, disbound and mounted, one
inscribed: Jasper Scambles, Kings Ward, and
some other slight pencil notes, watercolour
over pencil, accompanied by the original
leather binding
7¾ x 12½in (20 x 32cm) opened
£25,000-35,000 *S*

*Miller is best known for his views of the
architectural sights of London and
Westminster, but the present sketchbook sheds
new light on his work. Many of the views
depict the riverside villages up the Thames -
Lambeth, Fulham, Battersea and Putney,
providing a poignant reminder that only 200
years ago there were farms in Marylebone and
that the quickest way from Richmond to the
City was by boat. The illustrations show
Miller as a man who delighted in the
everyday side of London life in all its variety,
from the coffee houses and great sights of the
City, to the rural retreats and country inns
along the banks of the Thames.*

William P. Sherlock (1775-1822)
British
Somerset House from the Thames
Oil on canvas
20 x 35½in (51 x 90cm)
£5,600-6,600 *PCA*

James Baynes (1766-1837)
British
Lambeth Palace from the West
Watercolour over pencil heightened with
bodycolour
8 x 12½in (20.5 x 31.5cm)
£480-580 *S*

Rose Maynard Barton, R.W.S. (1856-1929)
Irish
Hyde Park Corner
Signed and dated 1892, pencil, watercolour
and bodycolour
13¼ x 20¼in (33.7 x 51.5cm)
£5,600-6,600 *C*

*The daughter of an Irish solicitor, the artist
specialised in atmospheric views of Dublin
and London.*

Joseph Mallord William Turner, R.A.
(1775-1851) British
Old Blackfriars Bridge
Signed Turner and inscribed, pencil and
watercolour
8¾ x 5⅜in (22.2 x 14.7cm)
£12,000-13,000 *C*

*Among Turner's finished topographical
watercolours of the mid-1790s, there are a
number concentrating on oblique views of
bridges both in London and elsewhere, for
instance Magdalen Tower and Bridge of 1794,
and Westminster Bridge of about 1796.*

John Paul (19thC) British
A View of Whitehall with the Banqueting
House
17 x 30in (43.2 x 76.2cm)
£2,300-3,300 *C*

English Provincial School (early 19thC)
Smithfield Market, with St Bartholomew's
Hospital, St Bartholomew's the Less, and the
Church of St Sepulchre
Oil on canvas
21½ x 36in (55 x 91cm)
£10,000-11,000 *S*

John Glover (1767-1849)
British
Greenwich
Inscribed on old label, watercolour over
pencil heightened with bodycolour
16¼ x 22⅝in (41.5 x 57.5cm)
£6,000-7,000 *S*

William Parrott (1813-69)
British
The Foresters' Day at Crystal Palace
Signed, watercolour heightened with white
9¼ x 14in (23 x 36cm)
£1,500-1,700 *HN*

J. C. Stadler (late 18th/early 19thC)
British, of German extraction
View of London taken from Albion Place,
Blackfriars Bridge
Coloured aquatint, after a drawing by N. R.
Black, published in London in 1802
£5,500-6,000 *OG*

*This is a view of the first Blackfriars Bridge
which was built in 1760-69 after the designs
of Robert Mylne.*

James Pollard (1792-1867)
British
The New General Post Office, London, 1849
Coloured aquatint and line engraving, part
printed in colours, originally published July
1849, by J. W. Laird, 2 Barge Yard,
Bucklersbury
17½ x 27in (44.5 x 68.5cm)
£300-400 *CSK*

*James Pollard specialised in coaching subjects
and by extension covered many themes
connected with post and the mail. He worked
mainly for dealers and private patrons
including Edward MacNamara, a close friend
who had the sole contract of the Royal Mail.
Highly successful in his early years, Pollard's
life was to end in sadness. In 1840, both his
wife and youngest daughter died, a blow from
which he never truly recovered, and as the
railways ousted the stagecoach in the middle
of the century, so his favourite subject matter
disappeared. Pollard, his vogue outlived,
died in poverty.*

William Bowyer (b1926)
British
Chiswick Green
Oil on canvas
30 x 36in (76 x 92cm)
£3,200-3,500 *BRG*

John Vicat Cole (b1903)
British
The Old Cheshire Cheese,
Fleet Street
Oil on panel
16 x 12in (41 x 30.5cm)
£1,100-1,500 *C*

Hilda Davis (20thC)
British
Covent Garden Market
Signed and dated 1938,
on canvas laid down
on board
28 x 36in (71 x 91.5cm)
£1,000-1,400 *CSK*

Frederick Gore (b1913) British
Charlotte Street
Oil on canvas
26 x 30½in (66 x 77.5cm)
£8,000-8,500 *BRG*

Anthony Gross (b1905) British
Girl on a Bicycle, Fulham, 1948
Signed, inscribed and numbered 31/50
6¾ x 7¾in (17 x 20cm)
£400-450 *BLD*

Louis Grimshaw (1870-1943)
British
St Paul's
Signed and dated 1901
11½ x 17¼in (29 x 44cm)
£6,000-7,000 *AG*

Norman Hepple (b1908)
British
St Martin's in the Fields
from the steps of the
National Gallery
Oil on canvas
36 x 28in (92 x 71cm)
£3,500-3,700 *BRG*

Jeremy King (20thC)
British
Westminster Bridge
Lithograph, 10 colours
16 x 24in (40.5 x 61cm)
£100-125 *CCA*

*'The limited edition print bridges the gap
between a painting and a poster,' explains
Ruth Tufnell of the CCA Galleries in London,
who specialise in prints by contemporary
artists, including Jeremy King. 'It is an ideal
way of providing original and affordable art.
People are more educated now and want
original works of art but not everybody has
perhaps thousands of pounds to spend. A
high quality, limited edition print, signed and
numbered by the artist, can cost less than
£100. Prints fill a very important gap in the
market, and can provide work, from the
artist's own hand, that many more people can
afford to enjoy.'*

Max Hofler (1892-1963)
British School
Summertime, Brompton Oratory
Signed, oil
20 x 24in (51 x 61cm)
£1,250-1,450 *Dr*

Alan Sorrell (1904-74)
British
Londinium Romanum
Signed and dated 1959, oil on canvas laid
down on board
102 x 144in (259 x 366cm)
£1,000-1,500 *C*

*This work was commissioned from the artist
by Balfour, Williamson & Co., and was
located in the main entrance hall of Roman
House, Wood Street in the City of London. It
depicts Roman London in the 3rd Century
A.D. and shows examples of Roman relics
which have been excavated in the Wood Street
area of the City.*

Rowland Suddaby (1912-72)
British
London Car
Oil on panel
25 x 17in (64 x 43cm)
£2,550-2,750 *BRG*

William Walcot, R.A. (1874-1943)
British
Carriages on a London Street
Signed, watercolour and pencil
7½ x 9¼in (19 x 23.5cm)
£3,300-4,000 *S(S)*

Charles Youldon (20thC)
British
London from Shooters Hill
Signed and dated 1945,
inscribed on label on
reverse
19½ x 26¼in (49.5 x 66.6cm)
£300-350 *CSK*

Carel Weight (b1908)
British
Fetter Lane 1908
Signed, oil on canvas
10 x 14in (25 x 35.5cm)
£13,000-13,500 *BRG*

Dutch & Flemish Towns

Dutch School (17thC)
A Landscape with Townsfolk on a frozen
Waterway by a Church
On copper
10¼ x 15¼in (26.2 x 38.7cm)
£40,000-50,000 *C*

Thomas Heeremans (active 1660-97)
Dutch
A Winter Landscape with Townsfolk on the
Ice by a Town Wall; and A Village on a River
with Peasants Smoking and Drinking outside
an Inn
The first signed and dated THMans 1697 (TH
in monogram)
19 x 25½in (48.3 x.64.5cm)
£23,000-30,000 *C*

Attributed to Frans de Momper (1603-60)
Flemish
A View in a Town in Winter
Oil on panel
15¼ x 20¼in (38.5 x 51.7cm)
£16,600-18,600 *S*

*As the present painting demonstrates, a work
does not have to be in perfect condition to find
a buyer. Modern day restoration techniques
have become highly sophisticated. A painting
that might look in a disastrous state to the
amateur will appear highly promising to the
professional eye. With the help of a good
restorer, the natural ravages of time can often
be halted and reversed. Far more damaging
to the value of a picture is poor restoration,
repainting or over-cleaning when the
individual qualities of a work have been lost
and the result is irretrievable. Pictures that
have never been touched will almost
invariably fetch better prices than those that
have been unsympathetically restored and,
where possible, auction houses will generally
advise vendors to offer works in their original
condition and to leave them as they are,
damage and all.*

Jacob van Liender (1696-1759)
Flemish
A View of the Ramparts of Utrecht with the
Bastion Zonnenburg near the Tolsteegpoort
and the Wittevrouwenpoort
Signed, pen and brown ink, watercolour,
heightened with white, pencil framing lines
8 x 12in (20 x 31cm)
£2,000-2,400 *C(Am)*

Elias Pieter van Bommel (1819-90)
Dutch
A Church Beside a Canal
Signed, oil on canvas
32¼ x 44in (82 x 112cm)
£27,000-35,000 *S*

Belgian School (19thC)
A Procession in the Meir,
Antwerp
Oil on panel
12¼ x 15¼in (31 x 39cm)
£4,700-5,700 *S*

Jacques Carabain (1834-92)
Belgian
A Busy Street Market in a Continental Town
Signed, oil on canvas
30¼ x 24½in (77 x 62cm)
£17,000-18,000 *P*

Cornelis Springer (1817-91)
Dutch
De Poort in Buuren by Zomer
Signed and dated 1865, oil on panel
10 x 8¼in (25.5 x 21cm)
£8,000-9,000 *CNY*

S* Van Der Ley** (19thC)
Dutch
The Jewish Quarter, Amsterdam
Signed, oil on panel
22 x 17¾in (55.8 x 45)
£1,500-2,000 *L*

William Dommersen (d1927)
Dutch
A View of Rotterdam with the Boompjes
Canal and Saint Laurent's Church in the
background
Signed, oil on canvas laid down on board
24 x 39¾in (61.5 x 101cm)
£2,900-3,500 *S*

Johannes Christiaan Karel Klinkenberg
(1852-1924)
Dutch
A View of a Dutch Town with Barges Moored
Beside the Harbour Wall
Signed, oil on canvas
15½ x 18½in (39 x 47.3cm)
£9,000-10,000 *P*

Jan Hendrick Verheyen (1778-1846)
Dutch
A Dutch Street Scene
Signed with initials, indistinctly dated, oil on panel
13 x 16in (33 x 41cm)
£3,800-4,500 *S*

Joselin Bodley (20thC)
British
Bruges
Signed inscribed, and dated 1936, oil on canvas
12¾ x 9½in (32 x 24cm)
£480-580 *LW*

Fredericus Jacobus Van Rossum Du Chattel (1856-1917)
Dutch
A View of Dordrecht
Signed, oil on canvas
22¾ x 33in (57.7 x 83.8cm)
£4,200-5,000 *C(S)*

J. F. Spohler (1853-94)
Dutch
Dutch Canal, and Street Scene with Figures
A pair, oil on panel
7 x 5½in (18 x 14cm)
£2,600-2,800 *HCH*

French Towns

Whereas the towns and buildings of Northern France attracted the artists of the 19thC, the 20thC saw them moving down south to the villages of Provence and the coastal resorts of the Riviera. Paris, however, has remained a continuously popular subject. Painters such as Eugène Galien-Laloue and Edouard Cortès devoted the majority of their careers to portraying Paris, famous buildings and sights, (Nôtre Dame, the Louvre, and the Arc de Triomphe) elegant backdrops for an endless stream of shoppers and bourgeois pedestrians promenading down the city's tree-lined streets and boulevards.

Miles Birket Foster (1825-99)
British
Fair at Quimper
Watercolour
4 x 7in (10 x 17.5cm)
£6,750-7,250 *ChG*

Charles Euphrasie Kuwasseg (1838-1904)
French
A View of Dieppe Harbour
Signed and dated 1883, oil on canvas
16 x 19¼in (41 x 49cm)
£2,800-3,400 *S*

Samuel Prout, O.W.S. (1783-1852)
British
Café de la Place, Rouen
Signed, inscribed as title and numbered 3, pencil and watercolour heightened with scratching out
27¾ x 20½in (70.5 x 52cm)
£5,800-6,800 *C*

Alexander Akerbladh (b1866)
British
The Harbour at St Tropez
Oil on board
14 x 18in (36 x 46cm)
£1,000-1,200 *ALT*

Charles Cousin (19th/20thC)
French
Ville Franche (Riviera)
Signed, oil on canvas
19¾ x 25½in (50.2 x 64.8cm)
£800-900 *S(NY)*

Raoul Dufy (1877-1953)
French
Sainte-Adresse
Signed, oil on board
9 x 21½in (22.5 x 55cm)
£17,000-18,000 *S*

*Technically, Dufy was astonishingly gifted.
When training at the Ecole des Beaux Arts in
Paris, according to his biographer Alfred
Werner, he achieved such virtuosity with his
right hand that he deliberately switched to
using his left, which he eventually came to
prefer. While his showman-like facility and
joyous, decorative canvases brought him
many wealthy clients and huge popular
success, his work did not always please the
critics. He was compared to a milliner, and
one commentator said scathingly that when
looking at Dufy's paintings, he heard the
tinkling of champagne glasses. 'If Fragonard
could be so gay about the life of his time,'
countered Dufy cheerfully, 'why can't I be just
as gay about mine?'*

Frederick William Elwell (19th/20thC)
British
Caravans at Cahors
Signed
15½ x 11½in (40 x 29.5cm)
£2,600-3,000 *DA*

John Maclauchlan Milne (1885-1957)
British
Street of the Four Winds, St Tropez
Signed and dated '33, oil on canvas
29 x 36in (74 x 91cm)
£16,000-16,500 *PaHG*

Glen Scouller (20thC) British
Stairs to the Castle, La Verdière
Watercolour
21 x 29in (53 x 74cm)
£1,000-1,150 *RB*

Elisée Maclet (1881-1962)
French
Bastia, Place de la Galetta, Corse
Signed, oil on canvas
25½ x 32in (64.8 x 81.3cm)
£7,000-8,000 *S(NY)*

Maurice Utrillo (1883-1955)
French
Scène de Rue
Signed and dated 1935, gouache
19½ x 24¾in (50 x 64cm)
£35,000-45,000 S

Maurice de Vlaminck (1876-1958)
French
Scène de Rue
Signed, oil on canvas
15 x 18½in (38.5 x 46.5cm)
£37,000-45,000 S

Paris

Alexandre Jean Noël (1752-1834)
French
A View of Paris with Nôtre Dame in the
Distance
Inscribed on boat lower left Vernet 1768
Oil on canvas
20 x 34in (50.8 x 86.4cm)
£22,000-30,000 S(NY)

*The artist was a student of Claude Joseph
Vernet and Louis Sylvestre, and exhibited
often in the Salons between 1800 and 1822.
He was a tireless voyager, and among the
places he visited were California, Spain and
Portugal.*

John Fulleylove (1847-1908)
British
Paris
Signed, pencil and watercolour
7¼ x 10¾in (18.3 x 27.3cm)
£900-1,100 Bon

Ian Armour-Chelu
(20thC)
British
Nôtre Dame, Paris,
Against a Sunset
Watercolour
8½ x 11½in (21 x 29cm)
£600-685 PHG

Ludwig Bemelmans (1898-1963)
American
Sacre Coeur and Nun on a Motorcycle
Signed, oil on canvas
42 x 30in (106.7 x 76.2cm)
£2,800-3,400 S(NY)

Antoine Blanchard (1910-88)
French
Moulin Rouge, Paris
Oil on canvas
18 x 21½in (46 x 54.5cm)
£9,000-9,500 *OM*

Amedée Julien Marcel-Clément (b1873)
French
Après l'Averse, Place de la Concorde
Signed, inscribed and dated 1911 (?) Paris, oil
on board
24 x 29in (61 x 73.7cm)
£5,100-6,000 *C*

Edouard Cortès (1862-1969)
French
Nôtre Dame, Les Quais, Paris
Signed, oil on canvas
13 x 18¼in (33 x 46.4cm)
£4,200-5,000 *C*

Jules Herve (1887-1981)
French
Grande Bassin des Tuileries, Paris
Oil on canvas
25 x 31½in (63 x 80cm)
£8,000-8,500 *OM*

Charles Jouas (1866-1942)
French
Building the Paris Metro
Signed, watercolour on paper
26¾ x 36¼in (68 x 92cm)
£3,800-4,500 *CNY*

Luigi Loir (1845-1916)
French
Twilight on the Avenue de Neuilly, Paris
Signed, oil on canvas
12¼ x 21¼in (31 x 54cm)
£7,200-8,000 *S*

Gaspar Miro Lleo (1859-1930) Spanish
The Seine with Nôtre Dame; and A Street
Scene, Paris
Both signed, one oil on panel and one oil on
board
9½ x 13in (24 x 33cm)
£2,100-2,600 *C*

William Bruce Ellis Ranken (1881-1941)
British
Fountains at Versailles
Signed, inscribed and dated 1939, oil on
canvas
29½ x 56in (75 x 142cm)
£3,400-4,000 *S*

Joaquin Pallares y Allustante (1853-1935)
Spanish
Signed and dated 1901, oil on canvas
15 x 18in (38 x 45.7cm)
£4,000-5,000 *C*

Georges Stein (20thC)
French
Elegant Figures before the Arc de Triomphe,
Paris
Signed and inscribed, pencil, watercolour and
coloured chalks
15 x 19in (38 x 48.2cm)
£1,500-2,000 *CSK*

Italian Towns & Views

George Heriot (1759-1839)
British
A Procession by Pisa Cathedral
Watercolour over pencil heightened with
bodycolour
5 x 8in (20.5 x 12.5cm)
£800-900 *S*

Jacob van der Ulft (1627-89)
Dutch
A View along the Walls of an Italianate City
Signed, pen and brown ink and wash, brown
ink framing lines
6 x 8in (15.6 x 20cm)
£2,000-3,000 *C(Am)*

Antonietta Brandeis (b1849)
Bohemian
Palazzo Vecchio from Boboli Gardens,
Florence
13¼ x 9¼in (33.7 x 23.6cm)
£7,200-8,000 *C*

Antonio Canal, Il Canaletto (1697-1768)
Italian
Mestre; and An Imaginary View of Padua
Etchings, before 1744, watermark Initial R
11 x 17in (30 x 43.3cm)
£5,800-6,800 *C*

*Canaletto was the leading Italian view
painter of his time and he enjoyed huge
commercial success in particular with
English patrons. According to many
contemporary reports, success definitely
spoiled him and he was not above exploiting
his many eager clients: 'The fellow is
whimsical and varies his prices every day,'
complained Owen McSwiney in a letter to
Lord March, later Duke of Richmond, in
1727, 'and he that has a mind to have any of
his work, must not seem to be too fond of it,
for he'll be the worst treated for it, both in the
price and the painting too. He has more
work than he can do in any reasonable time,
and well: but by the assistance of a particular
friend of his, I get once in two months a piece
sketched out and a little time after finished,
by force of bribery.'*

William Leighton Leitch (1804-83)
British
An Italian Hill Town at Dusk
Watercolour
6¾ x 10½in (17 x 28cm)
£1,000-1,200 *PCA*

Charles Earle, R.I. (1832-93)
British
In the Piazza del Erbe, Verona
Signed and inscribed, watercolour over pencil
heightened with bodycolour
20½ x 13½in (52 x 34.5cm)
£1,000-1,400 *S(S)*

Martin Rico y Ortega (1833-1908)
Spanish
A Sunlit Piazza
Signed, oil on canvas
22¼ x 18in (56.5 x 46cm)
£3,000-4,000 *CNY*

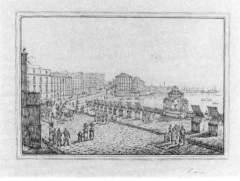

Antonio Senape (active c1830-50)
Italian
A Set of Six Views in Italy
Pen and ink
6 x 9½in (15.5 x 24cm)
£1,700-2,200 *P*

Michael Richardson (b1933)
British
Via Lazzaretto, Milan
Signed, oil
24 x 20in (61 x 51cm)
£400-450 *Dr*

Graham Clarke (b1941)
British
Italics
Etching, hand coloured, edition size: 400
10½ x 10in (26.5 x 25.5cm)
£125-155 *GCP*

Rome

Manner of Hendrik Frans van Lint
(1684-1763)
Flemish
The Colosseum, Rome
Oil on canvas
13½ x 17in (35.7 x 43.5cm)
£1,900-2,400 *CSK*

Italian School
The Pantheon, Rome; and Lake Mori
A pair, oil on vellum
6 x 9in (15.2 x 22.8cm)
£1,700-2,000 *CSK*

Jean-Achille Benouville (1815-91)
French
Villa Medici, Rome
Signed and dated 1860, oil on panel
21½ x 36in (55 x 91.5cm)
£21,000-30,000 *C*

Victor-Jean Nicolle (1754-1826)
French
A View of the Arch of Septimus Severus,
Rome
Signed and inscribed, pen and brown and
black ink, watercolour
6in (15cm) diam.
£3,400-4,000 *C*

Giovanni Battista Piranesi (1720-78)
Italian
Vedute di Roma: 111 plates
Etchings, 1748-75, presumably a set as
issued c1775.
23 x 32½in (58 x 82cm)
£61,000-75,000 *C*

*Architect, designer and engraver, Piranesi
was one of the most influential and
imaginative graphic artists of his period, and
Rome was his principle theme. 'Study the
sublime dreams of Piranesi, who seems to
have conceived visions of Rome beyond what
is boasted even in the Meridien of its
splendour,' exhorted Horace Walpole in 1771.
'Savage as Salvator Rosa, fierce as Michel
Angelo, and exuberant as Rubens, he has
imagined scenes that would startle geometry,
and exhaust the Indies to recognise. He piles
palaces on bridges, and temples on palaces,
and scales heaven with mountains of edifices.
Yet what taste in his boldness! What
grandeur in his wildness! What labour and
thought both in his rashness and details!'*

Circle of Paolo Sala (1859-1924) Italian
Figures on a Terrace beside a Fountain, a
View of Rome Beyond
Oil on panel
7 x 11in (18 x 28cm)
£330-450 *P*

Michele Cascella (b1892) Italian
Rome, The Forum
Signed and dated Roma 1932, pen and
watercolour
28 x 42in (96.5 x 106.7cm)
£3,200-4,000 *DN*

P. Götz Pallmann (1908-66) German
Piazza Navona, Rome
Signed, oil on board
19½ x 27in (49.5 x 68.5cm)
£3,000-4,000 *Bon*

John Yardley (b1936)
British
Green Shutters, Rome
Watercolour
9 x 12in (22.5 x 31cm)
£650-750 *Bne*

Classical & Ancient Ruins

Manner of Claude (17thC)
French
Classical Landscape with Figures Offering a
Sacrifice Before a Temple
Oil on canvas
28½ x 47½in (72.5 x 120.6cm)
£3,400-4,000 *S(S)*

Circle of Pier Francesco Cittadini
(1616-81)
Italian
A Garland of Assorted Flowers surrounding
an Architectural Ruin in a Garden with a
Fountain; and A Garland of Assorted Flowers
surrounding Classical Buildings beside a
Bridge
A pair, oil on canvas
25½ x 44in (90 x 112cm) and 35¾ x 43¾in (91
x 111cm)
£5,300-6,300 *P*

Follower of Viviano Codazzi (17thC)
Italian
A Capriccio of Classical Ruins with Peasant
Women and Philosophers
Oil on canvas
51½ x 39in (133.3 x 99.4cm)
£8,000-9,000 CSK

Jacob van der Ulft (1627-89)
Dutch
An Extensive Capriccio of a Mountainous
Shore, with Classical Ruins, a Castle and
Soldiers Leading Captives Towards a Ship
Signed, gouache on vellum, laid down on
panel
7½ x 10in (18.5 x 25.5cm)
£9,500-10,500 S(NY)
Van der Ulft's gouaches are very rare.

Louis François Cassas (1756-1827)
French
Grand Tourists and Greeks by the Monument
of Philopappos, Greece
Signed and dated 1821, pen, ink and
watercolour
27 x 42in (68.6 x 106.7cm)
£31,000-41,000 Bon

*The monument of Philopappos stands on the
crest of Mousein Hill near Athens. It was
erected in 114-116 A.D. in honour of the
exiled Prince of Commagene, C. Julius
Antiochus Philopappos, who settled in
Athens, assuming a number of civic and
religious offices. The monument contained a
burial chamber and was richly ornamented
on the exterior. It is thought to have
remained almost intact until the mid-15th
Century, when Cyriacus of Ancona recorded
the inscriptions on its façade.*

Giovanni Battista Busiri (1698-1757)
Italian
The Porta San Giovanni, Rome; the Pyramid
of Caius Cestius, Rome; The Porta Romana,
Florence; and Pilgrims on a Path in a Wooded
Landscape
Four, inscribed, black chalk, pen and brown
ink, fragmentary watermark A above
encircled paschal lamb on (1) and (3)
7 x 9in (17.2 x 22.8cm)
£1,200-1,600 C

Jacob Philipp Hackert (1737-1807)
German
The Tomb of the Horatii and Curiatii
Signed, inscribed and dated 1770, black
chalk, pen and black ink, watercolour,
watermark HONIG
13½ x 18½in (40 x 47.5cm)
£10,200-11,500 C

Attributed to Gilles-Marie Oppenord
(1672-1742)
French
A Ruined Classical Monument in a Park
Black chalk, pen and brown ink, grey wash,
watermark grapes
16¾ x 11in (42.6 x 27.8cm)
£2,700-3,200 *CNY*

Alexis-Nicolas Perignon (1726-82)
French
Landscape with a Rotunda and a Triumphal
Arch
Signed and dated 1776, black chalk,
watercolour, bodycolour
7½ x 12in (29.7 x 31cm)
£3,800-4,500 *CNY*

Amadeo, 5th Count Preziosi (1816-82)
Maltese
A Greek Guide Showing Visitors the
Parthenon, a View of Athens beyond
Signed indistinctly and dated 1881, pencil
and watercolour
16½ x 27in (41.5 x 69cm)
£5,300-6,000 *P*

**Jan Frans van Bloemen, called
Orizzonte** (1662-1749)
Flemish
Figures Resting Before the Tomb of the Orazi
and Curiazi
Oil on panel
14 x 18in (36 x 46cm)
£1,200-1,600 *P*

Studio of Giovanni Paolo Panini
(1691-1765)
Italian
A Capriccio of Classical Ruins with Marcus
Curtius
31 x 49in (78.3 x 12.7cm)
£19,000-22,000 *C*

*Whereas Canaletto was the leading view
painter of Venice, Panini was his equivalent
in Rome. He recorded views of the city, both
contemporary and archeological for the
visiting English 'mi-lords' and grand tourists.
As David Piper notes (see Biblio), he also
popularised the capriccio or 'ruinscape',
grouping several famous monuments of
antiquity together in one composition, thus
offering the thrifty visitor three or more views
for the price of one. Such skillful marketing
techniques were highly successful and
Panini's works were exported all over Europe.
His popularity continues today. Though only
catalogued as Studio of Panini, the work
doubled its estimate at auction.*

G. G. Lanza (b1827)
Italian
Extensive Italian Landscape with Figures
and Cattle in the foreground, Classical Ruins
and Mountains beyond
Signed
17 x 29in (42 x 72cm)
£950-1,200 *HSS*

Luigi Rossini (1853-1923)
Swiss
Avanzi di una Gran Sala Termale in Villa
Adriana Vicino a Tivoli
Etching, published in Rome, 1925, with 22
others similar
19 x 23½in (48 x 60cm)
£1,500-2,000 *P*

*** Tosatto (19thC) Italian
The Arch of Constantine, Rome
Signed, watercolour
9¼ x 16in (23.5 x 40cm)
£750-850 *S*

Eugène Berman (1899-1972)
Russian
Antique Fragments in a Roman Garden
Signed with initials and dated 1854, oil on
canvas
18 x 12in (45,7 x 30.5cm)
£1,500-2,000 *S(NY)*

Carl Werner (1808-94) German
A View of the Colossus of Thebes, Egypt
Signed and dated 1865 Thebes, watercolour
14½ x 24½in (37 x 62cm)
£2,600-3,200 *S*

Frederic James (20thC)
Olympia
Signed, titled and dated 55, watercolour and
pencil on paper
19¾ x 15¾in (50.2 x 40cm)
£300-400 *S(NY)*

Naples & Neapolitan Views

John 'Warwick' Smith (1749-1831)
British
Entrance to the Grotto of Posillipo, Naples
Signed and inscribed, 1780s, watercolour
over pencil
9 x 13¼in (23 x 34cm)
£2,600-3,100 *S*

Giuseppe Carelli (1858-1921)
Italian
Fishermen Tending Their Nets in the Bay of
Naples
A pair, indistinctly signed, oil on panel
10 x 18½in (25.5 x 47cm)
£4,100-5,000 *P*

Neapolitan School (mid-19thC)
Grotta di Pozzuoli; Eruzione de 22 Xbre,
1832; and Camaldoli di Napoli
Inscribed, bodycolour and gum arabic
8 x 11¼in (20.2 x 28cm)
£2,000-2,500 *C*

Xavier della Gatta (active 1777-1811)
Italian
A View from Mergellina of Palazzo
Donn'Anna, Posillipo in the Distance,
Fishermen in the Foreground
Signed and dated 1780, tempera
12½ x 22in (31.5 x 56cm)
£21,000-26,000 *S(NY)*

Carl Fredrik Aagaard (1833-95)
Danish
Amalfi dai Cappuccini
Signed and dated 1872, oil on canvas
28½ x 38¾in (72 x 98.5cm)
£13,000-14,000 *C*

Giacinto Gigante (1806-76) Italian
Figures on the Waterfront at Naples; and
Figures on a Terrace overlooking Naples
A pair, signed, oil on board
7½ x 10½in (19 x 26.6cm)
£14,500-16,000 *CSK*

Neapolitan School (19thC)
A View near Naples
Gouache
21 x 28½in (54 x 72.4cm)
£2,300-2,800 *Bon*

Neapolitan School (19thC)
Eruzione de 26 Otte 1822
Signed and inscribed, gouache
21 x 29¾in (53.3 x 75.5cm)
£1,400-1,800 *Bon*

This and the following work were from a set of 5 highly decorative gouaches, sold by Bonhams, and discovered by the vendor's father in a bombed hotel on the South Coast during the last war. Although told to throw them away, his daughter had concealed them in her attic. Worth very little 50 years ago, they all fetched sums of over £1,000 and more, suggesting that sometimes it is better not to listen to your parents!

Neapolitan School (19thC)
A View of Naples with Posillipo in the Background
Gouache
11½ x 17in (29 x 43cm)
£2,500-3,000 *S*

Attilio Pratella (1856-1949)
A Woman on a Terrace Overlooking the Bay
of Naples
Signed, oil on panel
8½ x 13½in (22 x 34.5cm)
£6,600-7,600 *P*

Charles Rowbotham (active 1877-1914)
British
Naples from Mergellina
Signed, water and bodycolour
8 x 16in (20.3 x 40.8cm)
£900-1,200 *Bon*

Jean-Charles-Joseph Remond (1795-1875)
French
Entrée du Port de Palerme
Signed, inscribed and dated 1842, oil on canvas
8½ x 14½in (21.6 x 36.9cm)
£3,900-4,600 *C*

Neapolitan School
(20thC)
On the Waterfront,
Naples Bears indistinct
signature and date
1847, oil on canvas
13 x 18in (33 x 45.7cm)
£8,300-9,300 *CSK*

Jan Hendrick Verheyen (1778-1846)
Dutch
A Canalside Town
Signed, oil on canvas
24¾ x 33½in (63 x 85cm)
£8,500-10,000 *S*

Rudolf von Alt (1812-1905)
Austrian
A View of the Michaelerplatz, Vienna
Signed and dated '888, watercolour
12¾ x 18½in (32.5 x 47cm)
£32,000-42,000 *S*

François-Antoine Bossuet (1798-1889)
French
Toledo
Signed and dated 1865, oil on canvas
20½ x 28½in (52 x 72.4cm)
£8,000-10,000 *C*

Louise Rayner (1832-1924)
British
Ludlow from Corve Street, looking towards
The Buttercross
Watercolour
17¾ x 23¾in (45 x 60cm)
£18,500-19,500 *Pol*

Myles Birket Foster, R.W.S. (1825-99)
British
Andernach on the Rhine
Signed with monogram, inscribed, pencil and
watercolour with touches of white heightening
6 x 9in (15 x 22.5cm)
£5,000-6,000 *C*

John Atkinson Grimshaw (1836-93)
British
Gourock Dock, Glasgow
Signed and inscribed, oil on canvas
12 x 18in (30.5 x 46cm)
£14,500-18,000 *C*

Anonymous (20thC)
Street Scene
Oil on board, naive
14½ x 18½in (37 x 47cm)
£200-250 *MBA*

Orlando Greenwood (1892-1989)
British
Rouen Cathedral
Oil on canvas
22 x 27in (56 x 69cm)
£2,700-2,900 *NZ*

Ian Houston (20thC)
British
A Canal in Choggia
Signed, oil on board
10 x 14in (25 x 36cm)
£500-550 *KHG*

Childe Hassam (1859-1935)
American
Harper's Ferry 2nd
Signed and dated April 1926, watercolour
on paper
16 x 19in (40.6 x 48.3cm)
£12,500-14,500 *S(NY)*

Bernard Buffet (b1928)
French
Saint Tropez
Signed and dated 58, oil on canvas
35½ x 51¼in (90 x 130cm)
£45,000-55,000 *S*

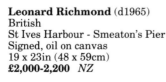

Leonard Richmond (d1965)
British
St Ives Harbour - Smeaton's Pier
Signed, oil on canvas
19 x 23in (48 x 59cm)
£2,000-2,200 *NZ*

Edwin Fletcher (1857-1945)
British
Tugs on the River Thames
Oil on canvas
22 x 30in (56 x 76cm)
£2,300-2,500 *F*

Harold Workman (20thC)
British
Chaos on London Bridge
Signed, oil on canvas
40 x 30in (102 x 76cm)
£4,000-4,500 *S*

Herbert Menzies Marshall (1841-1913)
British
Westminster
Signed, watercolour
17½ x 24½in (44 x 62cm)
£7,500-8,000 *Pol*

Ian Armour-Chelu (20thC)
British
Big Ben from the Jubilee Gardens,
Evening
Watercolour
7 x 10in (18 x 25cm)
£550-650 *PHG*

Edouard Cortès
(1882-1969)
French
Café de la Paix, Paris
Signed, oil on canvas
13¼ x 18½in (33.6 x
47cm)
£8,500-10,000 *C*

Georges Stein (20thC)
French
At the Folies Bergères, Paris, and
Westminster Bridge, London
A pair, both signed, watercolour with
coloured chalks
11½ x 15¼in (29 x 39cm)
£3,400-4,000 *S*

George Chenard-Huché
(1864-1937)
French
Montmartre at Twilight in
Winter
Signed and dated 1909, oil
on canvas
19¼ x 28½in (49 x 72cm)
£5,000-6,000 *S*

Eugène Galien-Laloue (1854-1941)
French
L'Arc de Triomphe, Paris
Signed, bodycolour with black charcoal on
card
8 x 12¾in (20.3 x 32.4cm)
£7,200-8,000 *C*

Peter Graham (b1959)
British
Jardin du Luxembourg
Oil on canvas
30 x 24in (76 x 61cm)
£1,000-1,200 *Bne*

Pierre Oulif (19thC)
French
A Young Woman by the Seine, Paris
Signed, oil on canvas
32 x 51½in (81 x 131cm)
£2,500-3,000 *S*

Leopold Blauensteiner (1880-1947) Austrian
A View of Rome
Signed and titled on reverse, oil on panel
24 x 25in (61 x 63.5cm)
£4,200-5,200 *S*

Jean-Victor-Louis Faure (1786-1879)
French
Forum Romanum; and The Colisseum, Rome
A pair, both signed, oil on canvas
25½ x 35½in (65 x 90cm)
£15,500-20,000 *C*

Ken Howard R.A. (b1932)
British
Piazza Republica, c1922
Signed, oil on canvas
7 x 11½in (18 x 29cm)
£800-1,000 *AdG*

Simone Pomardi (1760-1830)
Italian
A Panoramic View of Rome
and the Tiber from the Villa
Millini on Monte Mario
Pencil and watercolour
25¼ x 40¼in (64 x 102cm)
£17,000-20,000 *S*

Victor-Jean Nicolle (1754-1826)
French
View of the Piazza della Rotonda
with the Pantheon
Signed, pen and brown ink and
blue and brown wash
9½ x 15½in (24 x 40cm)
£7,500-8,500 *S(NY)*

Gustav Bauernfeind (1848-1904) Austrian
The Ruins at Baalbek
Signed with initials, oil on board
12 x 9in (30.5 x 22.8cm)
£9,000-10,000 *C*

Attributed to Filippo Giuntotardi (1768-1831)
Italian
A View of the Temple of Neptune at Paestum
Watercolour, 21 x 29½in (53 x 75cm)
£2,700-3,500 *S*

Charles-Louis Clérisseau (1721-1820)
French
A Pair of Capricci; Roman Ruins with Figures
Both signed and dated 1789, gouache
17½ x 14½in (44.2 x 37cm)
£14,500-18,000 *S(NY)*

Frank Taylor (20thC)
British
Numbers of Stones, Delphi
Watercolour
15 x 24in (38 x 61cm)
£450-550 *PHG*

Mary Jackson (20thC)
British
Luxor, Evening Light
Oil on canvas
8 x 10in (20 x 25cm)
£450-750 *BSG*

Franco Vassetti
(20thC)
Italian
Street Market, Naples
Oil on panel
12 x 8in (31 x 20cm)
£700-900 *OM*

Antonio Joli (c1700-77)
Italian
A Fair seen from the Balcony of the Royal Palace at Naples, 1763
Oil on canvas
30 x 50in (76 x 127cm)
£260,000-300,000 *S*

Gabriele Ricciardelli
(active 1740-80)
Italian
The Ponte Nuovo,
Naples
Oil on canvas
25 x 51in
(63.5 x 129.5cm)
£100,000-120,000 *S*

Franz Richard Unterberger (1838-1902)
Belgian
The Capucine Monastery, Amalfi
Signed, oil on canvas
45¼ x 39¾in (115 x 101cm)
£18,500-25,000 *S*

Otto Didrik Ottesen (1816-92)
Danish
Orange Trees with Vesuvius in the Background
Signed and dated 1883, oil on canvas
25½ x 21¾in (65 x 55cm)
£9,000-10,000 *S*

Francesco Guardi (1712-93)
Italian
Palazzo Ducale, Venice, Seen from the Sea
Oil on canvas
21¾ x 28¼in (55 x 72cm)
£190,000-250,000 *S(NY)*

Maurice B. Prendergast (1859-1924)
American
The Porch with the Old Mosaics, St Marks,
Venice
Signed and inscribed Venice, watercolour
and pencil on paper
16 x 11½in (40.6 x 29cm)
£186,000-220,000 *S(NY)*

Rubens Santoro (1859-1942)
Italian
The Grand Canal with the Campanile
of St Maria Gloriosa dei Frari, Venice
Signed, oil on panel
16¼ x 12¾in (41.3 x 32.5cm)
£43,000-50,000 *C*

**Giovanni Antonio Canal,
il Canaletto** (1697-1768)
Italian
The Church and Campo of Santa
Maria Zobenigo, Venice
Oil on canvas
11½ x 15in (29 x 38cm)
£220,000-300,000 *C*

Edward Pritchett
(active 1828-64)
British
The Doge's Palace, Venice
Oil on canvas
25 x 38in (64 x 96.5cm)
£23,000-25,000 *FAO*

Henry Pether (1828-65)
British
Santa Maria Della Salute, Venice - By Moonlight
Signed and dated 1862, oil on canvas
22 x 34in (56 x 86.5cm)
£11,500-12,000 *FAO*

Theresa Knowles (20thC)
British
Squera di San Trouasa, Venice
1992
11 x 8½ in (28 x 21.5cm)
£400-450 *A*

Roberto Ferruzzi (b1927)
Italian
Zattere, Venice
Gouache on paper laid onto canvas
35½ x 15¾in (90 x 40cm)
£4,200-5,600 *WFA*

Jeremy Barlow (b1945)
British
Behind The Salute
Oil on canvas
20 x 17in (51 x 43cm)
£750-850 *A*

Faith Shepherd (20thC) British
View in Venice, Gondola Boat Yard
Oil on canvas
13½ x 23in (34 x 59cm)
£350-400 *SAV*

Antonio Reyna (20thC)
Spanish
A View of Venice from the Laguna
Signed and inscribed, oil on canvas
13¾ x 29in (35 x 74cm)
£13,000-14,000 *CNY*

Roberto Ferruzzi (b1927)
Italian
Rio San Barnaba, gouache on paper
laid onto canvas
39 x 29½in (99 x 75cm)
£4,000-5,000 *WFA*

Henry Harris (1852-1926)
British
Tintern Abbey and the Anchor Inn from across The Wye
Oil on canvas
20 x 29½in (50 x 75cm)
£400-450 *ALL*

John Atkinson Grimshaw (1836-93)
British
At Nightfall
Signed and inscribed on reverse, oil on canvas
30 x 25in (76.2 x 63.6cm)
£35,000-45,000 *C*

Circle of Haytley (18thC)
British
A View of a Country House, possibly in the Thames
Valley, a group of Ladies taking Tea in the foreground
Oil on canvas
25 x 39½in (63.5 x 100.3cm)
£30,000-40,000 *Bon*

Captain Francis Grose (1731-91)
British
The Lavatory Tower, Canterbury, Kent
Pen and ink and watercolour
14½ x 20¼in (37 x 52cm)
£1,500-2,000 *S*

Edward Hopper (1882-1967)
American
Vermont Sugar House
Signed, watercolour on paper
14 x 20in (35.6 x 50.8cm)
£105,000-125,000 *S(NY)*

Jack Levine (b1915)
American
Old City Hall, Boston
Signed and dated '83, watercolour, pencil
and gouache on paper
11 x 14¾in (28 x 37.5cm)
£3,600-4,000 *S(NY)*

Ian Weatherhead (b1932) British
Villandry
Oil
24 x 30in (62 x 76cm)
£450-520 *Wyk*

Graham Clarke (b1941) British
Home Sweet Home
Etching, hand coloured, 10½ x 10in (26.5 x
25.5cm) **£135-155** *GCP*

Fred Cuming
(b1930) British
Studio, Evening -
By Moonlight
Oil on board
24in (62cm) square
£2,500-4,500 *BSG*

John Piper
(1903-92) British
Kirkham Priory
Gateway
Etching
£700-750 *CCA*

Weng Fang-Peng (20thC)
House
Oil on canvas, executed 1991
14 x 11in (36 x 28cm)
£2,500-3,000 *RMG*

Allan Bruce (20thC)
British
Skyline
Watercolour, 32 x 18in (81 x 46cm)
£400-450 *KHG*

Edmund Fairfax-Lucy
(20thC)
British
Interior with Silver
Candlesticks
Oil on board
10 x 7in (25 x 18cm)
£900-1,200 *Wa*

Brenda Evans (b1965)
British
A Little Night Music
14 x 10in (36 x 25cm)
£175-195 *KHG*

Keith Lucas (20thC)
British
The Balcony, Porta Polenca
Oil on canvas
23 x 26in (59 x 66cm)
£585-685 *AMC*

Timothy Easton (b1943)
British
Bella's Window
Oil on canvas
30 x 20in (76 x 51cm)
£2,000-3,000 *BSG*

Ken Howard (b1932)
British
Studio Interior, Mousehole
Oil on canvas
48 x 40in (122 x 101.5cm)
£5,000-6,000 *BSG*

Robert Palmer (20thC)
British
Still Life with Paper Flowers
Oil on canvas
28 x 36in (71 x 92cm)
£2,200-2,500 *BSG*

Raymond Oliver (20thC)
British
Provençal Afternoon
Gouache
20 x 14in (51 x 36cm)
£350-450 *KHG*

Jacqueline Williams (b1963)
British
Interior with Lamp
Oil on canvas
46½ x 34¾in (117 x 88.5cm)
£2,450-2,650 *BSG*

Richard Pikesley (b1951)
British
Bottle Garden and Spring Flowers
Oil on canvas
40 x 36in (101.5 x 92cm)
£1,000-2,500 *BSG*

Susan Ryder (20thC)
British
Bedroom with Blue Flowers
Signed, oil on canvas
30 x 36in (76.5 x 92cm)
£2,500-4,000 *BSG*

Daniel-Nicolas Chodowiecki
(1726-1801)
German
View of the Gardens of a Palace
with a Wide Avenue and Fountains,
Figures Promenading and
Gardeners Working, *verso* Figures
in a Ravine
Signed, gouache
16 x 23in (41 x 59cm)
£7,000-8,000 *S(NY)*

Ettore Roesler Franz (1845-1907)
Italian
A View from the Villa d'Este at
Tivoli
Signed, inscribed and dated 1901
Watercolour
13 x 27in (33 x 68.5cm)
£4,500-5,500 *S*

Claude Monet (1840-1926)
French
La Maison à Travers Les Roses
Oil on canvas, executed c1925-26
28¾ x 36in (73 x 92cm)
£260,000-280,000 *S*

Attributed to
Balthasar Nebot
(active 1730-after 1765)
British
A View of the Fountain Pond
at Hackfall, with the
Banqueting House Beyond
29 x 42½in (73.7 x 108cm)
£13,500-15,500 *C*

Charles Penny (20thC) British
Late Summer Shadows II
Watercolour, 30 x 22in (76 x 56cm)
£600-675 *AMC*

John Yardley (b1936)
Garden Shadows
Watercolour, 19½ x 25½in (50 x 65cm)
£1,000-1,250 *Bne*

Annette Kane (b1955)
British
A Place in the Shade
Signed and dated 1992, watercolour
19 x 30in (48 x 76cm)
£1,000-1,150 *TCG*

R. A. Gardner (active 1902-17)
British
The Pergola
Signed and dated 1915, oil on board
10¼ x 14in (26 x 36cm)
£200-250 *Gan*

Andrew Price (b1955)
British
Mediterranean Steps
Oil on canvas
40 x 30in (101.5 x 76cm)
£1,650-1,850 *AMC*

Ilana Richardson (20thC)
Israeli
Fontvielle Gardens
Watercolour
16 x 19¾in (40.5 by 50cm)
£1,000-1,250 *CCA*

Sir Hugh Casson (20thC)
British
Needs Ore Cottages, Beaulieu
Watercolour
12 x 16in (31 x 41cm)
£250-300 *OLG*

Henry John Sylvester Stannard
(1870-1951)
British
Girl Feeding Ducks
Watercolour
9 x 13in (23 x 33cm)
£1,450-1,650 *ChG*

Helen Allingham R.W.S.(1848-1926)
British
East End Farm, Moss Lane, Pinner
Signed, watercolour
13¼ x 17⅓in (34 x 44cm)
£30,000-32,000 *Pol*

Helen Allingham R.W.S. (1848-1926)
British
A Wiltshire Cottage
Signed, watercolour
6 x 9in (15 x 23cm)
£11,500-12,000 *MJA*

Charlotte Bathurst (20thC)
British
Owl House
Signed on stretcher, oil on canvas with additions
29 x 39in (74 x 99cm)
£450-500 *NBO*

Rowland Henry Hill (1873-1952)
British
Cottage Garden in Summer, Runswick
Signed and dated 1905, colour washes
heightened with white
£1,800-2,500 *P(L)*

Venice

Venice has always been a magnet for artists and tourists alike. In the 18thC it was a central stop on the Grand Tour, and painters provided innumerable elegant views of the city for wealthy visitors. Master of the genre was Canaletto, the most sought-after artist in his field: 'As for Canaletto, his metier is to paint views of Venice,' noted Charles de Brosses, a contemporary correspondent in 1739. 'In this genre, he surpasses all before him. His manner is clear, gay, lively, and in perspective, with admirable detail. The English have so spoilt this workman in offering for his paintings three times what he asks for them, that it is no longer possible to do business with him.'

The expansion of travel in the 19thC brought about a new breed of middle-class tourist to the city, and a demand for more sentimental and more anecdotal portrayals of Venetian life. In addition to straight views of the city, artists concentrated on its colourful inhabitants: pretty peasant girls, handsome gondoliers, mischievous 'ragazzi' - decorative genre pictures, where the figures are invariably as picturesque as the city itself.

Manner of Canaletto
(1697-1768)
Italian
A View of the Dogana and Santa Maria della Salute with a British Merchant Ship and other Vessels
Oil on canvas
26½ x 43in (67.3 x 109.3cm)
£23,000-28,000 *Bon*

Giovanni Antonio Guardi
(1699-1760)
Italian
A Masked Ball with Ladies and Gentlemen in Carnival Costume in the Grand Hall of the Ridotto in the Palazzo Dandalo, Venice
Oil on canvas
32 x 43in (81 x 109cm)
£340,000-400,000 *S*

One of an extremely rare group of paintings by Francesco and Giovanni Antonio Guardi depicting the interior of the Ridotto in Venice, with masked figures celebrating the carnival.

After Francesco Guardi
(1712-93)
Vedute of Venice, by F. Rizzi
Etching
16 x 12½in (40.5 x 32cm)
£420-520 *CSK*

Francesco Guardi (1712-93)
Italian
The Grand Canal with San Simeone Piccolo
Black chalk, pen and brown ink, brown wash, unidentified fragmentary watermark, the left and right sections partly incised, on 3 joined sheets of paper, the left and right sections rubbed with black chalk verso
11½ x 21in (29.2 x 53.6cm)
£53,000-63,000 *CNY*

Francesco Guardi (1712-93)
Italian
Venice, Island of Santa Maria
della Grazia
Inscribed on the reverse, probably
by the artist, oil on panel
9½ x 6⅝in (24 x 16.7cm)
£30,000-35,000 *S*

Giovanni Bernardino Bison
(1762-1844)
Italian
Gondolas Travelling Along a
Venetian Canal Beside a Palace
with a Bell Tower
Oil on paper, laid down on canvas
11¾ x 9in (30 x 22.5cm)
£2,300-3,000 *P*

Fred Burgess (active 1882-92)
British
Venetian Lagoon
Signed, watercolour
12 x 18½in (30 x 47cm)
£320-360 *FWA*

Circle of Francesco Tironi
(18thC)
Italian
St Mark's Square, Venice
Oil on canvas
29 x 44½in (74 x 113cm)
£10,000-11,000 *P*

William James (18thC)
British
A Regatta on the Grand Canal
with Gondolas and Bissone
Moored Before the Palazzo Balbi
from which People Watch the
Race
Oil on canvas
23½ x 35½in (60.6 x 90.5cm)
£46,000-56,000 *P*

Charles-Clément Calderon
(late 19thC)
French
The Bacino, Venice
Signed, oil on canvas
21½ x 32in (54.6 x 81.3cm)
£3,000-4,000 *C*

Guglielmo Ciardi (1842-1917)
Italian
A View of the Lagoon in Venice
Signed and dated 1890, oil on
canvas
21¾ x 39in (55 x 99cm)
£92,000-110,000 *S*

Federico del Campo (19thC)
Peruvian
Feeding Pigeons Before St.
Mark's, Venice
Signed, oil on panel
11¼ x 7⅓in (28.5 x 18.5cm)
£3,700-4,700 *P*

G. Feretti (19thC)
Italian
The Doge's Palace
Signed, oil on canvas
20 x 32in (50.8 x 81.3cm)
£950-1,200 *CSK*

Alexandre Defaux (1826-1900)
French
A Capriccio View of Venice
Signed and dated 1858, oil on
canvas laid down on board
18 x 28⅜in (46 x 73cm)
£3,000-3,500 *S*

James Hervé d'Egville (d1880)
British
Figures and Boats Before S.
Giorgio Maggiore, Venice
Signed with monogram,
watercolour and bodycolour
11¼ x 19in (28.6 x 48.2cm)
£450-550 *Bon*

Carlo Grubacs
(active early 19thC) Magyan
View of Santa Maria Della Salute
Pen and brown ink and gouache
10 x 16½in (25 x 42cm)
£5,500-6,500 *S(NY)*

*Grubacs appears to have been of Magyar
origin, born either in Eastern Europe or in
Venice. Biographical details are scarce and
sometimes contradictory, but sources
agree that he was a pupil of the elderly
Francesco Guardi and that he worked
principally in Venice. Bolaffi's 'Dizionario
enciclopedico dei pittori e degli incisori
Italiani' praises his work, saying that he
re-animated the language of Canaletto with
taste and evident self-confidence.*

William Logsdail (1859-1944)
British
A Venetian al Fresco
Signed and dated 1885, oil on
canvas
41 x 66in (103.8 x 167.7cm)
£46,000-60,000 *C*

*Logsdail lived and worked for
several years in Venice. When the
present work was shown at the
Royal Jubilee Exhibition in
Manchester in 1887, the Art
Journal described it as 'brilliantly
clever' and in 1898 it sold at
Christie's for 150 guineas. At
Christie's nearly a century later
the picture received an equally
enthusiastic reaction, creating an
auction record for an artist whose
works are usually expected to fetch
under £10,000.*

Pieter van Loon (d1873)
Dutch
Ponte Della Paglia con il Palazzo
Ducale, Venezia
Signed and dated 1845, oil on
canvas
24 x 35½in (61 x 90.2cm)
£6,500-7,500 *C*

Alexander Mann (1853-1908)
British
A Touch of Autumn, Venice
Signed and dated 1884, oil on
canvas
17 x 21in (43.2 x 53.3cm)
£4,000-5,000 *C(S)*

J. W. Milliken (active 1887-1930)
British
Piazza San Marco
Signed, pencil and watercolour
25½ x 37½in (64.8 x 95.2cm)
£3,000-4,000 *C*

Thomas Moran (1837-1926)
Venice, Reminiscence of Vera
Cruz, Mexico
Signed with monogram and dated
1886, oil on canvas
17½ x 27½in (44.5 x 70cm)
£38,000-45,000 *S(NY)*

Antonio Paoletti (1834-1912)
Italian
Il Mercatino del Pesce, Venezia
Signed, oil on canvas
21¾ x 32in (55.2 x 81.4cm)
£9,000-10,000 *C*

Alfred Pollentine (19thC)
British
Venice
Signed, oil on canvas
20 x 30in (51 x 76cm)
£3,250-3,500 *SH*

V. Pasini (19thC)
Italian
Water Carriers in the Courtyard
of the Doge's Palace, Venice
Signed, pencil and watercolour
14 x 8in (36 x 20cm)
£680-800 *CSK*

Edward Pritchett
(active 1828-64)
British
The Riva Degli Schiavoni with the
Ponte Della Paglia, Venice
Signed, oil on canvas
17 x 23in (43.2 x 58.4cm)
£5,000-6,000 *C*

Alberto Prosdocimi (b1852)
Italian
Figures Around the Well in the
Courtyard of the Doge's Palace
Signed, watercolour
22¼ x 37¾in (57 x 96cm)
£3,300-4,000 *P*

Luigi Querena (19thC)
Italian
The Piazzetta by Moonlight
Signed, inscribed and indistinctly
dated 1853 (?), oil on canvas
21¾ x 34⅛in (55 x 87cm)
£7,000-8,000 *S(S)*

August Siegen (19thC)
German
Gondolas and Sailing Boats on a
Venetian Canal
Signed, oil on panel
12½ x 16½in (31.5 x 42cm)
£2,200-2,800 *P*

**Antonio Maria Reyna
Manescau** (1859-1937)
Spanish
A View of the Venetian Lagoon
Signed, oil on canvas
13 x 28¾in (33.5 x 73cm)
£13,500-14,500 *S*

Félix Ziem (1821-1911)
French
A View of Venice
Signed, oil on panel
12¾ x 18½in (32.5 x 47cm)
£6,400-7,400 *S*

Francis Hopkinson Smith
(1838-1915)
American
Canal Scene, Venice
Signed, watercolour and gouache
on paper
20 x 12in (50.5 x 30.5cm)
£5,000-6,000 *S(NY)*

Nicholas P. Briganti (b1895)
American
The Grand Canal, Venice
Signed, oil on canvas
18¼ x 40½in (46.4 x 103cm)
£1,800-2,200 *S(NY)*

Albert Goodwin, R.W.S. (1845-1932)
British
The Hardy Norseman at Venice
Signed, inscribed and dated 1919,
oil on canvas
30 x 66in (76 x 167.5cm)
£6,000-7,000 *Bea*

Antoine Bouvard (d1956)
French
The Grand Canal with the Santa
Maria della Salute, Venice
Signed, oil on canvas
19¾ x 25½in (50.4 x 65cm)
£6,700-7,700 *C(S)*

Antonio Reyna (20thC)
Spanish
Venetian Canal Scene
Signed, oil on canvas
13½ x 29in (34.5 x 73.5cm)
£20,000-25,000 *CNY*

Arthur Knighton-Hammond
(1875-1970)
British
The Doge's Palace, Venice
Signed, watercolour
8 x 12in (20 x 31cm)
£1,000-1,250 *EG*

William Crosbie (b1915)
British
Signed, inscribed with title and
dated '56, watercolour with pen
and ink
5 x 7¼in (13 x 18.5cm)
£420-500 *S(S)*

Anthony Rickards (20thC)
British
Rio Ogmissanti, Venice
Oil on canvas
11½ x 13½in (29 x 34cm)
£550-600 *Wyk*

Amédée Rozier (19th/20thC)
French
St Mark's Square, Venice
Signed, oil on panel
17 x 12in (43 x 30cm)
£2,200-2,600 *S*

Edward Brian Seago, R.W.S.
(1910-74)
British
Evening on the Piazza, St Mark's
Square, Venice
Signed, watercolour over pencil
13½ x 20½in (34 x 52cm)
£8,000-9,000 *S*

Michael Hyam (20thC)
British
Venetian Doorway
Oil
10 x 6in (25 x 15cm)
£1,000-1,250 *PHG*

Vallin (Hugo Golli) (20thC)
Italian
Evening Shadows, Venice
Oil on canvas
24 x 36in (61 x 92cm)
£8,000-8,500 *OM*

Jerusalem & Israel

Gustav Bauernfeind
(1848-1904)
Austrian
Via Dolorosa, Jerusalem
Signed with initials, oil on board
9¼ x 6¼in (23.5 x 16cm)
£4,000-5,000 *C*

Carl Friedrich Heinrich Werner (1808-94)
German
David's Strasse, Jerusalem
Signed, inscribed and dated 1862,
pencil and watercolour
20 x 13¾in (50.8 x 34.8cm)
£1,700-2,300 *Bon*

Adrien Dauzats (1804-68)
French
A View of the Monastery of Saint
Catherine, Mt. Sinai
Signed, oil on canvas
21¼ x 26½in (54 x 67cm)
£13,500-14,500 *CNY*

Nathaniel Everett Green
(1833?-99)
British
The Church of the Holy
Sepulchre, Jerusalem
Signed, inscribed and dated 1884,
pencil and watercolour
heightened with white
22 x 31in (55.8 x 78.7cm)
£6,700-8,000 *C*

Otto Friedrich Georgi
(1819-74)
German
A View of Jerusalem
Signed, indistinctly inscribed and
dated 1863, oil on canvas
37½ x 56¼in (95 x 143cm)
£8,600-9,600 *S*

Spanish Towns

David Roberts, R.A.
(1796-1864)
British
The Chapter House, Burgos
Cathedral
Signed and dated 1835,
watercolour and bodycolour
16½ x 11½in (42 x 29.2cm)
£3,700-4,700 *Bon*

*The son of a shoemaker, David
Roberts was apprenticed for 7
years to a house painter and then
at 21 joined a travelling circus as
a scene painter. 'Sometimes I
enacted in the evening the part of
a robber,' he later recalled, '...
more for my own amusement than
by the manager's wish, for, in
playing a bandit one night, I was
so in earnest (as Scotsmen
generally are) that I fired the
pistol in his face, to the great
terror of the actor himself.
Fortunately it was not loaded.'*

David Roberts, R.A.
(1796-1864)
British
A Fountain at the Prado, Madrid
Signed, watercolour over pencil
heightened with touches of
bodycolour on grey/blue paper
9¾ x 6¾in (25 x 17cm)
£4,200-5,200 *S*

François-Antoine Bossuet
(1800-89)
Belgian
Xeres, Spain
Signed and dated 1879, oil on
panel
21½ x 16½in (54.6 x 42cm)
£4,500-5,500 *C*

Enrique Marin (19th/20thC)
Spanish?
A Sunlit Courtyard
Signed and inscribed Toledo,
watercolour and pencil
12½ x 9in (31.7 x 22.7cm)
£650-750 *S(S)*

Henry John Johnson (1826-84)
British
Crevillente, Spain
Inscribed, watercolour over pencil
10¾ x 15in (27.5 x 38cm)
£530-630 *S*

A. Moulton Foweraker
(1873-1942)
British
A Spanish Town by Moonlight
Signed, watercolour
20½ x 24in (21.4 x 61cm)
£2,800-3,300 *Bon*

PARKS & GARDENS

Parks and Gardens are perennially popular themes. For this year's Picture Price Guide, as well as the great landscaped parks of the 18thC and the cottage and country gardens of the 19thC, we have received more garden pictures by contemporary artists. As some of the dealers we have talked to have noted, in times of recession there is not only a move back to figurative, more traditional, art but also a distinct demand for bright and cheerful subjects, qualities epitomised by the theme of the garden.

Louis Gadbois (d1826)
French
The Alleys of a Park with Two
Ladies Walking
Signed, watercolour heightened
with white
10 x 13¼in (25.5 x 34.4cm)
£900-1,000 *CNY*

18th Century

Jean-Honoré Fragonard (1732-1806)
French
The Garden of an Italian Villa
with a Gardener and Two Children Playing
Drawn with a brush in brown
wash over black chalk
13 x 17¾in (33.8 x 45cm)
£235,000-270,000 *S(NY)*

This exceptionally beautiful drawing must have been made during, or soon after, Fragonard's second Italian journey of 1773-74, undertaken in the company of his patron. During this period, Fragonard explored the possibilities of wash and chalk, using delicate tones of wash to create atmosphere rather than subject matter, summoning up the most extraordinary and magical effects of shimmering light. 'Fragonard was the master of the dream world,' wrote the Goncourt Brothers (see Biblio.), and alongside Watteau, he was, in their opinion, the only true poet of the 18thC. Fragonard himself expressed his enthusiasm for his art with a little more gusto and a little less reverence as one might expect from a painter famed for his erotic creations. According to one contemporary report, his whole being was drawn towards the arts and even if he were to lose all his faculties, he declared: 'I would paint with my bottom.'

Hubert Robert (1733-1808)
French
A Figure Reading by the
Entrance to a Villa
Black chalk, pen and brown ink,
brown wash, watermark letters GR
7 x 9in (18 x 23cm)
£9,000-10,000 *C*

Anthony Devis (1729-1817)
British
A View of the Chinese Pagoda at
Studley Royal with Deer Grazing
in the Foreground
Pencil, pen and grey ink and
watercolour
12 x 17in (30.8 x 43cm)
£420-520 *C*

After being disgraced as Chancellor of the Exchequer during the time of the South Sea Bubble in 1720, John Aislabie retired to his estate at Studley Royal, near Ripon, where he consoled himself by laying out the grounds and building many ornamental gardens.

William Turner of Oxford
(1789-1862)
British
Dale Park near Arundel, Sussex
Pencil and watercolour with
scratching out
23 x 39¼in (58.4 x 99.7cm)
£3,500-4,000 *C*

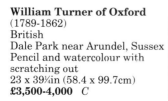

19th Century

William Ashburner
(active 1900-32)
British
Admiring the Borders
Signed, watercolour
7 x 10in (18 x 25cm)
£1,000-1,500 *TLG*

Alice Boyd (1825-97) British
A View of the Studio at Penkill
with Alice Boyd seated at an
Easel painting, William Bell Scott
in the Doorway
Oil on canvas
14 x 18in (35.3 x 45.7cm)
£2,000-2,500 *C(S)*

Alfred de Breanski
(1877-c1945)
British
Iris and Lilac
Signed and inscribed, oil on
canvas
£2,000-2,400 *BWe*

Henri Biva (1848-1928)
French
Le Lac du Parc
Signed, oil on canvas
25½ x 32in (65 x 81cm)
£6,250-6,750 *BuP*

*Grimshaw's endless repetition of
evening and moonlit views
inspired some suspicion among
his contemporaries. His obituary
in the Leeds Mercury observed
that his pictures 'showed no
marks of handling or brush work,
and not a few artists were
doubtful whether they could be
accepted as paintings at all.' As
Jeremy Maas notes (see Biblio.),
Grimshaw's landscapes do have a
'photographic vision with their
mists, the stencilling of branches
or masts against a moonlit sky,
the reflection of light....' And
Grimshaw himself devised a
technique whereby a master-
drawing was thrown on to a
canvas or board through a
photographic enlarger, and by
this method he was able to paint
several versions of the same
subject.*

John Atkinson Grimshaw (1836-93) British
Stapleton Park, Nr. Pontefract
Signed and dated 1879, oil on
board
10¾ x 13½in (27 x 34cm)
£8,200-9,200 *P(L)*

Arthur Hughes (1832-1915)
British
The Gardens at Penkill with Alice
Boyd walking her dog, Ogier
Signed and dated 1886, oil on
artist's board
10 x 14in (25.4 x 35.5cm)
£1,400-1,800 *C(S)*

Charles Kerr (1858-1907)
British
The Cure's Garden
Signed, painted verso with a
sketch of a lady's head
23¾ x 31¾in (60.5 x 80.5cm)
£2,200-2,800 *S(S)*

Tom Lloyd, R.W.S. (1849-1910)
British
Scything the Lawn
Signed and dated 1903,
watercolour
11¼ x 27½in (28.5 x 69.5cm)
£3,000-3,500 *S*

Beatrice Parsons (1870-1955)
British
An Arabian Night's Garden
Signed and inscribed, watercolour
9 x 6⅛in (22.5 x 15cm)
£1,200-1,800 *CSK*

E. Arthur Rowe (d1922)
British
Under the Apple Trees, The Old
Place
Signed and inscribed, watercolour
12 x 9in (30.5 x 22.8cm)
£1,800-2,200 *DN*

Isodore Meyer (19thC)
French
A Walk in the Park at
Chateauroux
Signed and dated 1884,
watercolour and gouache
10 x 16¼in (25.5 x 41.5cm)
£1,200-1,600 *S*

Charles Edward Wilson
(active 1891-1936)
British
My Lady's Garden
Signed, watercolour
9½ x 6¾in (24 x 17cm)
£5,800-7,000 *S*

William Wyld (1806-89)
British
Bagneres de Bigone, Pyrenees
Signed and dated Aout 73,
watercolour with touches of
bodycolour over traces of pencil
5¾ x 8¾in (14.5 x 22cm)
£3,200-4,000 *S*

20th Century

Edward Bawden (1903-89)
British
The Palm House
Signed and entitled in ballpoint
pen, linocut, printed in colours, on
wove
49¼ x 30¾in (125 x 78cm)
£550-650 *P*

Nigel Casseldine, R.W.A.
(b1947)
British
Al Fresco
Signed, oil on canvas
16 x 17¾in (41 x 45cm)
£650-700 *Wyk*

Ernest Albert Chadwick
(early 20thC)
British
The Delphinium Border
Signed and dated 1909,
watercolour
7½ x 10½in (19 x 27cm)
£1,200-1,600 *S*

Fred Cuming (b1930)
British
Patio
Signed, oil on board
20 x 24in (51 x 62cm)
£2,500-4,500 *BSG*

Robert Sowers (20thC)
American
Picnic in the Park
Signed and dated 8/19/86, oil on
canvas
40 x 50in (101.6 x 127cm)
£1,200-1,600 *S(NY)*

Peter Kuhfeld (b1952)
British
Florence in the Garden, c1986
Signed, oil on board
20 x 30in (51.8 x 77.2cm)
£1,600-2,000 *Bon*

Valerie Miller (20thC) British
The Secret Garden
Signed with initials, oil on board
9 x 14in (22.5 x 35.5cm)
£300-325 *TFA*

Ilana Richardson (20thC)
Israeli
Cordoba Garden
Silkscreen, 20 colours
23½ x 31½in (60 x 80cm)
£200-225 *CCA*

Luis Graner y Arrufi
(1867-1929)
Spanish
The Lake in Central Park
Signed and dated 1923, oil on
canvas laid down on board
25¼ x 33in (64 x 84cm)
£4,500-5,500 *CNY*

Tony Brummell Smith (20thC)
British
Figures in a Walled Garden
Signed, pastel
27 x 37in (68.5 x 94cm)
£800-875 *WG*

Norman Stevens (b1937)
British
Priory Garden
Etching, 2 colours
14½ x 17½in (37.5 x 45cm)
£450-500 *CCA*

Alfred Stockham (b1933)
British
Alice Nunn's Garden
Oil
36 x 28in (91.5 x 71cm)
£3,650-3,850 *KG*

Piero Vignozzi (20thC)
Italian
Seggiolina
Lithograph, 9 colours
27½ x 19¾in (70 x 50cm)
£125-150 *CCA*

David Tindle (b1932)
British
Yolanta Design
Signed and inscribed on reverse,
acrylic on panel
20 x 72in (51 x 182.5cm)
£6,000-6,500 *BRG*

Julian Trevelyan, R.A.
(1910-88)
British
The Cherry Tree
Signed twice and dated '46, oil on
canvas
20 x 24in (51 x 61cm)
£1,700-2,200 *S*

Guy Wiggins (1883-1962)
American
Winter Along Central Park
Signed, oil on canvas
25¼ x 30in (64 x 76.2cm)
£15,000-16,000 *S(NY)*

Jacqueline Williams (20thC)
British
Letter to Benedikt
Oil
45 x 36in (114 x 92cm)
£2,600-2,800 *PHG*

Gill Watkiss (b1938)
British
Winter in Morrab Park, Penzance
Signed and dated '91, oil on
canvas
18 x 24in (45.5 x 61cm)
£1,000-1,100 *NZ*

Nina Zborowska

Katherine Mary Fryer `Winter in the Park - Bath' watercolour 15 x 20 inches

20th Century British paintings and drawings
from 1900 to 1970

If you would like to know more about the gallery Please phone 0452 812460
Damsels Mill, Paradise, Painswick, Gloucestershire

ENGLISH COUNTRY COTTAGES

The market for 19thC British pictures has suffered during the recession. English cottage watercolours, so popular in the 1980s, have certainly been struggling in the salerooms over the last couple of years. But, if prices are not what they once were, recent results have seen artists such as Allingham and Arthur Claude Strachan holding their own at auction, and signs suggest that country cottages are coming back into fashion.

Walter Follen Bishop
(1856-1936)
British
Sun & Flowers, Porlock Weir
Signed and inscribed, watercolour
20½ x 14in (52 x 35cm)
£900-980 *LH*

Heather Cottage is situated close to the former home of Helen Allingham at Sandhills, and was painted on a number of occasions by the artist. Although they might look like idealised visions of rural delight, many of the cottages painted by the artist can be identified and still exist today.

Helen Allingham, R.W.S.
(1848-1926)
British
Heather Cottage
Signed, pencil and watercolour with scratching out
8¾ x 10½in (22.3 x 26.7cm)
£12,500-13,500 *C*

Jasper Francis Cropsey
(1823-1900)
American
Anne Hathaway's Cottage
Indistinctly inscribed, oil on canvas
18 x 30in (45.7 x 76.2cm)
£7,500-8,500 *S(NY)*

Owen Bowen (1873-1967) British
Old Cottage
Signed, oil on canvas
9½ x 13½in (23 x 34cm)
£1,100-1,500 *AH*

Florence Fitzgerald
(active 1887-1900)
A Time of Roses
Signed, oil on canvas
20 x 30in (51 x 76cm)
£1,800-2,200 *S*

Sir George Clausen, R.A.
(1852-1944)
British
Cottages on a Frosty Evening
Signed and inscribed, oil on
canvas
16 x 20in (41 x 51cm)
£5,000-5,500 *VDG*

*One of the most influential of the
British Impressionists, Clausen
trained in London then in Paris
under Bougereau and Robert-
Fleury. Returning to England, he
began to paint the life of the
agricultural labourer. Strongly
influenced by Bastien-Lepage, he
worked out of doors, spending
much time in the Essex
countryside sketching farmhands
at their daily work. Although like
the French Impressionists,
Clausen was preoccupied with
light, unlike them he retained
solidity of form.*

Benjamin D. Sigmund
(active 1880-1904)
British
Woman by a Thatched Cottage,
Sea Beyond
Signed, watercolour
10 x 14in (25 x 35.5cm)
£650-750 *TAY*

J. W. Gozzard (19thC)
British
Wayside Cottages
Signed, watercolour
17½ x 13⅛in (44 x 34cm)
£250-270 *HCH*

**Henry John Sylvester
Stannard** (1870-1951)
British
Feeding Granny's Pet, near
Tebworth, Beds.
Signed, watercolour
14¼ x 20½in (36.5 x 52cm)
£3,500-4,000 *P(S)*

James Matthews (19thC)
British
At Madehurst, Sussex
Signed and inscribed, pencil and
watercolour
9½ x 13½in (22.5 x 34cm)
£800-900 *CSK*

Lilian Stannard (1877-1944)
British
A Surrey Cottage near Haslemere
Signed, watercolour
9½ x 13½in (24.2 x 34.3cm)
£2,000-2,500 *Bon*

Warren Williams (1863-1918)
British
A Girl Feeding Chickens by a
Coastal Cottage; and Boys
Fishing by a Cove, a pair
Signed, watercolour
7½ x 10¾in (19 x 27.3cm)
£1,200-1,600 *Bon*

Arthur Claude Strachan
(c1865-1929)
British
A pair of Rural Country
Scenes
Signed, watercolour
7 x 10¼in (18 x 26cm)
£3,400-3,600 *F*

David Woodlock (1842-1929)
British
Welford, Near Stratford-on-Avon
Signed, watercolour heightened
with bodycolour
9½ x 11½in (24 x 29cm)
£700-800 *S*

Graham Sutherland (1903-80)
British
St Mary Hatch
Signed in pencil, etching, 1926
5¼ x 7¼in (13.3 x 18.3cm)
£600-700 *P*

HOUSES AND BUILDINGS

The market for architectural drawings remains difficult at present, but as in every other field, if something of exceptional quality, rarity and importance comes on to the market it will always find a ready buyer. Such is the case with Kent's design for the Marble Parlour at Houghton Hall (see page 192), which exceeded by far its auction estimate of £8,000-12,000 at Sotheby's in April 1993. Architectural drawings and designs can be a fascinating subject for the collector. Britain has undoubtedly produced some of the greatest architects and decorative designers in the world and an architectural drawing is not just a pretty picture, but a story of the collaboration between designer and patron, leading to the plan or drawing, and culminating (hopefully) in the creation of the object or building itself. The Royal Institute of British Architects in London houses one of the finest architectural libraries in the world, research into the history and provenance of architectural designs, and it is open daily to the general public.

Exteriors
17th Century

Jan Wildens (1585-1653) Flemish
A View of a Country House and
Formal Garden: April
Pen and brown ink and wash,
extensively incised
10¾ x 17½in (27.7 x 44.5cm)
£5,500-6,500 S

18th Century

William Alexander (1767-1816)
British
An Old Inn with a Butcher's Stall
Nearby
Signed, pencil and grey wash
10½ x 14¼in (27 x 36.5cm)
£450-550 S

Abraham Bloemaert (1564-1651) Dutch
A Farm
With number '4', black chalk, pen
and brown ink, brown and red-
brown wash, brown ink framing
lines
5¾ x 7½in (14.4 x 19cm)
£6,000-7,000 C(Am)

Follower of Jan Wyck
(1640-1702)
Dutch
A Panoramic View of
Fontainebleau with a Mounted
Nobleman in the Foreground
37¼ x 51¾in (94.6 x 131.5cm)
£17,000-18,000 C

Joseph Charles Barrow
(active 1775-1805)
British
A Gardener Working in the
Grounds of an Elegant House
Signed and dated 1788, pencil,
pen and grey ink and watercolour
9¼ x 12¼in (23.6 x 31cm)
£1,300-1,700 C

*Barrow exhibited at the Royal
Academy from 1789-1802 and did
a series of views of Strawberry
Hill for Horace Walpole.*

William Ashford (c1746-1824)
British
View of Shane's Castle on Lough
Neagh
Signed and dated 1786, oil on
canvas
28¼ x 40¼in (72 x 102.5cm)
£23,000-30,000 *S*

*Shane's Castle stood at the north
east corner of Lough Neagh near
Antrim Bay. Shortly before this
view was painted, Mrs Siddons
stayed at Shane's Castle and
noted how the guests would pluck
their desert from the conservatory
whilst the waves splashed outside,
and likened the luxury of the
house to 'an Arabian Nights
entertainment'. During storms,
however, the noise of the wind and
waves was considerable and spray
is said to have reached the attics
of the castle. Nash was
commissioned to enlarge the castle
early in the 19thC but it was
burnt down in 1816. A new castle
was built in the 1860s, but was
burnt down in 1922.*

**Attributed to François Louis
Thomas Francia** (1772-1839)
French
Conway Castle
Pencil and watercolour
11½ x 17in (29.2 x 43.2cm)
£500-600 *C*

Jan de Beijer (1703-c1785)
Dutch
The Castle 'De Haar' at
Haarzuilens, near Utrecht
Signed and dated 5 October 1744,
pencil, pen and grey ink,
watercolour, grey ink framing
lines, fragmentary watermark
Pro Patria
5½ x 7½in (13.6 x 18.8cm)
£2,000-2,500 *C(Am)*

Thomas Girtin (1775-1802)
British
Marine Barracks at Stonehouse,
Plymouth
Signed, pencil and watercolour
6½ x 11in (16.5 x 28cm)
£3,500-4,500 *C*

*'If poor Tom had lived, I should
have starved,' Turner is reputed to
have said about his friend and
contemporary, Thomas Girtin.
Though he died at the age of only
27, Girtin won an undisputed
place among the great masters of
watercolour painting, ranking
with Turner and Constable. As
Hardie notes (see Biblio.), not only
were his style and technique bold
and innovative, but above all he
imposed his own personality on
the development of watercolour
painting in Britain, transforming
it from a cool and controlled craft
of dispassionate portrayal into an
art form that embraced chance,
imagination and the widest self-
expression.*

Isaac de Moucheron
(1667-1744)
Dutch
A Classical Villa with a
Vase on a Terrace; and
Part of a Fountain
with a River God
A pair, signed, black lead,
pen and brown ink,
grey wash, brown ink
framing lines,
fragmentary watermark
with letter V
6 x 3in (15.5 x 8cm)
£1,000-1,500 *C(Am)*

Thomas Jones (1742-1803)
British
View of the Roofs of an Italian
Villa, Mountains Beyond
Oil on paper
10¼ x 15½in (26 x 39cm)
£17,000-19,000 *S*

Hugh O'Neill (1784-1824)
British
Old Houses near a Church
Watercolour over pencil with pen
and brown ink
6¾ x 10¼in (17 x 26cm)
£1,900-2,400 *S*

John Inigo Richards, R.A.
(c1720-1810)
Tonbridge Castle, Kent
Signed and dated 1796,
watercolour over pencil
9½ x 13¾in (24 x 35cm)
£700-800 *S*

Hendrik Meyer (1744-93)
Dutch
A Rustic Scene with Peasants by
a Tumbled Down Watermill
Signed and dated 1778, pen and
black ink and watercolour
11¾ x 15½in (30 x 39.7cm)
£6,500-7,500 *S(NY)*

William Tomkins, A.R.A.
(c1730-92)
British
A View of Boldre Hill House,
Lymington
Signed with monogram and dated
1769
23½ x 38½in (59.6 x 97.8cm)
£9,000-10,000 *C*

John Wells (active late 18thC)
British
Morden Hall, Surrey
A pair, both signed and inscribed,
watercolour over pencil with wash
line borders
15¾ x 22½in (40.5 x 57cm)
£2,700-3,200 *S*

19th Century

Thomas Allom (1804-72)
British
Osborne House, Isle of Wight
Pencil and brown wash
heightened with white
8 x 15¾in (20.7 x 40cm)
£950-1,200 *C*

Cecil Charles Windsor Aldin
(1870-1935)
British
The Chequers Inn, Tonbridge,
Kent
Signed, pencil
18½ x 16in (47 x 40.6cm)
£600-700 *DN*

*This is the original drawing for
Page 116 of Cecil Aldin's 'Old
Inns'.*

George Price Boyce (1826-97)
British
From a Window of the Hôtel du
Lion d'Or, Vézelay
Inscribed and dated 1885,
watercolour
5¼ x 11¼in (13.2 x 28.5cm)
£550-650 *Bon*

Attributed to Sam Bough
(1822-78)
British
Windsor Castle
Bears signature
11 x 18in (28 x 45.5cm)
£700-800 *S(S)*

John Buckler (1770-1851)
British
North View of Littlecot House;
South View of Littlecot House
A pair, signed and dated 1806,
pen and monochrome wash
6 x 8¾in (15.2 x 22.2cm)
£220-300 *DN*

John Constable, R.A. (1776-1837)
British
St Peter's Church, Sudbury,
Suffolk
Pencil with wash on laid paper
6¼ x 6in (16 x 15cm) **£5,500-6,500** *S*

Samuel Colman (1832-1920)
American
Puebla, Mexico
Signed and dated '92, watercolour
and gouache on brown wove paper
7½ x 15¼in (19 x 38.7cm)
£2,800-3,300 *S(NY)*

John Constable, R.A.
(1776-1837)
British
A Water Mill
Watercolour over pencil
heightened with bodycolour and
scratching out
7½ x 9½in (19 x 24cm)
£42,000-50,000 *S*

Lewis Nockalls Cottingham
(1787-1847)
British
Perspective View of a Design for
the South Front of Combe Abbey,
Warwickshire; and a Louis XIV
Drawing Room at Combe Abbey
Two, watercolours over pencil,
one with scratching out
One 19¼ x 37in (49.5 x 94cm), the
other 23 x 31in (58.5 x 79cm)
£2,600-3,000 *S*

*'The sound of water escaping from
mill dams, etc., willows, old rotten
planks, slimy posts, and
brickwork, I love such things.
Shakespeare could make
everything poetical; he tells us of
poor Tom's haunts among 'sheep
cotes and mills'. As long as I do
paint, I shall never cease to paint
such places ... Those scenes made
me a painter and I am grateful.'
John Constable, letter to the Rev.
John Fisher, 1821.*

David Cox (1783-1859)
British
Guy's Cliff, Warwickshire
Watercolour over traces of pencil
with scratching out
13¾ x 18¼in (35 x 46.5cm)
£4,200-5,000 *S*

*Guy's Cliff was a popular tourist
spot in the 19thC as the home of
Guy of Warwick who lived there in
a cave in the 10thC. According to
legend Earl Guy, having slain the
Danish giant Colbrand, strangled
a wild boar and killed several
dragons, and retired to live the life
of a hermit in the cave that bears
his name. There are also many
other caves cut into the great cliff
where later hermits followed his
example.*

Henry Hadfield Cubley
(active 1882-1930)
British
Conway Castle
Signed, oil on canvas
17½ x 24in (44 x 61cm)
£500-575 *BCG*

English Provincial School
(early 19thC)
Prospect of Harewood House,
Yorkshire
Oil on canvas, unlined
16 x 19¾in (40.5 x 50.5cm)
£650-750 *S*

Richard Bankes Harraden
(1778-1862)
British
A View of Emmanuel College,
Cambridge
10 x 14¾in (25.4 x 37.5cm)
£2,000-2,500 *C*

**Victor Philippe Auguste de
Jonquières** (active 1838-70)
French
Cathedral Scenes
A pair, one signed, watercolour
heightened with white
16¼ x 13in (41.3 x 33cm)
£1,700-2,300 *Bon*

George Moore Henton
(1861-1924)
British
The School Yard, Eton
Signed and dated 1894, oil on
canvas
15 x 22½in (38 x 57cm)
£2,000-2,500 *S*

Alfred Parsons (1847-1920)
British
The Rose Garden
Signed, pencil and watercolour
heightened with bodycolour
10½ x 15in (27 x 38cm)
£200-300 *CSK*

J. J. Murray (c1820-c1880)
British
Prospect of a Scottish Castle
Signed and dated 1858, pencil,
pen and red ink and watercolour
15½ x 23¾in (39.4 x 60.4cm)
£550-650 *C*

James Paterson, R.S.A., R.W.S.
(1854-1932)   British
Bullen's Yard, Cambridge
Signed, inscribed and dated 1909,
watercolour heightened with
bodycolour
14½ x 21in (37.2 x 53.3cm)
£2,500-3,000 *C(S)*

Thomas Sully (1783-1872)
English (active USA)
Springfield in Chester County,
Pennsylvania
Inscribed and dated March 10th
1820, pencil and watercolour
7½ x 13in (19.4 x 32.7cm)
£2,800-3,300 *C*

Thomas Taylor (active 1850s)
British
A Folio of Designs for the Free
Grammar School, Swansea
Including a complete set of plans,
elevations and details, Articles of
Agreement, specifications and
prices, 26, all signed and dated
September 1852 and January
1853, pen and black ink and
coloured washes
20½ x 28¾in (52 x 73cm) each
£2,400-2,800 *S*

Valter Williams (1835-1906)
British
Rievaulx Abbey; and Fountains
Abbey
a pair, both signed and dated 78,
oil on canvas
12 x 18in (30.5 x 46cm)
£5,800-7,000 *C*

Hilaire Thierry (19thC)
French
The Arcade of the Palais Royale,
with figures walking, the borders
with views of palaces and other
Royal residences surmounted by
the arms of the Duc d'Orleans
and the Princess Amelia of
Naples
Signed and inscribed, black chalk,
watercolour and bodycolour,
watermark
10 x 12¾in (25.4 x 32.5cm)
£9,500-10,500 *C*

20th Century

Charles Bittinger (b1879)
American
The Old Homestead
Signed, oil on canvas
16 x 20in (40. 6 x 50.8cm)
£900-1,200 *S(NY)*

Thomas P. Anshutz (1851-1912)
American
The Summer House
Watercolour on paper, executed
c1900
13¼ x 20in (33.7 x 50.8cm)
£5,000-6,000 *S(NY)*

James Brown (20thC)
British
Passing By
Oil on board
24 x 20in (61 x 51cm)
£700-750 *BRG*

Graham Clarke (b1941)
British
Cat at the Corner, Alba (Ardèche,
France)
Signed and dated 1992,
watercolour
8½ x 10½in (21.5 x 26cm)
£1,500-1,800 *WILD*

*Graham Clarke, author,
illustrator and humourist, is one
of Britain's most popular
printmakers, writes critic Judith
Bumpus. His watercolour
paintings are usually derived
from topographical sketches and
these can be considered as both a
preparation for the etching and as
a separate activity. What is
particularly interesting is that
they are at once more serious and
more idiosyncratic. The medium
is employed in an even more
random and playful fashion.
Blotches and lines and colours
have a life of their own, and
Graham enjoys controlling the
accidental effects of watercolour
on paper. These passages of pure
artistic pleasure are then
programmed for the viewer by the
same clever, cartoon-like line that
he employs in his etchings.*

Marcel Dyf (1899-1985)
French
L'Eglise de Martigues
Signed, oil on canvas
23¾ x 28¾in (60 x 73 cm)
£1,400-1,800 *CSK*

Peter Evans (b1943)
British
Boucherie Dienis
Acrylic
30in (76cm) square
£5,500-6,000 *CSG*

Stuart Davis (1892-1964)
American
Chinatown
Signed and dated 1912, oil on
canvas
37 x 30¼in (94 x 76.8cm)
£40,000-50,000 *S(NY)*

Herbert Jackson (1909-89)
British
Four designs for 'A Private Yacht
Club on the Mediterranean',
executed for the Tite Prize
Inscribed and stamped 1928, pen,
ink and watercolour
Front elevation 27 x 39¼in (68.6 x
99.7cm)
£850-1,000 *Bon*

Henry Gasser (1909-81)
American
The Hoffman House
Signed, watercolour on paper
15½ x 22½in (39.4 x 57.2cm)
£1,700-2,000 *S(NY)*

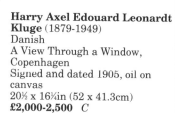

**Harry Axel Edouard Leonardt
Kluge** (1879-1949)
Danish
A View Through a Window,
Copenhagen
Signed and dated 1905, oil on
canvas
20½ x 16¼in (52 x 41.3cm)
£2,000-2,500 *C*

Edward Hopper (1882-1967) American
Gloucester Houses
Signed, watercolour on paper
16 x 21¾in (40.6 x 55.2cm)
£230,000-250,000 *S(NY)*

*Executed in 1926 or 1928, this
watercolour is also known as
Houses on a Hill.
'It was in Gloucester in 1923 that
Hopper embarked on the
watercolours of houses and village
streets that were to become his
first generally known type of
subject - for a while, one might
say, his trademark,' writes
Hopper's biographer, Lloyd
Goodrich. He liked the spare
wooden houses and churches of
the early years, their puritan
severity sometimes relieved by
jigsaw ornamentation; or the more
ambitious flamboyant mansions
of the late 19thC with their
mansard roofs, wide spreading
porches, and jutting dormers and
bay windows. But equally he
liked the poorer run down
sections.....Never before had the
American small town been
subjected to such candid scrutiny.
When these watercolours were
first shown, the general reaction,
from critics and public, was that
they were satire. 'We were not yet
used to seeing such commonplace,
and to some of us ugly, material
used in art. But actually there
was no overt satire. Hopper was
painting an honest portrait of an
American town, with all its native
character, its familiar ugliness
and beauties.'*

Edward Hopper, New York, 1978.

John Marin (1870-1953)
American
Old Church at Ranchos, New
Mexico
Signed and dated '30, watercolour
on paper
13¾ x 18½in (35 x 47cm)
£42,000-50,000 *S(NY)*

Walter Murch (1907-67)
American
Girders and Factory
Gouache on paper
10¼ x 14in (26 x 35.6cm)
£800-1,000 *S(NY)*

Phillip Stuart Paice
(1892-1961)
British
Higher Bebington Mill, Cheshire
Signed, oil on canvas
20 x 24in (51 x 61.5cm)
£550-600 *BCG*

John Piper (1903-92)
British
Duchene Fountain, Blenheim
Silkscreen, 15 colours
16½ x 23¼in (42 x 59.5cm)
£700-750 *CCA*

Reginald Marsh (1898-1954)
American
Grain Elevator
Annotated WC NB-156, stamped
on reverse, watercolour on paper
14 x 20in (35.6 x 50.8cm)
£3,000-4,000 *S(NY)*

Ellen Robbins (1828-1905)
American
Lincoln Boat House, Sandy Pond
Signed and dated 1890,
watercolour on board
9¾ x 25in (50.2 x 63.5cm)
£2,700-3,200 *S(NY)*

Robert Spencer (1871-1931)
British
Misty Evening
Signed, oil on canvas
20 x 24in (51 x 61cm)
£8,000-9,000 *DN*

Frank Taylor (20thC)
British
Old Orchard Ocean Pier
Acrylic and oil
12 x 18in (31 x 46cm)
£350-400 *PHG*

Ian Weatherhead
(b1932)
British
Chateau d'Usse
Watercolour
16 x 26in (41 x 51cm)
£400-450 *Wyk*

Interiors
17th & 18th Centuries

Pieter Neeffs the Elder (c1587-c1661)
Flemish
A Cathedral Interior with Figures
Signed, and bears a Teniers
monogram, oil on panel
17½ x 26¾in (44.5 x 68cm)
£40,000-50,000 *S(NY)*

**François de Nomé, called
Monsù Desiderio**
(c1593-after 1644)
French
A Church Interior
Oil on canvas
11½ x 20¼in (29.5 x 51.7cm)
£2,300-3,000 *S*

William Kent (c1685-1748)
British
Design for the Marble Parlour at
Houghton Hall
Signed, pen and grey and brown
ink with brown wash
10¼ x 15in (26 x 38cm)
£22,000-26,000 *S*

Bolognese School (18thC)
Capricci of Palace Interiors at
Night with Classical Figures
A pair, both oil on canvas
36¼ x 45¼in (92.5 x 115cm)
and 37¼ x 46in (94.5 x 117cm)
£18,500-22,000 *S*

Giacomo Quarenghi
(1744-1817)
Italian
Design for a Ceiling Decoration
with an Allegorical Female Figure
in the Central Medallion
Pen and black ink and
watercolour
13½ x 18¾in (34.5 x 47.5cm)
£3,500-4,000 *S(NY)*

Roman School (18thC)
The Interior of Saint Peter's, Rome
Oil on canvas
33 x 50¾in (84 x 129cm)
£18,000-20,000 *S*

Johannes Rienkzn. Jelgerhuis
(1770-1836)
Dutch
The Interior of the Church of St
Laurens, Alkmaar
Signed and dated 1829, black
chalk, black ink, watercolour,
pencil framing lines
19 x 14¾in (48.3 x 37.3cm)
£1,600-2,000 *C(Am)*

19th Century

Carl Holsøe (1863-1935)
Danish
An Interior
Signed, oil on canvas
16½ x 13¾in (41.6 x 35cm)
£6,500-7,500 *C*

Louis Haghe (1806-85)
Belgian
A Chapel in St Clementi, Rome;
and The North Transept of St
Marco, Venice
A pair, both signed and dated
1865 and 1866, pencil and
watercolour heightened with
bodycolour
24½ x 18in (62.5 x 46cm)
£1,000-1,200 *CSK*

John Foulston
(1772-1842)
British
The Civil and Military
Library, Devonport
Inscribed, pencil
and watercolour
with touches of
white heightening
6¼ x 8¾in (16 x 22.3cm)
£1,400-1,800 *C*

English School (c1883)
The Drawing Room, Woodford
Cottage, Gibraltar
Inscribed, pencil and watercolour
heightened with white and
scratching out
8 x 11½in (20 x 29.2cm)
and another interior, possibly in
the same house, by the same
artist. **£3,000-3,500** *C*

C. Ando (19th/20thC)
Japanese
Inside a Japanese Temple
Signed and dated 1893, oil on
canvas
42 x 30in (106.7 x 76.2cm)
£7,000-8,000 *S(NY)*

A. Armand (19thC)
French
A Library with Antiquities
Signed AA, black lead, pen and
brown ink, brown wash,
watermark Whatman
5¾ x 5in (14.4 x 13cm)
£600-700 *CNY*

Ludwig Michalek (1859-1942)
Austrian
A Study in a Palais on the
Ringstrasse, Vienna
Signed, watercolour
18½ x 24in (47 x 61cm)
£2,000-2,600 *S*

Frederick Nash (1782-1856)
British
The Nave, Exeter Cathedral
Watercolour over pencil
heightened with gum arabic
19¼ x 23½in (49 x 65cm)
£1,400-1,800 *S*

Joseph Nash (1808-78)
British
The Carved Parlour, Crewe Hall
Watercolour, heightened with
white
11 x 17in (28 x 43cm)
£800-850 *BCG*

William Lake Price (1810-91)
British
Sala di Gran Senata, Venice; and
Byron Meditating in the Palazzo
Mocenigo, Venice
A pair, both signed and dated
1839, watercolour over pencil
heightened with bodycolour
13½ x 19in (34 x 49cm)   **£2,500-3,000** *S*

Herbert Davis Richter
(1874-1955)
British
The Oriel Window
Signed, coloured chalks
30 x 25in (76 x 63.5cm)
£600-700 *S(S)*

Circle of Hilaire Thierry
(19thC)
French
The Interior of a Grand Salon,
traditionally identified as Roche-
Guyon, with 2 ladies playing the
harpsichord, another listening
Signed and inscribed, black chalk
and watercolour
6½ x 10in (16.5 x 24.8cm)
£1,800-2,200 *C*

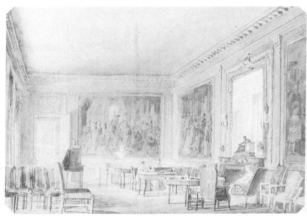

20th Century

Alison Griffin (20thC)
British
The Window Seat
Signed, acrylic
6 x 5in (15 x 12.5cm)
£300-330 *FI*

Derrick Greaves (b1927)
British
Italian Interior
Signed and dated 53, oil on
canvas
40 x 33in (102 x 84cm)
£4,200-5,000 *S*

Michael Schreiber (b1949)
German
Orangerie
Lithograph, 6 colours
27¼ x 19½in (69.5 x 49.5cm)
£175-195 *CCA*

John Rideout (b1933)
British
The White Hat
Signed, gouache
14 x 20in (35.5 x 51cm)
£200-225 *Dr*

William Henriksen (1880-?)
Danish
A Sunny Corner
Signed, oil on canvas
16¾ x 19½in (42.5 x 50cm)
£2,000-2,500 *S*

Dame Laura Knight
(1877-1970)
British
Theatre Box, Amsterdam
Signed and dated 2 Aug 1925,
watercolour over black chalk
14 x 10in (36 x 25cm)
£5,300-5,600 *JMI*

Robert Panitzsch (1879-?)
Danish
A Lady Sitting on the Porch
Signed and dated, oil on canvas
19¼ x 23in (48 x 58.5cm)
£3,500-4,000 *S*

MARINE

'There has been a very keen interest shown in marine pictures over the first six months of this year,' said Martin Gallon of Sotheby's, speaking to us at the beginning of June 1993. 'In our January sale, over 90% of works sold, a very strong result. Interest was shown in artists from every period, in particular the 20th century with pictures by Montague Dawson proving very popular, and fetching high prices.' At marine auctions, it is not just dealers but also private collectors who make up a significant percentage of those who attend and buy. Bonham's January marine sale, for example, is traditionally timed to coincide with the Earls Court Boat Show, when many seafaring folk come to town. 'Marine pictures tend to be bought by those with a very specific marine interest,' explains Gallon, 'specialist collectors who understand the field.'

With marine pictures, it is not only the name of an artist that can attract a buyer, but the identity of a ship, the portrayal of a particular naval engagement or celebrated yacht race. In marine auctions, many works come complete with long catalogue entries detailing a vessel's full history. Depending on the importance of the subject portrayed, research can help a great deal with selling a work, and can also be extremely enjoyable in its own right. As well as consulting books on marine artists and maritime history, specialist advice can be obtained from museums. The most famous in this field is the National Maritime Museum at Greenwich which houses a superb art collection and a wonderful library, covering every aspect of maritime history, and which is open to the general public.

F. Huys After Pieter Brueghel the Elder
(1512-69)
Flemish
Three Men of War in a Tempest, Sailing to the Right
Engraving, 1565
8¾ x 11in (22 x 28.5cm)
£6,700-7,700 *C*

Lorenzo Castro (active late 17th/early 18thC)
Spanish? Active in Netherlands and Britain
A British Squadron with Levantine Galleys and other Shipping in The Straits of Messina
Oil on canvas
30 by 63¾in (76 by 162cm)
£23,000-30,000 *S*

16th-17th Century

Attributed to Jan van de Capelle
(1626-79)
Dutch
Fishermen and Sailing Boats on an Estuary in a Calm
Pen and brown ink, grey wash, brown ink framing lines
5½ x 10¾in (14 x 27.3cm)
£2,800-3,500 *C(Am)*

Although one of the most expensive and admired of all Dutch marine painters, Capelle was not a professional artist but a wealthy businessman who painted for pleasure. He was a major art collector in his own time and left a vast fortune to his seven children.

Bonaventura Peeters (1614-52)
Flemish
Shipping in a Stiff Breeze off a walled Port
Signed and dated BP 1639, oil on panel
21½ x 39in (54 x 99cm).
£34,000-40,000 *C*

Jan Porcellis (c1584-1632)
Dutch
Dutch Shipping off a Pier in a Choppy Sea
Oil on panel
15¼ x 17½in (39 x 45cm)
£32,000-40,000 *S(NY)*

Attributed to Matthieu van Plattenberg
(1608-60)
Flemish
Ships Labouring in Heavy Seas off a Rocky
Shore
Oil on canvas
36½ x 48in (93 x 122cm)
£3,000-4,000 *P*

*Plattenberg specialised in portraying storms
and ships wrecked on rocky coasts.*

Pieter van de Velde (1634-after 1687)
Flemish
Shipping off the Dutch Coast
Oil on canvas
32 x 48¼in (81 x 123cm)
£10,500-11,500 *S(NY)*

Salomon van Ruisdael (1600-70)
Dutch
A River Landscape with Farmers ferrying
Cattle
Oil on canvas
27½ x 39½in (70 by 100cm)
£83,000-95,000 *S*

Follower of Willem van de Velde
(17th/18thC)
Dutch
Fishing Boats moored in a Calm at a Jetty
Oil on canvas
19 x 17in (48 x 43cm)
£2,300-2,600 *CSK*

18th Century

William Anderson (1757-1837)
British
A Harbour Side
Signed and dated 1797, watercolour and pen
and black ink
11¾ x 15⅜in (30 x 40cm)
£2,700-3,200 *S*

Charles Brooking (1723-59)
British
Dutch Barges in a Calm
Oil on canvas,
21 x 30¾in (53 x 78cm)
£7,000-8,000 *S*

Hendrick Cornelisz Vroom (1566-1640)
Dutch
Elegant figures conversing on a Beach before
a Coastal Fortress in front of which a Man-
O'-War with Numerous Passengers Sets Sail
amongst a Flotilla of Various Vessels
Signed, oil on panel
12½ x 24in (32 x 61cm)
£8,000-9,000 *P*

*Although Pieter Brueghel painted a few
marine pictures, Vroom is generally regarded
as the father of marine painting.*
*Born in Haarlem, Vroom travelled extensively
as a young man. Planning to visit Seville, he
painted some religious works to support him
while he was abroad. Support him they did
and in the most unlikely way. The ship he
was travelling on was wrecked on the coast
near Lisbon where the inhabitants, thinking
the survivors were English corsairs, planned
to kill them. Fortunately, Vroom had
managed to save his pictures and was able to
show them to the Portuguese. On seeing them
they said 'These men are not Englishmen they
are Christians,' and Vroom and his
companions were saved.*
*Rather than putting him off, Vroom's
experiences at sea fostered his interest in
marine painting. He became the master in
his field, pioneering the portrayal of naval
scenes and battles in a manner never seen
before. He taught the first generation of
Dutch and Flemish School Marine painters,
and was a major inspiration to all those who
followed him.*

William Anderson (1757-1837)
British
A British Man-O'-War and other Shipping at
Anchor
Signed and dated 1814, oil on canvas
19¾ x 30in (50 x 76cm)
£7,500-8,000 *VDG*

> *Condition is a
> major factor in a
> picture's price*

English Provincial School (c1726)
The Jolly Sailor Inn, at Saltford Weir and
Lock, Nr Bristol
Oil on panel
25¼ x 66½in (64 x 169cm)
£7,000-8,000 *S*

Jacob Cats (1741-99)
Dutch
A Stormy Scene with Figures Unloading
Boats near a House on the Water's Edge
Signed and dated 1785, drawn with a brush
in grey and blue wash over traces of black
chalk
10½ x 13½in (26 x 34.5cm)
£22,000-28,000 *S(NY)*

Dutch School (c1765-69)
The Walenburgh and other Dutch
Merchantmen at anchor in Table Bay, South
Africa, with the Castle of Good Hope to the
left
Pencil, pen, black ink and watercolour
9 x 14¼in (23 x 36.2cm)
£2,500-2,800 *C*

Robert Cleveley (1747-1809)
British
Shipping in the Pool of London
Watercolour over pencil
6 x 9¼in (15 x 24cm)
£600-800 *S*

**Charles François Grenier de Lacroix,
called Lacroix de Marseille** (c1700-82)
French
Imaginary Views of Mediterranean Harbours
A pair, both signed and dated 1776, oil on
canvas
each 41¼ x 57in (105 x 144.5cm)
£85,000-100,000 *S(NY)*

Francis Holman (d1790)
British
The ships 'London', 'Integrity', 'Elizabeth' and
'Nancy' with other vessels off Yarmouth
Signed, oil on canvas
34 x 59in (86.5 x 150cm)
£28,000-35,000 *S*

*Painted c1780, it has been suggested that this
painting shows a group of merchantment in
Yarmouth Roads gathering as a convoy before
embarking for the Baltic. At that time British
ships were forced to form convoys for their
own safety due to the hostile forces of Russia,
Denmark & Sweden (the League of Armed
Neutrality) and France which had allied itself
to the revolutionaries during the American
War of Independence. The Baltic was the
principal source of all mast timber and tar
and therefore the Baltic trade was vital to
Britain and had to be carried on in spite of
the risks.*

Peter Monamy (1681-1749)
British
The Royal William firing a Salute
Oil on canvas
24 x 30¼in (61 x 76.5cm)
£31,000-40,000 *C*

John Laporte (1761-1839)
British
Loading Slate at Bangor Ferry
Inscribed PS, pencil and bodycolour
14½ x 21½in (37 x 54.5cm)
£4,700-5,700 *C*

*Much of Laporte's work was influenced by
Paul Sandby, hence the false inscription with
Sandby's initials.*

Philippe James de Loutherbourg, R.A.
(1740-1812)
French
Fishermen Launching a Boat at Worthing,
Sussex
Pen, brown ink and watercolour over traces
of pencil heightened with touches of
bodycolour
8½ x 14¼in (21 x 36cm)
£2,000-2,500 *S*

Thomas Mitchell (exh 1774-1789)
British
A Frigate off Portsmouth with Spithead
beyond
signed and dated 1780, oil on canvas
17 x 28in (43 x 71cm)
£5,000-6,000 *CSK*

Thomas Luny (1759-1837)
British
The U.S. Ship 'Granville' off Deptford
signed and indistinctly dated 1799, oil on
canvas
28 x 47in (71 x 119cm)
£21,000-25,000 *S*

*Luny was clearly a man of remarkable
strength of character. He trained as an artist
with Francis Holman, then subsequently
joined the Royal Navy from which he was
forced to retire c1810 due to rheumatoid
arthritis. His disability was severe - he was
confined to a wheelchair and since his hands
were also affected, he either held the brush
between both hands or strapped it to his
wrists. In spite of this, he painted a
prodigious number of works, in some months
according to his diaries) turning out a
picture every working day. Most of his
paintings sold for £5, a proportion for £10
while a few went for as much as £25 a piece.
See Bibliography E.H.H. Archibald,
Dictionary of Sea Painters, 1982.*

Francis Nicholson (1753-1844)
British
Unloading a Wrecked Ship at Scarborough,
Yorkshire
Signed and dated 1793, pen, grey ink and
watercolour over traces of pencil heightened
with gum arabic and scratching out, on
original wash line mount
11¾ x 16½in (30 x 42cm)
£2,700-3,200 *S*

Charles Martin Powell (1775-1824)
British
Dutch Pinks and a Man-O'-War thought to be
off Amsterdam
signed, oil on canvas
17¾ x 24in (45 x 61cm)
£5,300-6,300 *C*

Jan Claesz. Rietschoof (c1652-1719)
Dutch
Dutch Men-O'-War moored to a Quayside and
other Vessels in a Harbour
Signed with monogram, oil on canvas
21 x 25¼in (53 x 64.2cm)
£5,600-7,000 *Bon*

Anton Schranz (1769-1839)
Austrian active in Minorca and Malta
Ships in Mahon Harbour, Minorca
Oil on canvas
16½ x 25in (42 x 64cm).
£14,000-15,000 *OSG*

Francis Swaine (c1715-82)
British
Men-O'-War in a stiff Breeze
Signed, oil on canvas
25 x 49in (64 x 124.5cm)
£4,500-5,000 *S*

Thomas Whitcombe (1763-1824)
British
Ramsgate Harbour
Signed with initials, oil on canvas
12 x 17in (31 x 43cm).
£4,700-5,700 *CSK*

Cornelis van de Velde (active 1710-29)
British
An English Naval Two-decker, c1710, with a
Hoy alongside
Oil on canvas
25 x 40in (64 x 101.5cm)
£5,500-6,500 *C*

19th Century

Thomas Buttersworth (1768-1842)
British
The French Ship Droits de L'Homme, 74
guns, manoeuvering to avoid being raked by
H.M.S. Amazon and H.M.S. Indefatigable's
guns
Signed, oil on canvas
10¼ x 14¼in (26 x 37cm)
£2,700-3,200 *CSK*

> ### Locate the Source
> *The source of each
> illustration in Miller's can
> be found by checking the
> code letters below each
> caption with the list of
> contributors.*

James Edward Buttersworth (1817-94)
British
A British Man-O'-War off the coast of Cadiz
Signed, oil on canvas
17½ x 23½in (45 x 60cm)
£11,500-12,500 *S*

Thomas Buttersworth (1768-1842)
British
The Action of Commodore Dance and The
Comte de Linois off The Straits of Malacca,
15th February 1804
Indistinctly signed, oil on canvas
31 x 47¼in (79 x 120cm)
£19,000-25,000 *S*

*This painting commemorates one of the most
unusual actions in British naval history. On
31st January 1804 the East India Company's
fleet of merchant vessels left Canton
commanded by Commodore Nathaniel Dance,
nephew of the artist Nathaniel Dance. On
February 11th, the fleet, consisting of only 16
Indiamen and 11 smaller ships met a French
squadron commanded by Admiral Linois off
Pulo Aor in the straits of Malacca. The
French admiral concluded that 3 of Dance's
ships were men-o'-war and Dance's bold
attitude in ranging his fleet in line of battle
reinforced this belief. The next morning,
Dance made the signal to engage the enemy
and the attack was led by the 'Royal George'
under Captain Timmins followed by the
Gange's and the 'Earl Camden', Dance's ship.
Linois believed that the attack came from
ships of the line and after a few badly aimed
broadsides decided to flee. Dance signalled
his fleet to chase the French and for 2 hours
the merchantmen pursued the powerful
French squadron. The only loss on the
English side was one man killed and one
wounded, and no ships were damaged. On
28th February Dance's fleet met 2 English
warships which escorted them to St Helena.
On his return home Dance was knighted and
voted a pension from grateful East India
Company.
Buttersworth's painting shows 5 French ships
on the right firing at the Indiamen which are
returning fire.*

Frederick Calvert (d1845)
British
Fishing Vessels off the Coast
Oil on canvas
12 x 15¾in (30 x 40cm)
£2,200-2,400 *PCA*

Nicolas Cammillieri (active 1830-55)
Maltese
H.M.S. Revolutionaire leaving Valetta
Harbour
Signed, inscribed and dated 1822, pen, black
ink and watercolour on paper
13¾ x 20in (35 x 51cm)
£1,800-2,200 *CSK*

Consalvo Carelli (1818-1900)
Italian
Fishing off Capri
Signed and inscribed Capri, oil on panel
10½ x 16¾in (26 x 43cm)
£8,000-9,000 *P*

Guiseppe Carelli (1858-1921)
Italian
Sorrento, Fishing Boats on a Calm Sea
Signed, oil on canvas
12½ x 19½in (32 x 49cm)
£5,000-6,000 *E*

John Wilson Carmichael (1800-69)
British
Port of The Brill,
Signed and dated 1860, oil on canvas
13 x 20in (33 x 51cm)
£20,000-21,500 *BuP*

George Chambers (1803-36)
British
The Battle of Trafalgar, October 21st, 1805
Signed and dated 1823, oil on panel
18½ x 22in (47 x 56cm)
£7,200-8,000 *CSK*

Henry Barlow Carter (1803-67)
British
A View of Whitby from the end of the West
Pier
Colour washes, with scratching out
6¾ x 9½in (17 x 24cm)
£1,200-1,500 *P(L)*

Chinese School (19thC)
Northbrook
Oil on canvas
24 x 36in (61 x 92cm)
£3,500-4,000 *CSK*

*On 19 January 1885, Northbrook, built in
1874, sailed from San Francisco bound for
Falmouth with a cargo of grain. After a near
record passage down the west coast of South
America, she ran into a tremendous storm off
Cape Horn and was soon in difficulties.
Losing her main and mizzen masts in quick
succession, it was only thanks to the courage
of her two apprentices - one of whom was
Quinton Rhodes - that the foremast was
saved. Northbrook finally made Falmouth on
18 June where she was cheered into port and
her crew given a hero's welcome. For his
gallantry in saving the mast and thus the
ship herself, Rhodes was awarded the bronze
medal of the Board of Trade and also received
a purse of gold from the ship's underwriters.
Sold with the painting was a fascinating
archive of documentation comprising a
quantity of letters and character references
concerning Rhodes conduct in 1885 as well as
his later career as a captain in the Merchant
Marine, together with various newspaper
cuttings recounting the events of 1885 (but
dating from the late 1920's when the story
was publicised).*

William Clark (1803-83)
British
The Yacht Avon Winning the Opening Cruise
of the Clyde Yacht Club
Signed and dated 1871, oil on canvas
27 x 44in (69 x 112cm)
£17,500-20,000 *S*

**Nicholas Matthew
Condy** (1818-51)
British
Shipping off the Coast
Signed and dated 1834, oil on board
11½ x 15½in (29 x 40cm)
£6,000-7,000 *Bea*

Colonial School (early 19thC)
An extensive view of Table Bay
Inscribed Cape Town, watercolour and
scratching out, unframed
10¼ x 31¾in (26 x 81cm)
£4,300-5,300 *Bon*

Henry Thomas Dawson (active 1860-78)
British
Navy Vessel off Plymouth
Signed and dated 1870, oil
16 x 24in (41 x 61cm)
£3,800-4,200 *Dr*

Hans Dahl (1849-1937)
Norwegian
With the Wind
Signed, inscribed on stretcher, oil on canvas
38 x 61¾in (97 x 156cm)
£26,000-28,000 *BuP*

Pieter Christian Dommersen (1834-1908)
Dutch
Delfshaven on the Maas, Holland
signed and dated 1882, oil on panel
10¾ x 15in (27 x 38cm)
£8,000-9,000 *C*

Edward Duncan (1803-82)
British
Dutch Shipping off the Coast in a choppy Sea
Signed and dated 1861, pencil and
watercolour with scratching out and touches
of white heightening
11½ x 23½in (29 x 60cm)
£4,500-5,500 *C*

William Dommersen (d1927)
Dutch
Vollerhoven on the Zuider Zee, Holland
Signed, oil on canvas
15¼ x 23½in (29 x 60cm)
£4,700-5,500 *S*

Luigi Maria Galea (1847-1917)
Maltese
Out into the Mediterranean: H.M.S.
Dreadnought clearing Grand Harbour,
Valetta
Signed, oil on card
10¼ x 28½in (26 x 72cm)
£3,000-4,000 *C*

H.M.S. Dreadnought was laid down in Pembroke Dockyard in 1872, launched in 1875 and completed in 1879, her staggering cost of £619,739 making her the most expensive warship in the Royal Navy to date. Designed by W.H. White, she was a notable ship for various reasons; she was the first warship to have a longitudinal bulkhead amidships, the first to be fitted with compound engines and the first to have artificial ventilation.

Charles Gregory (1810-96)
British
The America
Oil on canvas
16 x 24in (41 x61cm)
£25,000-30,000 *VDG*

*This important painting of the famous
schooner yacht 'America' was completed in
1851, the year of the Great Exhibition and the
yacht is shown in her transatlantic rig prior
to any racing.
Great Britain had always dominated the
sport of yacht racing, but in 1851 'America'
challenged the British at Cowes in a now
legendary race and carried off the Hundred
Guinea Cup to the United States.*

Gian Gianni (19thC)
Italian
A Steamer in Valetta Harbour
Signed, oil on board, in the shape of an
artist's palette
6¾ x 8¼in (17 x 21cm)
£1,700-2,000 *S*

Bernard Finnegan Gribble (1873-1902)
British
Signed, oil on board
14 x 18in (36 x 46cm)
£2,000-3,000 *TBJ*

Henriette Gudin (exhibited 1850s)
French
Fishing Boats at Dusk
Signed, oil on panel, original frame
5 x 8in (13 x 20cm)
£1,000-1,800 *CGa*

Thomas Bush Hardy (1842-97)
British
The Return of the Fishing Fleet
Signed, oil on canvas
30 x 50in (76 x 127cm)
£14,000-15,000 *OSG*

Edwin Hayes (1820-1904)
British
St. Aubin's Fort, Jersey
Oil on canvas
11 x 17in (28 x 43cm)
£3,400-3,800 *C*

Joseph Heard (1799-1859)
British
The Philomela off Harrington, Cumbria
Dated 1846, oil on canvas
24 x 35¼in (61 x 90cm)
£9,500-10,500 *S*

On the skyline can be seen the chimneys of the Harrington Chemical Company. The coastal railway was opened in 1847, the year following this painting. Such major features in the course of construction were not infrequently anticipated and justifiably included to introduce an element of novelty.

Gerardus Hendriks (late 19thC)
Dutch
The Ferry
Signed, oil on panel
11¼ x 17½in (29 x 44cm)
£4,700-5,500 *C*

Heinrich Hiller (19thC)
German
A Coastal Scene
Signed, oil on canvas
11¾ x 19⅜in (30 x 53cm)
£1,700-2,000 *S*

Alfred Herbert (1820-61)
British
The Fishing fleet at Dawn
Watercolour
21 x 34in (53 x 86cm)
£1,450-1,650 *PCA*

Charles Hoguet (1821-70)
German
Fishing Vessels in a Strong Breeze offshore, a
Lighthouse Beyond
Signed and dated 1865, oil on canvas laid
down on board
34½ x 56¼in (87 x 142cm)
£3,400-4,000 *C*

Henry George Hine (1811-95)
British
Brighton Beach, c1855
Signed, watercolour
12 x 19in (31 x 48cm)
£1,450-1,650 *EG*

Eugène Isabey (1803-86)
French
Le Port de Boulogne
Signed with initials, oil on canvas
20½ x 15½in (52 x 39cm)
£4,000-5,000 *S*

Antonio Nicolo Gasparo Jacobsen
(1850-1921) American
S.S. Devon
Signed, inscribed and dated 1886, oil on
canvas
22 x 36in (56 x 92cm).
£4,800-6,000 *C*

Abraham Hulk Snr (1813-97) British
Fishing Vessels in a Calm Estuary
Signed, oil on panel
10¼ x 9¼in (25.5 x 23.5cm).
together with a companion painting
£5,700-7,000 *P(L)*

William Joy (1803-67)
British
Preparing to Sail
Pencil and watercolour
10¾ x 15¾in (27 x 40cm)
£6,000-7,000 *CSK*

Jan Hermanus Koekkoek (1778-1851)
Dutch
Fishing Boats off a Jetty
Signed, oil on panel
12 x 17¼in (31 x 44cm)
£5,000-6,000 *S*

Fernand Legout-Gerard (1856-1924)
French
Retour des Pecheurs à Concarneau
Signed, oil on panel
21¾ x 18in (55 x 46cm)
£6,000-7,000 *CNY*

Hermanus Koekkoek (1815-82)
Dutch
Fishing Smacks in a Swell off a Jetty
Signed and dated 1839, oil on canvas
12 x 36in (31 x 92cm)
In a carved and giltwood frame
£5,000-6,000 *C*

William J. Leatham (active 1840s and 50s)
British
The Three sections of Captain Taylor's
Breakwater Moored off Brighton in a Gale,
January 22nd, 1845
Signed and inscribed watercolour over pencil
heightened with white
25¼ x 39in (64 x 99cm)
£1,800-2,200 *S*

*The artist exhibited storm scenes and sea
dramas from 1840-1855.*

John Lynn (19thC)
British
The Spartan, Capt. J. Brenton, Engaging the
French Squadron in the Bay of Naples, 3rd
May 1810
Signed and indistinctly dated, oil on canvas
23¼ x 35½in (59 x 90cm)
£12,700-14,000 *S*

Georges Philibert Charles Maroniez
(1865-1934)
French
Fin de Journée
Signed, oil on canvas
23 x 36in (59 x 92cm)
£9,000-10,000 *VDG*

William Kimmins McMinn (1818-98)
British
The Duke, in Two Positions, off St. Helena
Signed and dated 1845, oil on canvas
16 x 25in (41 x 64cm)
£9,500-10,500 *S*
*The Duke (609 tons) was built in Liverpool by
Thomas Royden & Co. and launched in 1843
by Miss Anne Royden. The ship is shown
centrally in starboard profile, and also from
the port quarter aspect on the right of the
painting.*
*It was often customary to paint a ship twice
from different angles.*

William Frederick Mitchell (c1845-1914)
British
H.M.S. Northumberland
Signed, inscribed, dated 1902, and numbered
1877, watercolour
11 x 17½in (28 x 45cm)
£1,375-1,575 *CGa*

François Etienne Musin (1820-88)
Belgian
The Royal Prince aground on Galloper Sands, 1666
Signed, oil on canvas
30 x 51in (76 x 130cm)
£14,000-15,000 *C*

The mid-17thC witnessed 3 major conflicts with the Dutch, the second of which began in the spring of 1665. After numerous encounters, the two opposing fleets met again at the so called Four Days' Battle which, lasting from 1st-4th June 1666, was one of the most prolonged and hard fought actions in naval history. Beginning off the North Foreland of Kent, by the third day Admiral Sir George Ayscue decided to withdraw his squadron westwards down the English Channel when his flagship Royal Prince, one of the finest ships in the fleet, ran aground on the Galloper Sands. Attempts to refloat her were unsuccessful and, before long, she was overwhelmed by the Dutch. Ayscue himself was taken prisoner and, to his horror, Royal Prince was put to the torch and burned where she had stranded. It was a black day for the Royal Navy and a bitter humiliation made even worse by the eventual loss of the battle.

Auguste Henri Musin (b1852)
Belgian
Awaiting the Tide
Signed, oil on canvas
30 x 50½in (76 x 128cm)
£12,800-13,800 *S*

Arthur Wilde Parsons (1854-1931)
British
Calling for a Pilot off Dover
Signed and dated, pencil and watercolour
31½ x 43in (80 x 109cm)
£1,800-2,200 *CSK*

Philip J. Ouless (1817-85)
British
The Rescue of the Express off La Corbière
Oil on canvas
11¾ x 16in (30 x 41cm)
£8,000-9,000 *C*

The Rescue depicts the packet steamer Express which hit the rocks and sank off the Guernsey coast in September 1859. Almost all her 200 passengers and crew were saved together with the horses. The work depicts the artist painting the scene in the foreground, although it is not proven that he actually attended the incident.

William Henry Pearson (Active 1880-1908)
British
Below Bridges
Signed and inscribed, watercolour
9½ x 19in (24 x 48cm)
£600-650 *TBJ*

William James Durant Ready (1823-73)
British
Coastal Scene at Low Tide
Signed with initials, oil on board
9 x 13½in (23 x 34cm)
£800-1,000 *Bon*

Henry Redmore (1820-87)
British
Shipping off Whitby
Signed and dated 1879, oil on canvas
22½ x 36½in (57 x 93cm)
£7,600-8,600 *C*

Thomas Sewell Robins (1814-80)
British
Fisherfolk and Barges in an Estuary
Pencil and watercolour heightened with
white and scratching out
15¾ x 23¼in (40 x 59cm)
£5,200-6,000 *C*

Josef Karl Berthold Puttner (1821-81)
Australian
Mending the Nets at Low Tide
Watercolour with body colour
12 x 9in (31 x 23cm)
£750-850 *PCA*

John Robertson Reid (1851-1926)
British
The Young Fishermen
Signed, dated '97 and inscribed, oil on canvas
30¼ x 25in (77 x 64cm)
£3,700-4,200 *C*

François Geoffroi Roux (1811-82)
French
Le Louis Napoleon arriving in Marseilles on
29 May 1854 from Martinique
Signed, inscribed and dated 1855, pencil, pen
and watercolour heightened with white
20 x 27in (51 x 69cm)
£12,200-13,500 *CSK*

Tommaso de Simone (c1859)
Italian
Three deckers from a British Squadron at
anchor in the Bay of Naples
Signed and dated 1859, oil on canvas
18 x 25½in (46 x 65cm)
£4,200-5,000 *CSK*

John Robert Charles Spurling
(1870-1933)
British
Dashing Wave passing Boston Light
Signed and inscribed, pencil, pen and
watercolour
15½ x 17¾in (39 x 45cm)
£750-850 *CSK*

John Francis Salmon (1808-86) British
A Harbour Scene
A pair, watercolour with body colour
10 x 14in (25 x 36cm)
£850-950 *PCA*

Petrus Jan Schotel (1808-65)
Dutch
The Rescue Party
Signed, oil on canvas
30½ x 39in (77 x 99cm)
£7,000-8,000 *S*

Fred Stead (active late 19thC) British
Whitby Harbour
Signed and dated 1888
28¾ x 19¼in (73 x 49cm)
£4,000-4,500 *AH*

Henry King Taylor (active 1857-69)
British
Fishing Boats entering Port - Rye, Sussex
Signed, oil on canvas
30 x 48in (76 x 122cm)
£8,500-9,000 *VDG*

*'A great 19thC exponent of the inshore scene.
His work has become well regarded and
sought after in recent years; his style is
vigorous but also shows excellent
draughtsmanship and perspective, and he
clearly understood the sea and how to paint
it. All the better 19thC artists had a style
which was distinctly their own, as
unmistakable as a characterful signature,
and this comment applies fully to Henry King
Taylor.
He lived in London at Hammersmith, Notting
Hill, Sloane Street, Covent Garden, Pall Mall
and Tichborne Street between 1859 and 1867
and obviously spent much time travelling to
and from the coast. Between 1859 and 1864
he exhibited 6 paintings at the Royal
Academy and 24 at the British Institution.'
From British 19th Century Marine Painting
by Brook-Hart (1967).*

Henry Scott Tuke (1858-1929)
British
The Fisherman's Yarn,
Signed and dated '93, watercolour
15 x 10in (38 x 25cm)
£5,600-5,800 *EG*

J. K. E. Tudgay (19thC)
British
The Clipper Bark, Wildfire, Sailing off the
Coast
Indistinctly signed, oil on canvas
26 x 36½in (66 x 93cm)
£3,200-3,800 *CNY*

Louis Verboeckhoven (1802-89)
Belgian
A Coastal Landscape with a beached Fishing
Boat
Signed and dated 1831, oil on board
8¾ x 13in (22 x 33cm)
£3,100-3,800 *C*

George Vincent (1796-1831)
British
Fisherfolk sorting their Catch on a Quay
Dated 1825, oil on panel
13½ x 19in (34 x 48cm)
£6,400-7,400 *C*

Joseph Walter (1783-1856)
British
The Red Squadron at anchor in the Bristol
Channel
Oil on canvas
16 x 26in (41 x 66cm)
£7,200-8,200 *C*

William Edward Webb (1862-1903)
British
Shipping in Portsmouth Harbour
Signed and indistinctly dated, oil on canvas
22 x 38in (56 x 96.5cm)
£3,000-4,000 *S*

James Webb (1825-95)
British
Mills at Dordrecht
Signed and dated 1875, oil on canvas
£18,000-18,500 *OSG*

John James Wilson (1818-75)
British
A Fresh Breeze off Etretat, France
Signed with initials and dated 1850, oil on
canvas
36 x 56in (92 x 142cm)
£9,000-11,000 *S*

Félix François Georges Philibert Ziem
(1821-1911)
French
Constantinople
Signed, oil on canvas
24½ x 30½ (62.2 x 77.5cm)
£23,000-28,000 *CNY*

20th Century

Thomas Hart Benton (1889-1975)
American
On Menemsha Pond
Signed and dated '71, acrylic on paper
18¼ x 24in (46.5 x 61cm)
£45,000-60,000 *S(NY)*

John Ambrose (20thC)
British
Polperro
Oil on canvas
20 x 28in (51 by 71cm)
£1,000-1,250 *GeC*

Sven Berlin (20thC)
British
Tending Nets
Signed and dated '47, pen, brush and black
ink
11¾ x 15in (30 x 38cm)
£600-700 *CSK*

E. Blanche Terry (20thC)
British
Morning Twilight
Dated 1934, oil on canvas
17½ x 24in (44.5 x 61cm)
£550-650 *MBA*

John Steven Dews (20thC)
British
'Ariel' and 'Taeping' running up the Channel,
1866 Tea Race
Signed and inscribed with title on the frame
Oil on canvas
30 x 30in (51 x 76cm)
£6,500-7,500 *S*

George Fagan Bradshaw (20thC)
British
Boats of Hayle
Signed, tempera
22 x 29in (56 x 74cm)
£950-1,000 *Dr*

Montague Dawson (1895-1973)
The Frigate 'United States' and the British
Frigate 'Macedonian'
Signed, oil on canvas
40 x 50in (101.5 x 127cm)
£60,000-70,000 *S*

*In 1812 the British frigate 'Macedonian', on
route to the West Indies, was intercepted by
the 'United States', captained by Stephen
Decatur, in the general area of Madeira.
Decatur attempted to gain the weather gauge
but was baulked by the British Captain John
Carden, however the American ship managed
to fire two broadsides from her 24 pounders.
Decatur's manoeuvres induced the British
ship to close from astern and enabled him to
bring more guns to bear. The American guns
were handled rapidly and accurately and
soon 'Macedonian's' rigging was shot to pieces
and a third of her ship's company was dead
or wounded.*

*When sold at auction in London in January
1993, this work fetched one of the highest
prices paid for a work by Dawson in recent
years.*

Louis Dodd (20thC)
British
A view of Hong Kong showing dragon boats
racing and the clipper Black Prince outward
bound, 1870
Signed, oil on panel
16 x 24in (40.5 x 61cm)
£3,400-4,000 *CSK*

Patrick Downie (1854-1945)
British
A Silvery Sea, Firth of Clyde
Signed and dated 1931, oil on board
13¾ x 20½in (35 x 52cm)
£800-1,000 *Bon*

Charles Dixon (1872-1934)
British
The Lower Pool
Signed and inscribed with title and dated '07
Watercolour heightened with bodycolour
10¾ x 30½in (27 x 77cm)
£2,600-3,000 *S(S)*

Donald Hamilton Fraser (b1929)
British
Skerra
Silkscreen
21¾ x 29½in (55 x 75cm)
£200-225 *CCA*

Snow Gibbs, (active 1916-32)
British
On the Broads
Oil on board
8¼ x 11in (21 x 28cm)
£200-250 *Gan*

*After training at the Central School of Arts
and Crafts, Gibbs studied in New York and at
the École des Beaux Arts in Paris. His work
was shown at the Paris Salon, and at most of
the significant British galleries. Snow Gibbs'
dashing brushwork and bright palette make
him an obvious minor star of the future, notes
the Gandolfi House*

Charles Napier Hemy, R.A. (1852-1937)
British
Crab Pots, Falmouth
Signed and dated 1904, oil on canvas
30 x 20in (76 x 51cm)
£4,700-5,700 *S*

Bernard Finegan Gribble (1873-1962)
British
Shipping on The Thames
Signed, title on label on reverse
23½ x 35½in (60 x 90cm)
£1,700-2,200 *P(L)*

Brian Jones (20thC)
British
Clipper Running Downwind
Signed, oil on canvas
15½ x 25½in (39 x 65cm)
£300-350 *LH*

Ludvig Karsten (1876-1926)
Norwegian
Fra Nyhavn
Signed and dated 23, oil on canvas
39½ x 47¼in (100.3 x 120cm)
£23,000-30,000 *C*

Wilfrid Knox (1884-1966)
British
With a Steady Breeze
Signed and dated 1919, watercolour
9¾ x 14¼in (25 x 36cm)
£425-475 *BCG*

Georgina Moutray Kyle (1865-1950)
Irish
At the turn of the dyke Volandam
Signed, oil on canvas board
17½ x 12in (44.5 x 30.5cm)
£400-600 *DN*

Guy l'Hostis (b1945)
French
Ailia Britannia et Erin
21 x 29in (53 x 74cm)
£1,000-1,250 *OSG*

André Lhote (1885-1962)
French
Bateaux sur la Plage
Signed, watercolour
10¾ x 14¾in (27.5 x 37.5cm)
£2,000-2,500 *S*

Frank Henry Mason (1876-1965)
British
A Three Masted Ship off Scarborough
Signed, watercolour
10 x 30in (25.4 x 76.2cm)
£1,500-1,800 *DN*

M O** Minards** (20thC)
R.M.S. Empress of Canada; Mauretania;
M.V. Shropshire; M.V. Derbyshire
Four, one signed and dated 1953, 2 signed on
reverse
Oil on board
12 x 16in (30.5 x 40.5cm)
£750-1,000 *S*

Martyn R. Mackrill (b1962)
British
Meteor II and Ailsa, Cowes Week 1896
Watercolour
14 x 22in (36 x 56cm)
£1,100-1,350 *CFA*

R. E. Nickerson (20thC)
American
White Wings of Baltimore
Signed and inscribed, oil on canvas
26 x 36in (66 x 91.5cm)
£2,000-2,500 *C*

*The American barquentine White Wings was
built by C. Norton Stewart at Baltimore,
Maryland, in 1889.*

John Anthony Park (1880-1962)
British
Summer, St. Ives
Oil on board
12½ x 15in (32 x 38cm)
£3,000-3,500 *Mon*

Bertram Priestman (1868-1951)
British
H. M. Yacht crossing from Cowes with coffin
of Queen Victoria
Inscribed, dated and signed on reverse, oil on
canvas
8½ x 16in (21 x 41cm)
£2,000-2,500 *NBO*

Harry Hudson Rodmell (1896-1984)
British
Victoria Pier, Proposed New Pier and
Landing Stage
Signed, inscribed and dated 1919, pen and
ink with colour washes
25 x 44in (64 x 111cm)
£2,200-2,600 *P(L)*

Joseph Henry Sharp (1859-1953)
American
Crow Camp
Signed with the artist's initials, oil on canvas
15 x 20in (38 x 50.5cm)
£9,000-10,000 *S(NY)*

*In the summer of 1948 while at the Crow
Agency, Sharp became involved in a film
based upon Longfellow's The Song of
Hiawatha. The making of the movie proved
to be a disaster and it was never finished.
According to Forrest Fenn: 'A canoe was
central to the film because Hiawatha, the
hero, was supposed to paddle gracefully
around a bend in the river to a cove where the
beautiful Minehaha waited in an elaborately
beaded buckskin dress.' The actors were not
able to manoeuvre the canoe and doomed the
movie. But, Fenn continues, 'Sharp
photographed the canoe on the bank of the
Little Big Horn and used the photograph as a
guide for Crow Camp and the painting, Night
Gigging.'*

Ronald William Fordham Searle (b192◌
British
Hamburg Haven
Signed, inscribed with title and dated 196◌
pen, ink and monochrome watercolour
19½ x 15in (49.5 x 38cm)
£1,550-1,750 *CBL*

Paul Signac (1863-1935) French
Rivière de Vannes
Signed, titled and dated 28 Mai 192◌
watercolour and pencil
11½ x 17⅜in (29.5 x 45cm)
£12,200-13,200 *S*

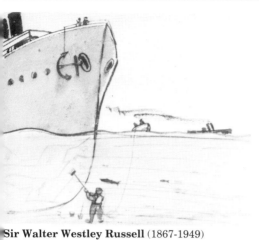

Sir Walter Westley Russell (1867-1949)
British
Painting the Ship
Signed, watercolour
7¼ x 8in (18 x 20cm)
£180-200 *ALT*

F. W. Scarbrough (active 1896-1939)
British
Evening, Boston Deeps
Signed, watercolour
13½ x 9½in (34.5 x 24cm)
£600-700 *BWe*

Dorothea Sharp (1874-1955)
British
The Harbour Mouth, St. Ives
Signed, oil on canvas
15 x 18in (38.5 x 40.5cm)
£5,500-5,700 *Dr*

Charles E. Turner (1883-1965)
British
Welcome to Amethyst, Plymouth, November
1949
Signed and inscribed, oil on canvas
£1,500-2,000 *S*

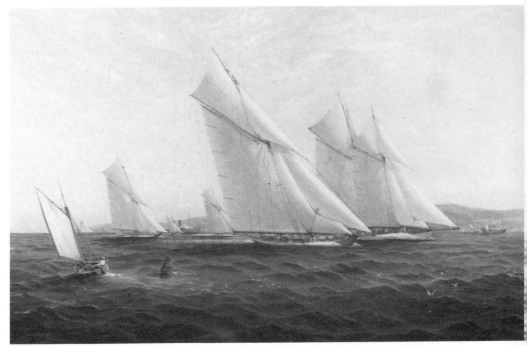

Michael J. Whitehand (b1941)
British
Shamrock racing Westward
Signed and dated '93, oil on canvas
30 x 47in (76 x 120cm)
£5,000-6,000 *CSK*

Shamrock was one of the series of legendary racing yachts, each of the same name, built for Sir Thomas Lipton, the tea magnate and one of the greatest yachtsmen of its golden age.

Alfred Wallis (1855-1942)
British
Boat and Lighthouse
Signed, pencil and oil on card
8 x 13½in (20 x 34.5cm)
£8,700-10,000 *C*

Edith Wright (active 1922-25)
British
Old Fishing Boat, Rye Harbour, Sussex
Signed, oil on board
10½ x 15½in (26 x 39cm)
£250-300 *Gan*

Attributed to Isaac Sailmaker (c1633-1721)
British
The Royal Prince and The St.Michael at the
Battle of Texel, off Holland, 13th August 1673
Bears signature, oil on canvas
33¼ x 63½in (84.5 x 161.5cm)
£5,700-6,700 *S*

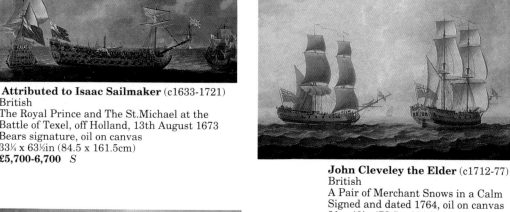

John Cleveley the Elder (c1712-77)
British
A Pair of Merchant Snows in a Calm
Signed and dated 1764, oil on canvas
31 x 40in (78.5 x 101.5cm)
£17,500-20,000 *C*

Thomas Luny (1759-1837)
British
Two Views of a British Frigate
Signed and dated 1802, oil on canvas
29 x 48in (74 x 122cm)
£13,500-16,000 *CSK*

Peter Monamy (1681-1749)
British
The Royal Yacht Dublin
Signed, oil on canvas
35 x 47½in (89 x 121cm)
£25,000-30,000 *Bon*

Willem van der Hagen (active 1722-45)
Dutch
Shipping in a Fresh Breeze
Oil on canvas
48½ x 39¾in (123 x 101cm)
£11,500-13,500 *S*

Ludolf Bakhuizen (1631-1708)
German
Fleet of Dutch Three Deckers off the Coast of Holland
Signed and dated 1705, oil on canvas
26 x 37in (66 x 94cm)
£13,000-14,000 *HFA*

William Roxby Beverley (1811-89)
British
Bridlington, Yorkshire
Signed and dated 1876, watercolour
9 x 13in (23 x 33cm)
£2,300-2,500 *NBO*

Constantin Bolonakis (1835-1907)
Greek
Fishing Vessels at Anchor
Signed, oil on canvas
21¼ x 17in (54 x 43cm)
£35,000-50,000 *C*

Thomas Buttersworth (1768-1842)
British
The Battle of Trafalgar, 21st October 1805
Oil on canvas
31¼ x 47½in (79 x 120.5cm)
£9,000-10,000 *CSK*

Alfred Thompson Bricher (1837-1908)
American
Drying the Main at Anchor
Signed with artist's monogrammed signature
Watercolour on paper
22½ x 15in (57 x 38cm)
£6,500-7,500 *S(NY)*

**Attributed to William Clark of
Greenock** (1803-83), British
The Brig Lady Octavia
Oil on board
30 x 44in (76 x 112cm)
£10,500-12,500 *CSK*

Luigi Maria Galea (1847-1917) Maltese
The Pride of the Mediterranean Fleet
Signed and inscribed, oil on card
10¼ x 28½in (26 x 73cm)
£2,300-3,000 *C*

Frederick James Aldridge (1850-1933)
British
Boats in Shoreham
Watercolour
13 x 20in (33 x 51cm)
£850-950 *F*

Hermanus Koekkoek Snr. (1815-1882)
Dutch
Sailing Vessels and a Cross Channel Packet
Steamer, possibly off Folkestone
Signed, oil on canvas
27 x 39½in (69 x 101cm)
£25,000-30,000 *C*

William Griffin of Hull (19thC)
Wanderer and William Darley in a crowded shipping lane
Signed, inscribed and indistinctly dated 1839?, oil on
canvas
28½ x 41in (73 x 104cm)
£13,500-15,000 *CSK*

Vassilios Hatzis (1870-1915)
Greek
A Sailing Vessel in a light Breeze
Signed, oil on canvas laid down on board
18½ x 13in (47 x 33cm)
£10,500-12,000 *C*

Antonio Nicolo Gasparo Jacobsen (1850-1921)
American
SS Alfred Dumois
Signed and dated 1891, oil on canvas
22 x 36in (56 x 91.5cm)
£3,600-4,600 *CSK*

Thomas Bush Hardy (1842-1897)
British
On the Dutch Coast
Signed, inscribed and dated 1890, watercolour
8½ x 11¼in (21 x 28cm)
£3,650-3,850 *MJA*

Raphael Monleon y Torres (1847-1900)
America
Signed, inscribed and dated 1886, oil on canvas
31 x 59in (79 x 149.5cm)
£5,000-6,000 *CSK*

John Lynn (active 1828-1838)
British
A Schooner of the Royal Yacht Squadron off the
Eddystone Lighthouse, other shipping beyond
Signed and dated 1831, oil on canvas
25½ x 39in (65 x 99cm)
£7,500-8,500 *S*

Arthur Wilde Parsons (1854-1931)
British
Autumn morning on the Avon
Signed and dated 1915, pencil and watercolour
24½ x 40in (62 x 101.5cm)
£3,000-3,800 *C*

Heinrich Andreas Sophus Petersen (1834-1916)
German
The Steamer Gitana off a Hanseatic Port
Signed and dated 1863, oil on canvas
19 x 27½in (48 x 70cm)
£5,000-6,000 *CSK*

Thomas Sewell Robins (1814-1895)
British
Windy day off Dover, the Castle beyond
Signed and indistinctly dated 1867?, pencil and
watercolour heightened with white
17½ x 26¼in (44.5 x 66.5cm)
£3,000-4,000 *C*

William Webb (1862-1903)
British
Unloading the Catch
Signed, oil on canvas
30 x 46in (76 x 116.5cm)
£8,500-9,000 *HFA*

John Bentham-Dinsdale
(20thC)
British
Ariel and Taeping
Oil on canvas
30 x 40in (76 x 101.5cm)
£4,400-4,800 *OM*

Charles Ernest Cundall, R. A., (1890-1971)
British
New York Harbour, thought to be painted from
Brooklyn Bridge, with the Statue of Liberty
beyond
Signed, oil on canvas
20 x 36in (51 x 91cm)
£4,500-5,500 *CSK*

Charles Dixon (1872-1934)
British
Off Tilbury
Signed, inscribed and dated 18,
watercolour heightened with bodycolour
7 x 10½in (18 x 26cm)
£2,500-3,000 *S(S)*

Montague Dawson (1895-1973)
British
A Naval Sloop
Signed, oil on canvas, unframed
40 x 50in (101.5 x 127cm)
£45,000-55,000 *S*

J. Steven Dews (b1949)
British
Racing on the Solent
Oil on canvas
36 x 60in (92 x 152cm)
£30,000-35,000 *OSG*

Richard Eurich R.A. (b1903)
British
The Ship Inn, Weymouth
Oil on canvas
20 x 24in (51 x 61cm)
£5,000-6,000 *S*

Colin Hayes (20thC)
British
Fishing Boats in Chios, Greece
Oil on canvas
24 x 30in (62 x 76.5cm)
£3,500-3,800 *BSG*

Moira Huntley (20thC)
British
Woodbridge, Suffolk
Watercolour
21 x 28¾in (53 x73cm)
£650-750 *A*

**Donald Hamilton
Fraser** (b1929)
British
Close Hauled
Silkscreen, 35 colours
23 x 15½in (58.5 x 39.5cm)
£200-225 *CCA*

Georges Laporte
(b1926)
French
Calm and Serene
Original zinc plate
lithograph
15 x 22in (38 x 56cm)
£120-140 *TES*

Michael J. Whitehand (20thC)
British
Racing off Cowes
Signed and inscribed on the stretcher, c1930, oil
on canvas
27 x 39in (68.5 x 99cm)
£2,400-3,000 *C*

Albert Marquet (1875-1947)
French
L'Eau Bleue
Signed, oil on panel, 1938
13 x 16in (33 x 41cm)
£28,000-35,000 *S*

Martyn R. Mackrill (20thC)
British
HMS Albion
Oil on canvas
28 x 36in (71.5 x 92cm)
£3,300-3,500 *CFA*

S. Robert Watson (active 1939-1958)
British
Drying the Sail, Mevagissey
Signed, oil on canvas
20 x 24in (51 x 61cm)
£550-600 *Cae*

Willy Makrozhitski (b1928) Russian
Saluting the Sailors, Sebastopol Port, The Black Sea
Oil on canvas, c1958
24 x 39in (61 x 99cm)
£13,000-15,000 *RMG*

Barry Mason (b1947)
British
The Rising Glass, Taitsing and Flying Spur
Signed and inscribed, oil on canvas
36 x 48in (91.5 x 122cm)
£3,500-4,000 *CSK*

l. **Daniel Mytens**
(c1590-1647)
Dutch
Portrait of Sir James
Oxenden of Deane
Oil on canvas
82¾ x 49in (209 x
124.5cm)
£27,000-40,000 *S*

r. **John Clostermann**
(1660-1711)
British
Portrait of a Gentleman,
with Classical
Landscape beyond
Oil on canvas
50 x 41in (127 x 104cm)
£6,500-7,500 *C*

German School (16thC)
A Nobleman on Horseback, a Dog before
Him and two Men in the Distant Landscape
Oil on panel, 7½ x 8in (19 x 20cm)
£42,000-55,000 *S(NY)*

Louis Carrogis, called Carmontelle
(1717-1806)
French
Monsieur de Cormainville in his Library, writing
at his Desk
Inscribed, black lead, red chalk, watercolour
heightened with white
11¾ x 7in (30.3 x 18cm)
£47,000-50,000 *C*

r. **Andrea Previtali** (c1475-1528)
Italian
Portrait of a young Gentleman, wearing Ermine
trimmed Coat
Signed, inscribed and dated 1506, oil on panel
13 x 10½in (33 x 27cm).
£170,000-200,000 *C*

English School (c1770)
Portrait of an Officer holding a
Spontoon, in a Wooded River Landscape
Oil on canvas
30 x 23in (76 x 59cm)
£9,500-10,500 *C*

Studio of Jean Etienne Liotard (1702-89)
Swiss
Portrait of William Ponsonby, 2nd Earl of
Bessborough
Oil on canvas, in carved wood frame
47 x 40in (119 x 101.5cm)
£43,000-55,000 *S*

Jean Baptiste Wicar (1762-1834)
French
Portrait of an Officer of the Queen's Regiment
Oil on canvas
29¾ x 24½in (76 x 62cm)
£12,000-13,000 *S(NY)*

Thomas Gainsborough, R.A. (1727-88)
British
Portrait of a Gentleman, thought to be General
Thomas Meyrick
Oil on canvas
30 x 25in (77 x 64cm)
£56,000-70,000 *C*

Attributed to Louis-Michel van Loo and Studio
(1707-71)
French
A Portrait of King Philip V of Spain
Oil on canvas
41¼ x 33in (105 x 84cm)
£9,000-10,000 *C*

William Bradshaw
(19thC)
American
Portrait of James Todd
Signed and dated verso
1845, oil on canvas
30 x 25in (76 x 64cm)
£500-550 *Cae*

Fernand Léger (1881-1955) French
Tête d'Ouvrier
Signed with initials and dated 52, gouache, brush
and indian ink over pencil, 19¼ x 15in (49 x 38.5cm)
£42,000-50,000 *S*

Isidor Kaufmann (1853-1921)
Austrian
Young Rabbi with Blue Tallis
Signed, oil on panel
9¼ x 11½in (23 x 29cm)
£48,000-60,000 *S(NY)*

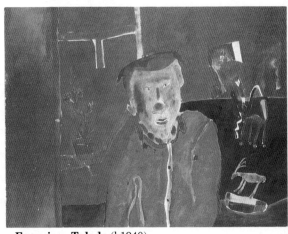

Francisco Toledo (b1940)
Mexican
Self Portrait, 1965
Signed and inscribed, watercolour, gouache, pen and ink
18½ x 25in (47 x 64cm). **£4,500-5,500** *P*

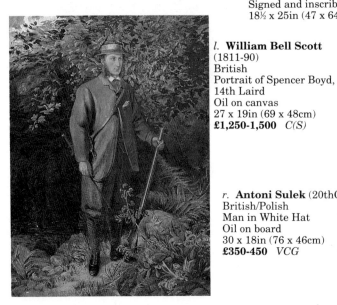

l. **William Bell Scott**
(1811-90)
British
Portrait of Spencer Boyd,
14th Laird
Oil on canvas
27 x 19in (69 x 48cm)
£1,250-1,500 *C(S)*

r. **Antoni Sulek** (20thC)
British/Polish
Man in White Hat
Oil on board
30 x 18in (76 x 46cm)
£350-450 *VCG*

Ambrosius Benson (active 1519-50)
Flemish
Portrait of a Lady, holding a Rosary
Oil on panel
15¾ x 12¾in (40 x 32.5cm)
£1,000,000-1,250,000 *C*

Sir Peter Lely (1618-80)
British
Portrait of Mary Bagot, Countess of Middlesex and
Dorset (1645-79)
Inscribed
49 x 39in (124.5 x 99cm)
£30,000-40,000 *C*

Govaert Flinck (1615-60)
Dutch
Portrait of a Lady holding a Bunch of Flowers
Signed and dated 1658, oil on canvas
30 x 25in (76 x 64cm)
£53,000-65,000 *DN*

Cornelis Jonson
(1593-1661)
British
Portrait of a Lady,
Alathea, Countess of
Arundel
Signed and dated
1619, oil on panel,
26¾ x 20in
(68 x 51cm)
£14,000-15,000 *C*

Circle of George Gower (c1540-96)
British
Portrait of Elizabeth I
Oil on panel
33¾ x 26¼in (86 x 67cm)
£13,500-15,000 *S*

Allan Ramsay (1713-84)
British
Portrait of Anne, Countess Winterton
Oil on canvas
30 x 25in (76 x 64cm)
£15,500-18,000 *C*

Arthur Devis (c1711-87)
British
Portrait of Miss Warden of Cuckfield Park,
Sussex
Signed, oil on canvas
29½ x 24½in (76 x 62cm)
£56,000-70,000 *S*

l. **John
Wollaston**
(active 1736-67)
British
Portrait of a Lady
in a Blue Dress
Oil on canvas
30½ x 24¾in
(77 x 63cm)
£6,000-7,000
CNY

Joseph Highmore (1692-1780)
British
Portrait of Mrs Iremonger of Wherwell Priory
Signed, oil on canvas, in carved wood frame
49¼ x 39¼in (126 x 100cm)
£12,500-14,500 *S*

Attributed to Sir Thomas Lawrence (1769-1830)
British
Portrait of a Lady, said to be Sally Siddons
Oil on canvas
29½ x 24½in (76 x 62cm)
£16,500-20,000 *S*

l. **Jacques-Laurent Agasse** (1767-1849)
Swiss
Miss Cazenove, mounted on a Grey Hunter, a Dog running alongside
Signed with initials
30½ x 25½in
(78 x 65cm)
£80,000-90,000 *C*

r. **James Jacques Joseph Tissot** (1836-1902)
French
Study for 'Le Sphinx', Woman in an Interior
Oil on canvas
43¾ x 27in
(111 x 69cm)
£610,000-700,000
S(NY)

Eugen von Blaas (1843-1931)
Austrian
A Maiden with a Basket of Roses
Signed and dated 1900, oil on panel
50½ x 25in
(128 x 64cm)
£45,000-55,000 *S*

Albert Joseph Moore (1841-93)
British
Ellen Terry as Portia
Signed and inscribed, oil on canvas
11½ x 9in (29 x 23cm)
£11,500-13,500 *C*

Abbey Altson (active 1894-1917)
British
Fair Ladies
A pair, signed, oil on canvas
28 x 18in (71 x 46cm)
£4,600-5,000 *HFA*

Alfred Stevens (1823-1906)
Belgian
L'Inde à Paris; Le Bibelot Exotique
Signed, oil on canvas
29 x 23½in (74 x 60cm)
£78,000-90,000 *S(NY)*

Grigory Bobrovsky (1873-1942)
Russian
Leisurely Read
Signed and dated 1909, oil on canvas
30 x 25in (76 x 64cm)
£9,000-9,500 *EG*

l. **Isa Thompson** (1850-1926)
British
Apple Blossom Time
Signed, oil on canvas
30 x 20in (76 x 51cm)
£11,500-12,000 *BSG*

Below l.
Emile Vernon
(19thC)
French
Under the Apple Tree
Signed, inscribed and dated
1919, oil on canvas
25½ x 21½in (65 x 54cm)
£9,600-11,000 *P*

Paul César Helleu (1859-1927)
French
Camara
Signed and inscribed, pastel on linen
41½ x 38½in (105 x 98cm)
£35,000-45,000 *S(NY)*

Below
Thomas Mackay (active 1898-1913)
British
Steps to the Pool
Signed, watercolour
8 x 5¾in (20 x 14.5cm)
£2,000-2,200 *CGa*

J. D. Fergusson
(1874-1961)
British
Blonde
Signed, inscribed
and dated 1937, oil
on board
13 x 10in
(33 x 25cm)
£5,800-7,000 *P(Sc)*

Trinh Cung (b1939)
Portrait
Oil on canvas, 1990
21 x 16in (53 x 41cm)
£3,000-4,000 *RMG*

Mary Fedden (b1915)
British
The Picnic, Glyndebourne
Signed and dated 1991, oil on canvas, 12 x 16in (31 x 41cm)
£1,000-3,000 *BRG*

l. **Cathy**
Fenwick
(20thC)
British
Study of an Old
Woman
Oil on board
31½ x 22in (80
x 56cm)
£3,550-3,750
EW

Marcel Dyf (1889-1988)
French
Claudine à sa Toilette
Oil on canvas
28½ x 23½in (72 x 60cm)
£1,300-1,500 *OM*

r. **Harold Knight**
(1874-1961)
British
Mending the Glove
Signed L.L., oil on
canvas
18 x 18in (46 x
46cm)
£14,000-14,500
EG

Richard Smith (b1957)
British
Pensive
Oil on canvas
12 x 16in (31 x 41cm)
£1,750-2,000 *BSG*

Henry Matisse (1869-1954)
French
Marie Jose en Jaune
Signed in pencil and numbered 73/100,
aquatint
21 x 16½in (53 x 42cm)
£32,000-40,000 *S*

Andy Warhol (1930-1987)
American
Marilyn
Set of 10 silkscreens, 1967, signed in pencil on verso, stamp
numbered 199/250, published by Factory Additions, New York
Each sheet 36 x 36in (92 x 92cm)
£127,000-140,000 *S*

Anna Shirokova (b1937)
Russian
Portrait of Natasha Kasimao
Oil
72 x 36in (182.5 x 92cm)
£2,000-2,500 *A*

Linda Sutton (20thC)
British
Robot Cat in Red
Mixed media
30 x 40in (76 x 101.5cm)
£2,000-2,300 *OLG*

PORTRAITS & PICTURES OF THE HUMAN FIGURE

The art of portraiture has always been particularly attractive to the English. As Andrew Wilton, Keeper of the British Collection at the Tate Gallery, notes: 'England is perhaps the last remaining country on earth where portraiture is still a flourishing practice.' David Poole, former President of the Royal Society of Portrait Painters, agrees: 'There is more demand for portraits today than there has been for many years - people are more enlightened and recognise the difference between a photograph and a portrait.'

The role of the modern portrait painter differs very little from that of his or her predecessors. Today, as in the past, the portrait painter's work is divided between private and public commissions: 'You get far more emotional upsets with family portraits,' warns Poole, 'husbands getting upset because their wives look more beautiful than they do or vice-versa. I prefer the official portrait - military and boardroom pictures.' Such works are generally commissioned by committees. 'There will always be someone on the board who wants to complain about something,' sighs Poole, 'but James Gunn (1893-1964), another former President, handed down a useful tip to the members of the Society: 'Always do a little thing deliberately wrong, an incorrect ribbon on a military uniform, or another small detail. It gives the complainer something to complain about, keeps him happy, and stops him looking for anything

more serious.' A popular myth about portraiture is that the artist should have a special rapport with the subject. 'You don't have to like your sitter,' concludes Poole, firmly. 'According to legend, when Goya painted the Duke of Wellington he hated his guts, but it is still a great portrait.'

With historical portraits, as in every other field, it is the 'great' pictures that maintain their value, even in the most difficult circumstances.

'Throughout the recession, anything which is important or the best of its type has made good money, not flowery crazy prices but good money,' says dealer Tony Haynes, of Haynes Fine Art. 'There is a desperate shortage of good paintings. Museums will always buy something if it is important and the big dealers have been buying throughout the recession.'

In the past year, buyers seem to have become increasingly discriminating, requiring pictures that are high in quality, fresh to the market and in preferably untouched condition. 'No matter what field you are interested in, always buy the best of its kind,' advises Haynes. 'If you've got £5,000 to spend and want a 19thC landscape, don't buy a poor Alfred de Breanski Senior, choose a Cooper or a David Bates instead; when buying a figure painting, don't just chase a famous name, but a good picture - never go for the second rate, always buy the best.'

Men
14th-16th Centuries

Frederico Barocci (1526-1612)
Italian
Study of the Head of a Bearded Man Turned to the Left
Inscribed, black, red, yellow and white chalk, on faded blue paper
9½ x 7in (23.5 x 17.7cm)
£14,000-15,000   C

This is a study for the head of Saint Joseph in Barocci's Circumcision in the Louvre.

Umbrian School (c1380)
A Draped Figure Holding a Book
Silverpoint heightened with white, on green/blue prepared paper, losses
7½ x 4½in (19.4 x 11.2cm)
£30,000-40,000   CNY

School of Bruges (late 15thC)
Portrait of Jacob Obrecht (d1505), a female saint en grisaille on the reverse
Inscribed in gold, inscribed and dated 1496, oil on panel, in original frame
20¼ x 14¼in (51.4 x 36.2cm)
£1,700,000-2,000,000   S(NY)

Follower of Ambrosius Benson
(d1550)
Flemish
Portrait of a Gentleman, in a fur- lined black
coat, with red sleeves and a gold chain
Oil on panel
13½ x 10in (34 x 25.7cm)
£13,500-14,500 *C*

Follower of Agnolo Bronzino
(1503-72)
Italian
Portrait of a Gentleman
Oil on panel
24½ x 19½in (62 x 49.2cm)
£6,500-7,500 *C*

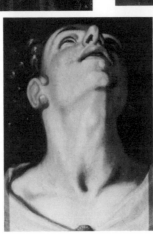

Circle of Giovanni de Busi,
called Cariani (16thC)
Italian School
A Portrait of a Gentleman
Oil on canvas
29¾ x 25in (75.5 x 63.5cm)
£2,300-3,000 *P*

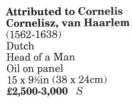

Attributed to Cornelis
Cornelisz, van Haarlem
(1562-1638)
Dutch
Head of a Man
Oil on panel
15 x 9½in (38 x 24cm)
£2,500-3,000 *S*

Attributed to Joos van Cleve
(active 1511-d1540/41)
Dutch
Portrait of a Bearded Gentleman
aged 36
Inscribed and dated 1526, oil on
panel
21½ x 19in (55 x 48cm)
£17,000-19,000 *C*

This picture provides an
interesting reflection of the
fluctuations in the market place.
Offered unsuccessfully by
Christie's in July 1992 with an
estimate of £20,000-30,000, the
work reappeared in the following
April with a distinctly more
conservative £6,000-8,000 price
range.

Studio of Lucas Cranach the Younger (1515-86)
German
A Portrait of a Bearded Gentleman before an Extensive Landscape
Oil on canvas
24 x 19½in (61 x 49.5cm)
£4,500-5,500 *P*

Etienne Dumonstier II (1520-1603)
French
Portrait of a Gentleman, aged 42
Inscribed and dated 1580, oil on canvas
23¼ x 16½in (59 x 41.6cm)
£1,700-2,200 *C*

Attributed to Gortzius Geldorp (1553-1618)
Flemish
Portrait of a Gentleman
Inscribed and dated 1600, oil on panel
38¼ x 27½in (97 x 70cm)
£2,200-2,500 *S*

English School (16thC)
Portrait of Sir Anthony Browne KG (d1548)
Inscribed, oil on panel
31 x 25¼in (79 x 64.2cm)
£9,500-11,000 *C*

Browne was an important figure in Henry VIII's court. He represented the King during his divorce from Catherine of Aragon and his marriage to Anne of Cleves, and after Henry's death he was appointed guardian to his children, Prince Edward and Princess Elizabeth. Granted vast amounts of land and property during the Dissolution of the Monasteries (including Battle Abbey and a considerable part of Hastings), Browne married twice, his second wife Lady Elisabeth Fitzgerald (known as 'the fair Geraldine'), being only 15 when she married the 60 year old courtier.

George Gower (c1540-96)
British
Portrait of a Gentleman of the Dacre Family, probably Francis Dacre
Inscribed with the sitter's coat-of-arms, and dated 1571, oil on panel
27½ x 23¼in (70 x 59cm)
£7,500-8,500 *S*

Florentine School (1576)
Portrait of a Scholar
Dated 1576, oil on panel
34¼ x 25½in (87 x 64.4cm)
£7,200-8,000 *S*

Hendrick Goltzius (1558-1617)
Dutch
A Portrait of a Man in Historical
Costume
Signed with monogram and dated
1607, pen and brown ink and
wash
Laid down around the edges on
reinforcing strips of paper
11½ x 8in (29.6 x 20.2cm)
£24,000-30,000 *S(NY)*

Circle of Daniel Mytens
(1590-1648)
Dutch
Portrait of a Gentleman, said to
be Sir Hugh Middleton
Inscribed on a fragment of the
original canvas on reverse, and
dated 1609, oil on canvas
46¼ x 34⅜in (117.5 x 89.5cm)
£2,700-3,200 *S*

Follower of Jan Roos I
(1591-1638)
Flemish
Portrait of a Nobleman, wearing a
coronet and the Order of Saint
John of Malta
18¾ x 14in (47.8 x 35.4cm)
£2,000-2,500 *C*

Circle of Jakob Seisenegger
(1504/5-67)
Austrian
Portrait of a Nobleman
Dated '1.5.5.5' on frame, oil on
panel
26 x 19in (66.2 x 48cm)
£4,000-5,000 *C*

**Andrea Piccinelli,
il Brescianino** (active 1505-25)
Italian
A Courtier
Oil on panel
17¾ x 12in (45 x 31cm)
£18,000-20,000 *C*

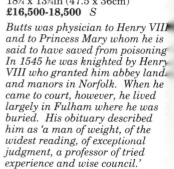

Studio of Hans Holbein
(1497-1543)
German
Portrait of Sir William Butts
(1485?-1545)
Inscribed, oil on panel
18¾ x 13¾in (47.5 x 36cm)
£16,500-18,500 *S*

*Butts was physician to Henry VIII
and to Princess Mary whom he is
said to have saved from poisoning.
In 1545 he was knighted by Henry
VIII who granted him abbey lands
and manors in Norfolk. When he
came to court, however, he lived
largely in Fulham where he was
buried. His obituary described
him as 'a man of weight, of the
widest reading, of exceptional
judgment, a professor of tried
experience and wise council.'*

Jacopo Robusti, called Tintoretto (1518-94)
Italian
Portrait of Bearded Venetian Nobleman
Bears inscription, oil on canvas
44 x 35½in (112 x 90cm)
£72,000-85,000 *S*

Charles Beale (1660-1714)
British
Portrait of a Gentleman of the Packer Family
Signed with monogram, oil on canvas
49 x 39in (124.5 x 99cm)
£6,500-7,500 *S*

17th Century

Antwerp School (c1635)
Portrait of a Gentleman
Oil on panel
27¼ x 21⅞in (69 x 55.5cm)
£1,200-1,600 *S*

Follower of Hans von Aachen
(1596-1623)
German
Portrait of a Nobleman, wearing Armour and the Order of the Golden Fleece
29½ x 24in (74.6 x 61cm)
£4,400-5,400 *C*

Attributed to Sebastiano Bombelli (1635-1719)
Italian
Portrait of a Nobleman, said to be Lorenzo Onofre Colonna, 6th Duke of Pagliano (1637-89)
Oil on canvas, in a carved and giltwood frame
83 x 51in (211 x 129.5cm)
£7,800-9,000 *S*

Bartolomeo Cesi (1583-1649)
Italian
Portrait of a Young Man
Inscribed, red and white chalk on blue paper
11½ x 6in (29 x 15cm)
£17,000-18,000 *CNY*

Gerard Ter Borch (1617-81)
Dutch
Portrait of a Gentleman
28½ x 23½in (72.5 x 59.7cm)
£46,000-60,000 *C*

John Closterman (1660-1711)
German
Portrait of Thomas Eyre of
Hassop, Derbyshire
Inscribed, oil on canvas, in a
carved wood frame
48½ x 39in (123 x 99cm)
£2,900-3,500 *S*

Dutch School (17thC)
Portrait of a Gentleman, said to
be Wouter Crabeth
Oil on copper, in a carved and
giltwood frame
3½ x 2¾in (9 x 7cm)
£1,700-2,200 *S*

**Circle of Sir Anthony van
Dyck** (1599-1641)
Flemish
Portrait of William Cavendish,
1st Duke of Newcastle (1593-
1676)
49½ x 39½in (125.8 x 100.4cm)
£6,400-7,400 *C*

Circle of Edward Bower
(active 1629-66)
British
Portrait of Sir William Fairfax
(1609-44)
Oil on canvas, in a carved wood
frame
80¾ x 50½in (205 x 128cm)
£17,500-20,000 *S*

**Attributed to Louis
(Ferdinand) Elle I** (1612-89)
French
Portrait of a young Gentleman
Oil on canvas
43 x 33in (109 x 84cm)
£15,000-17,000 *C*

English School (early 17thC)
Portrait of a Gentleman
Unsigned, oil on panel
32 x 22in (81 x 56cm)
£900-1,200 *S*

English School (17thC)
Portrait of Nicholas Fortescue, aged 31
Inscribed and dated 1627, oil on canvas
33 x 31¾in (84 x 80.7cm)
£2,200-3,000 *C*

Dirck Helmbreker (1633-96)
Flemish
A Sleeping Youth at a Table
Red chalk, black chalk framing lines
10½ x 8½in (26.4 x 21.4cm)
£4,500-5,500 *C(Am)*

Jan van den Hoecke (1611-51)
Flemish
Portrait of the Artist (?) as a
Shepherd
Signed with monogram IVH
Oil on panel
34¾ x 27in (88.4 x 69cm)
£16,500-18,000 *C*

Italian School (17thC)
A Portrait of King Charles V; and
A Portrait of a Gentleman
A pair, oil on canvas
40½ x 33½in (102.5 x 85cm)
£3,500-4,000 *P*

English School (17thC)
Portrait of a Gentleman
Oil on panel
14½ x 12¼in (37 x 31cm)
£1,500-2,000 *AH*

Sir Tho. Wendy, Kt

Cornelis Jonson (1593-1661)
Dutch
Portrait of Sir Thomas Wendy,
c1640
Inscribed, oil on canvas
30 x 25in (76.2 x 63.5cm)
£10,000-11,000 *C*

As Ellis Waterhouse notes (see Biblio.), Jonson (who was born in England of Dutch parents, and also spelt his name Johnson) is regarded as the first British-born master of the portrait tradition. He was 'the first to seize (as only an Englishman could) upon the shy and retiring streak in the English temper, whose presence in a portrait is a sure sign of native English art.' Like a miniaturist, he specialised in heads, concentrating on the face and character of his sitters rather than their clothes and surrounding trappings. His sensitive portrayals represent a landmark in the development of domestic as opposed to public portraiture.

'I paid Sir Godfrey Kneller a visit but two days before he died and I think I never saw a scene of so much vanity in my life,' recalled Alexander Pope. 'He was lying in his bed, contemplating the plan he had made for his own monument. He said many gross things in relation to himself and the memory he should leave behind him. He said he should not like to lie among the rascals at Westminster. A memorial there would be sufficient; and desired me to write an epitaph for it. I did so afterwards and I think it the worst thing I ever wrote in my life.'

Sir Godfrey Kneller, Bt.
(1646-1723)
British
Portrait of Don Jose Carreras y
Coligo
Oil on canvas, in a carved wood
frame
29 x 24¼in (73.5 x 61.5cm)
£8,700-10,000 *S*

Follower of Kneller (1646-1723)
British
Portrait of a Gentleman, wearing
the Costume of a Roman General
Oil on canvas
18¾ x 15in (46.3 x 38.2cm)
£1,300-1,600 *Bon*

After Sir Godfrey Kneller, Bt.
(1646-1723)
British
Portrait of King William III
wearing Garter Robes
Oil on canvas, in a carved wood
frame
49 x 39in (124.5 x 99cm)
£4,700-6,000 *S*

*After the full length portrait in the
Royal Collection.*

Circle of Pieter van Laer
(1582-1642)
Dutch
A Man Putting on his Boots
Black and white chalk on blue
paper, brown ink framing lines
8 x 5½in (21 x 14cm)
£1,700-2,200 *C(Am)*

Attributed to John Kerseboom
(active 1680s-1708) **and John
Vandervaart** (1653-1727)
British School
Portrait of a Gentleman
Oil on canvas, in a carved wood
frame
48¾ x 39in (123.5 x 99cm)
£4,700-6,000 *S*

Follower of Sir Peter Lely
(1618-80)
Portrait of Philip Packer (1656-
1739)
Oil on canvas, in original carved
wood frame
49 x 39in (124.5 x 99cm)
£3,000-4,000 *S*

Circle of Sir Peter Lely
(1618-80)
British
Portrait of Charles II
Oil on canvas
49¼ x 40in (125 x 102cm)
£650-800 *S(S)*

Sir Peter Lely (1618-80) **and
Studio**
British
Portrait of Oliver Cromwell
(1599-1658)
Inscribed, oil on canvas
30 x 25½ in (76.5 x 64.8cm)
£11,000-12,000 *C*

*Cromwell's attitude to having his
portrait painted was typically
direct and puritanical: 'Mr Lely, I
desire you would use all your skill
to paint my picture truly like me,
and not flatter me at all; but
remark all these roughnesses,
pimples, warts and everything as
you see me, otherwise I never will
pay a farthing for it.'*

Jan Lievens (1607-74)
Dutch
A Bearded Old Man
Oil on panel
23½ x 20½in (59.5 x 52cm)
£28,000-38,000 *C*

Attributed to Isaac Luttichuys
(1616-73)
Dutch
Portrait of Charles II
Oil on canvas
96 x 49¼in (243.5 x 125cm)
£7,800-9,000 *S*

Circle of Jacob van Oost
(1601-71)
Flemish
Portrait of a Gentleman
21½ x 19in (55 x 48cm)
£4,700-5,700 *C*

Follower of Jürgen Ovens
(1623-78)
German
Portrait of a Gentleman
52¾ x 39in (134 x 99cm)
£1,100-1,500 *S(S)*

**Anthonie Palamedesz., called
Stevers** (1601-73)
Dutch
Portrait of a Gentleman
Signed and dated 1657
32¾ x 27¼in (83.2 x 69.2cm)
£23,000-30,000 *C*

Rembrandt Harmensz. van Rijn (1606-69)
Dutch
Bust of an Old Man with a Flowing Beard
Etching, 1630, with a few touches of grey wash
3¾ x 3in (9 x 7.6cm)
£1,900-2,400 *C*

Bernardo Strozzi (1582-1644)
Italian
The Head of a Man
Black and white chalk, on light brown paper
6 x 4½in (15.4 x 11.3cm)
£7,200-8,000 *C*

Circle of Thomas van der Wilt (1659-1733)
Dutch
A Portrait of a Gentleman
Oil on canvas
28¾ x 23¼in (73 x 59cm)
£900-1,200 *P*

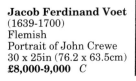

Follower of Hyacinthe Rigaud (1659-1743)
French
Portrait of Louis de France, Le Grand Dauphin
53 x 37½in (134.5 x 95cm)
£2,600-3,000 *C*
This was derived from Rigaud's three-quarter length portrait of 1697, now at Versailles, and the full-length version at Vaux-le-Vicomte.

Jacob Ferdinand Voet (1639-1700)
Flemish
Portrait of John Crewe
30 x 25in (76.2 x 63.5cm)
£8,000-9,000 *C*

John Riley (1646-91)
British
Portrait of Samuel Pepys (1633-1703)
Oil on canvas, in a carved wood frame
24 x 18¾in (61 x 48cm)
£18,000-22,000 *S*
'Here we have a mouth pouting, moist with desires,' wrote Robert Louis Stevenson on looking at Pepys' portrait: 'eyes greedy, protruberant and yet apt for weeping too, a nose great alike in character and dimensions; and altogether a most fleshly, melting countenance ... it could never be the face of an artist; it is the face of a viveur...' Pepys, Secretary to the Admiralty and President of the Royal Society, is chiefly remembered for the diary which he compiled between 1660 and 1669, the year his wife died and his eyesight began to fail him.

18th Century

George Beare (active 1741-47)
British
Portrait of Captain George
Brydges Rodney, R.N. (1719-92)
Signed and dated 1744, oil on
canvas
34½ x 27in (87.6 x 68.6cm)
£14,000-15,000 *S(NY)*

Louis Leopold Boilly
(1761-1845)
French
A Portrait of a Young Man
Oil on canvas
8½ x 6½in (21.5 x 16.8cm)
£4,000-5,000 *P*

**Louis Carrogis, called
Carmontelle** (1717-1806)
French
The Duke of York on a Quay in a
Flag Officer's Uniform
Inscribed, dated 1768, black lead,
red chalk, watercolour heightened
with white, watermark Strasburg
lily
11¾ x 7in (30 x 17.6cm)
£19,000-24,000 *C*

*Edward Augustus, Duke of York
KG (1739-67) was the second son
of Frederick, Prince of Wales and
his wife Princess Augusta of Saxe-
Gotha. His eldest brother
succeeded as King George III.*

Francis Cotes (1725-70)
British
Portrait of a Young Man
Signed and dated 1751, pastel
23¾ x 17¾in (60 x 45cm)
£3,800-4,500 *S*

*After Reynolds and
Gainsborough, Cotes was the most
fashionable portrait painter of the
day, as reflected in his charges.
For a head in pastel he charged
25 guineas, while works in oils
were priced at 20, 40 and 80
guineas respectively for head,
half-length and full-length
portraits. Cotes was above all a
pretty painter of pretty people,
hence his popularity. As Ellis
Waterhouse remarks (see Biblio.),
'he was concerned only with
fashion and handsome likeness
and not with character ... his
sitters usually have milk-and-
roses complexions and their
clothes are always bright, new
and fashionable.'*

Jacob Buys (1724-1801)
Dutch
A Portrait of the Actor Anthony
Spatsier as Warenar
Signed, inscribed and dated 1770,
pencil, pen and brown ink,
watercolour, black ink framing
lines, watermark D & C Blauw
12½ x 9¾in (31.6 x 24.6cm)
£4,000-5,000 *C(Am)*

*Anthony Spatsier born in 1721 in
Amsterdam, was a shoemaker but
also a poet and actor, most
appreciated in comedies.*

After Francis Cotes (1725-70)
British
Paul Sandby; and The Nut-Brown
Maid (Anne Sandby)
Mezzotints, 1763, a pair engraved
by Edward Fisher
15½ x 11in (39.4 x 27.5cm)
£225-300 *P*

Anonymous, Cuzco School
(18thC)
Capac Yupanqui, Quinto Rey Inca
Oil on canvas
18 x 15¼in (46 x 39cm)
£6,000-7,000 *S(NY)*

*Capac Yupanqui was the 5th
emperor and the first to conquer
lands outside the Cuzco Valley.*

English School (mid-18thC)
Portrait of Richard Hume of
Blakesware, MP, Commissioner
of Trade and Plantations
Oil on canvas
47 x 37½in (120 x 95cm)
£4,000-5,000 *HOK*

**Attributed to Joseph
Highmore** (1692-1780)
British
Portrait of a Gentleman
Oil
27½ x 23¾in (70 x 60cm)
£1,000-1,200 *S(S)*

Georg Christoph Grooth
(1716-49)
German
Portrait of an Elegant Nobleman,
wearing the Star and Blue Sash
of the Russian Order of Saint
Andrew
Oil on canvas, laid down
34¼ x 26½in (87 x 67.3cm)
£4,500-5,000 *S(NY)*

*George Christoph Grooth, born in
Stuttgart, had his greatest
commercial success at the court of
St Petersburg, where he moved in
1743.*

Thomas Hudson (1701-79)
British
Portrait of Henry Courthope
Campion of Danny
Oil
30 x 25in (76 x 64cm)
£5,200-6,000 *C*

Nicolas Lancret (1690-1743)
French
A seated Man leaning forward
Black, red and white chalk
5¾ x 6¼in (15 x 16cm)
£15,000-18,000 *CNY*

John Jackson, R.A. (1778-1831)
British
Portrait of William Pitt the
Younger (1759-1806)
Oil on canvas
29¼ x 24¼in (74.5 x 62cm)
£7,200-8,000 *S*

John Hoppner, R.A. (1758-1810)
British
Portrait of Richard Colley, 1st Marquess of
Wellesley, in the uniform of the Hon. East
India Company wearing the Breast Star
and Sash of the Order of Saint Patrick
Oil on canvas
49½ x 39½in (125.5 x 100cm)
£23,000-30,000 *C*

Attributed to Jens Juel
(1745-1802)
Danish
A Portrait of a Gentleman
Oil on canvas
21 x 16¾in (53.2 x 43cm)
£1,600-2,000 *P*

Justus Juncker (1703-67)
German
Portrait of the Artist, seated at
his easel with a portrait of a lady,
a pupil copying a sketch behind
Oil on panel
16¾ x 12¾in (43 x 32.5cm)
£34,000-44,000 *C*

James Latham (1696-1747)
Irish
Portrait of the Artist
Oil on canvas
30 x 25in (76 x 63.5cm)
£7,500-8,500 *S*

*The most distinguished Irish
artist of the early 18thC, Latham
was born in Tipperary. He
studied in Antwerp in 1724, and
later went on to study in Paris.*

Thomas Gainsborough, R.A.
(1727-88)
British
Portrait of Thomas Butcher
Oil on canvas
29¼ x 24¼in (74.5 x 61.5cm)
£40,000-50,000 *S*

*Gainsborough bitterly resented the
fact that he was forced to earn his
living as a fashionable portrait
painter. 'I am sick of portraits,' he
wrote sadly to one acquaintance,
'and wish very much to take my
viol de gamba and walk off to
some sweet village where I can
paint and enjoy the fag-end
of life in quietness and ease.'
According to Henry Angelo
('Reminiscences' 1828), if
Gainsborough had a portrait on
the easel he would be in a
growling temper, when however he
was engaged on a landscape 'he
was all gaiety, his imagination in
the skies.'*

Bartolomeo Nazzari
(1699-1758)
Italian
A Portrait of a Soldier
Oil on canvas
22½ x 18½in (57.3 x 47.3cm)
£1,700-2,200 *P*

Sir Henry Raeburn (1756-1823)
British
Portrait of the Rt. Hon. Robert
Blair of Avontoun
Oil on canvas
50 x 40in (127 x 101.5cm)
£11,000-12,000 *C*

After Sir Thomas Lawrence
(1769-1830)
British
The Baring Brothers and Dr.
Charles Wall by J. Ward
Mezzotint, second state of three
20 x 26in (51 x 66cm)
£380-450 *CSK*

Peale Studio (18th/19thC)
American
Washington at the Battle of
Princeton, 1779
Oil on canvas
40 x 29in (101.6 x 74cm)
£23,000-28,000 S(NY)

*The present painting is a copy
after Charles Willson Peal's
Washington at the Battle of
Princeton, 1779, which was
commissioned by the Supreme
Council of Pennsylvania in 1779.
Peale replicated this portrait
many times both for official bodies
and for Washington's friends.
Washington himself, as he
admitted in a letter to a friend in
1785, had become over the years
well used to the attentions of
portraitists: 'I am so hackneyed to
the touches of the painter's pencils
that I am now altogether at their
beck...at first I was as impatient
and as restive under the operation
as a colt is of the saddle. The next
time I submitted very reluctantly,
but with less flouncing. Now, no
dray horse moves more readily to
his thill than I do to the painter's
hair.'*

Robert Pyle (active 1760-69)
British
Portrait of a Gentleman
traditionally identified as
Tregonwell Frampton, Keeper of
the Running Horses at
Newmarket
Oil on canvas,
signed and inscribed
20½ x 16½in (52 x 42cm)
£1,500-12,500 C

Thomas Phillips, R.A.
(1770-1845)
British
Portrait of Sir Joseph Banks
wearing the Order of the Bath
Oil on canvas, in a carved wood
frame
55½ x 43¾in (141 x 111cm)
£65,000-80,000 S

Sir Henry Raeburn (1756-1823)
British
Portrait of Alexander, Lord
Abercromby of Tullybody
Oil on canvas
26 x 14¼in (66 x 36cm)
£5,800-6,800 S

**Attributed to Thomas Phillips,
R.A.** (1770-1845)
British
Portrait of Thomas Moore
Oil on canvas
23 x 19½in (58.5 x 49.5cm)
£5,000-6,000 S

*A lifelong friend of Byron, who left
Moore his memoirs, which he later
destroyed. The sitter was one of
Ireland's most prominent poets
and musicians.*

Allan Ramsay (1713-84)
British
A Portrait of a Naval Officer
Signed and dated 1747, oil on
canvas
30 x 25in (76.2 x 63.5cm), in a
carved giltwood frame
£8,500-10,000 C(S)

Sir Joshua Reynolds, P.R.A.
(1723-92)
British
Portrait of William Augustus,
Duke of Cumberland
Oil on canvas, in a carved wood
frame
24 x 19¾in (61 x 50cm)
£7,000-8,000 S

*It is clear that between 1762 and
1765 Reynolds produced a
number of versions of George II's
third son, the celebrated victor of
Culloden. The prime original is
the full length at Chatsworth
showing him in Garter robes.
Reynolds also painted him in
military uniform and replicas
were produced for officers who
had served under him.*

Circle of George Romney
(1734-1802)
British
Portrait of Mr. Green
Oil on canvas
23½ x 15½in (59.5 x 40cm)
£600-800 *S(S)*

Giovanni Battista Tiepolo
(1696-1770)
Italian
The Head of a Youth looking to
the left, recto; The Head of a man
looking upwards to the left, verso
Red and white chalk, recto, black
chalk verso
8 x 5¾in (20 x 15cm)
£17,000-20,000 *CNY*

Gilbert Stuart (1755-1828)
American
Portrait of General Robert
Cunninghame, later 1st Lord
Rossmore
Oil on canvas
29¾ x 24¾in (76 x 63cm)
£13,500-15,000 *C*

*The present picture is dateable to
c1790, during the artist's period
in Dublin in 1787-93.*

Cornelis Troost (1696-1750)
Dutch
Portrait of Jeronimus Tonneman
Signed and dated 1736
Pastel and gouache on blue paper
24½ x 19in (62.4 x 48.7cm)
£10,500-11,500 *S*

*The notable Amsterdam collector
Jeronimus Tonneman (1687-1750)
was one of Troost's most
important patrons.*

Samuel de Wilde (1748-1842)
British
Portrait of Joseph Shepherd
Munden
Oil on canvas
14½ x 11in (37 x 28cm)
£1,700-2,200 *C*

*Joseph Shepherd Munden (1758-
1832) was one of the best
comedians of his day, particularly
in elderly parts. He made his
London debut in Susannah
Centlitre's The Busy Body, the
subject of the portrait, at Covent
Garden on 2 December 1790. The
picture shows Munden as Sir
Francis Gripe chinking a bag of
coins and exclaiming 'Well, Sir
George, ha! ha! ha! take the last
sound of your guineas, ha! ha!
ha!'*

Giovanni Domenico Tiepolo
(1727-1804)
Italian
Head of an Oriental Man
Oil on canvas
29¾ x 22½in (76 x 57.5cm)
£63,000-80,000 *S*

Paul Sandby, R.A. (1730-1809)
British
Portrait of Francis Grose
Pen and grey ink and grey washes
5½ x 3½in (14 x 9cm)
£1,000-1,500 *S*

*Always a fat man, and known to
his contemporaries as the Greatest
Porter Drinker of the Age, he died
suddenly in Dublin and was
buried at Drumcondra, where his
tombstone records that Grose
'whilst in cheerful conversation
with his friends, expired in their
arms without a sigh 18 May 1791
aged 60.' The St. James's Evening
newspaper pithily commented that
'Death put an end to his Views
and Prospects.' Captain Francis
Grose, F.S.A. (1731-1791) was
born in Greenford, Middlesex, the
son of a Swiss jeweller who
modelled George II's crown. He
was a noted amateur
topographical draughtsman, but
extravagant living quickly
exhausted the fortune left him by
his father and forced him to earn
an income from his hobby.*

19th Century

American School (19thC)
Portrait of a Gentleman
Painted c1850
Oil on canvas
31 x 24in (78.7 x 61cm)
£1,200-1,500 *S(NY)*

Charles Edmund Brock
(1870-1938)
British
They Called Him Trotty from his
Pace
Signed and inscribed, watercolour
11 x 6½in (28 x 16cm)
£1,250-1,450 *CBL*

Paul Cézanne (1839-1906)
French
Portrait de Charles le Brun après
Coysevox
Pencil
8½ x 4¾in (21.5 x 12cm)
£7,600-8,600 *S*

*Executed c1892-95, after the bust
of Charles Le Brun by Charles
Antoine Coysevox in the Louvre.
During the early 1890s Cézanne
became increasingly reclusive;
finding the streets of Paris too
animated to work, he went to the
Louvre to draw. 'The sketches he
made in the museums were
doubtless supposed to take the
place of studies on the motif, or
even more, from the living model.
He began to copy ancient and
modern sculpture in the Louvre..'
(John Rewald, Cézanne,
A Biography, London 1986, p194).*

Ford Madox Brown (1821-1983)
British
Thomas Gray; A Cartoon for
Stained Glass at Peterhouse,
Cambridge
Inscribed, pencil, black chalk and
grey wash
24½ x 16½in (62.3 x 42cm)
£2,000-2,500 *C*

*This drawing is a fragment of a
cartoon for a window in the hall
at Peterhouse, Cambridge,
installed by William Morris & Co.
1872-1874. Thomas Gray (1761-
1771) best known for his Elegy
written in a Country Churchyard,
was Professor of Modern History
at Cambridge and a Peterhouse
man. According to Samuel
Johnson, Gray was not altogether
an inspiring companion. 'He was
a dull fellow,' he assured Boswell.
'He was dull in a new way; and
this made people think him great.
He was a mechanical poet.'*

Edward Clifford (1844-1907)
British
Portrait of a Gentleman
Signed and dated 1876, in gilt
frame
27¼ x 20¼in (69 x 51cm)
£350-450 AH

Edward Clifford (1844-1907)
British
Portrait of John Charles, Earl of
Seafield, K.T.
Signed, inscribed and dated 1882
Pencil, watercolour and
bodycolour with scratching out
23½ x 20⅛in (60 x 53cm)
£950-1,200 C

*A follower of Burne-Jones,
Clifford specialised in portraits of
the aristocracy. Angela Thirkell
said of him that he 'astonishingly
united a deep and active feeling
for religion, a passion for
duchesses and a marvellous gift of
watercolour painting.'*

Jean Baptiste Camille Corot
(1796-1875)
French
Portrait of Daumier
Oil on Panel
8 x 5¾in (20 x 15cm)
£30,000-40,000 CNY

*This spontaneous sketch is one of
the most interesting of all types of
portraiture - that of an artist
painting his fellow artist. Corot
has depicted Daumier, working on
a lithographic stone. Corot was a
true friend to the artist. 'Poor
Daumier,' recalled one
contemporary, 'he made no
provision for the future,' Towards
the end, when he was almost
blind, and could no longer pay the
rent to the place he had in the
country, Corot got wind of the
situation - he bought the house
and gave Daumier the deeds on
his birthday. The moment was
deeply moving for them both.
Daumier threw himself into
Corot's arms, eyes full of tears,
and said 'Oh Corot - you are the
only one from whom I could take a
gift like this and not feel
humiliated.'*

Continental School (19thC)
Portrait of Napoleon
Oil on canvas
25 x 17in (63.5 x 43.2cm)
£600-700 *DN*

Harry Windsor Fry
(active 1844-93)
British
Lorenzo
Inscribed and dated '91, gouache
and watercolour
17½ x 13½in (44.5 x 34.5)
£1,400-2,000 *Bon*

Henry F. Farny (1847-1916)
American
Ukchekehaskan Minneconjue
Sioux
Signed and titled, watercolour on
board
9½ x 6¼in (24 x 16cm)
£11,500-12,500 *S(NY)*

Frederick Dielman
(1847-1935)
German
The Scholar
Signed with the initials, oil on
canvas
36 x 16in (91.5 x 40.6cm)
£800-900 *S(NY)*

Robert Fox
(b1810, active to 1868)
Portrait of an Indian Gentleman
Oil on canvas laid on panel
22¼ x 17½in (56.5 x 44.5cm)
£3,200-3,800 *S*

French School (c1810)
A Portrait of a Gentleman
Oil on canvas
55 x 37in (140 x 94cm)
£7,500-8,500 *S*

Max Gaisser
(1857-1922)
German
A Lively Discourse
Signed and dated '63
Oil on panel
14½ x 18¾in (37 x 48cm)
£3,000-4,000 *P*

Manner of Francisco Goya y Lucientes
(1746-1828)
Spanish
Portrait of King Ferdinand VII, wearing the Order of the Golden Fleece
Oil on canvas
41½ x 32in (105.5 x 81.3cm)
£2,500-3,000 *CSK*

François-Pascal-Simon, Baron Gérard
(1770-1837)
French
Portrait of King Charles X of France
Oil on canvas
24 x 17in (61 x 43cm)
£11,500-12,500 *C*

In 1824 Gérard was commissioned by the Ministère de la Maison du Roi to paint a portrait of the new sovereign, King Charles X, in coronation robes. It was exhibited in 1825 at the salon, where it enjoyed considerable success. Numerous large versions of the portrait were executed in the artist's studio, with finishing touches added by the master.

Vincent Van Gogh (1853-90)
Dutch
Vieux se Chauffant
Signed, executed c1881, pencil, charcoal and pen and ink and wash
13¾ x 10in (35 x 25.4cm)
£140,000-160,000 *S*

In 1880 Van Gogh underwent a spiritual crisis and resolved to give up preaching for painting. In Spring 1881, he moved to Etten where he was confident he would find models for his life drawing at a reasonable price. Van Gogh's preferred subject was peasant figures, painted directly from life. 'It might seem that there is nothing simpler than painting peasants or rag pickers and other labourers,' he wrote to his brother Theo, 'but there are no subjects in painting as difficult as these everyday figures! As far as I know there isn't a single academy where one learns to draw and paint a digger, a sower, a woman hanging a pot over a fire or a seamstress.'

Dudley Hardy (1867-1922)
British
Self Portrait
Signed and dated 1901
Pen, ink and monochrome
watercolour with bodycolour
9½ x 8in (23.5 x 20cm)
£1,000-1,250 *CBL*

Carl Heuser (19thC) German
The pipe smoker, and the
companion portrait
A pair, signed, oil on panel
6¼ x 4¾in (16 x 12cm)
£2,000-2,500 *L*

Robert Henri (1865-1929)
American
La Jartigo
Signed and dated 1924
Oil on canvas
32¼ x 26in (82 x 66cm)
£25,000-30,000 *S(NY)*

Edwin Harris (1855-1906)
British
Portrait of a Fisherman
Signed, oil on panel
8 x 5½in (20 x 14cm)
£2,800-3,400 *C*

Hugo Kauffmann (1844-1915)
German
An Old Man with a Pipe
Signed and dated '86, oil on panel
9¾ x 7¾in (25 x 20cm)
£6,000-7,000 *CNY*

Attributed to John Neagle
(1796-1865)
American
Portrait of a Man
Oil on canvas laid down on board
29¾ x 24¾in (75.6 x 63cm)
£1,500-1,800 *S(NY)*

Andrew Robertson (1777-1845)
British
Portrait of a Gentleman
Signed and dated 1839, pencil
and watercolour with touches of
white heightening
18½ x 12½in (47 x 32cm)
£750-850 *C*

Sir Edwin Landseer, R.A.
(1802-73)
British
Portrait of William Lamb, 2nd
Viscount Melbourne (1779-1848)
Oil on canvas
15 x 12½in (38 x 32cm)
£26,500-35,000 *S*

*Divorced husband of Caroline
Lamb, famous for her infatuation
with the poet Byron, Melbourne
was a noted statesman, politician
and Prime Minister 1834-41.
During that period he was
responsible for guiding the young
Queen Victoria in the early years
of her reign. 'He is the person who
makes me feel safe and
comfortable,' Victoria confided to
her diary in 1838. Charles
Greville recalled that Melbourne
was as 'passionately fond' of the
young queen as he would have
been of his own daughter, all 'the
more because he is a man with a
capacity for loving without
anything to love.'*

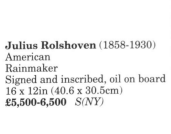

Julius Rolshoven (1858-1930)
American
Rainmaker
Signed and inscribed, oil on board
16 x 12in (40.6 x 30.5cm)
£5,500-6,500 *S(NY)*

Isidor Kaufmann (1853-1921)
Austrian
Portrait of a Rabbi
Signed, oil on panel
6¾ x 5¼in (17 x 13.3cm)
£16,500-18,500 *S(NY)*

Thomas Sully (1783-1872)
British
Portrait of Levi Fletcher
Signed with monogrammed
initials and dated 1830, oil on
canvas
30 x 25in (76.2 x 63.5cm)
£9,500-10,500 *S(NY)*

Attributed to Samuel Lovett Waldo
(1783-1861)
American
Portrait of William Steele
Oil on canvas
29½ x 24⅛in (75 x 62cm)
£2,200-2,800 *S(NY)*

Périclès Pantazis (1849-84)
Greek
Portrait of a Gentleman
Signed, oil on canvas laid down
on board
18½ x 15in (47 x 38cm)
£10,200-11,200 *C*

Werner Zehme (b1859)
German
The Money Lender
Signed and dated 1902, oil on
canvas
38 x 30in (96.4 x 76.6cm)
£4,000-5,000 *C*

Henry Wyatt (active 1817-38)
British
Portrait of a Young Gentleman
Signed, oil on board
11¾ x 9¾in (30 x 25cm)
£4,400-5,400 *S(S)*

After Thomas Weaver
(1774-1843)
British
Portrait of John Coates Esq. MP
for the County of Salop, W. Ward
Mezzotint, proof published March
17, 1810, by Thomas Weaver,
Shrewsbury
23¾ x 29½in (60.5 x 75cm)
£650-750 *CSK*

20th Century

Tony Bevan (b1951)
British
Head
Signed, dated and inscribed,
sand and acrylic on canvas
34 x 26in (86.5 x 66cm)
£5,000-6,000 *C*

Hans Bellmer (1902-75)
French
Portrait of Max Ernst
Signed and dated 1944, pencil
5 x 4½in (12.4 x 11.3cm)
£4,000-5,000 *S*

*Bellmer's friendship with Max
Ernst dates from 1939 when, at
the outbreak of the Second World
War, both artists, as German
subjects living in France, were
interned at the Camp des Milles,
near Aix-en-Provence. Ernst
recalled their hatred of the camp,
a converted brick factory.*

*'There were bits of bricks and piles
of brick dust everywhere ... this
red dust got into the pores in our
skin. It was as if we were destined
to become brick debris ourselves.
Hans and I drew all the time, in
order to overcome our anger and
our hunger.'
Bellmer portrayed Max Ernst on
several occasions and they
collaborated on a number of
projects.*

Florencio Molina Campos
(20thC)
Gaucho
Signed and dated 1940, gouache
on paper laid down on board
7¾ x 10½in (19.7 x 26.7cm)
£400-500 *S(NY)*

Fernando Botero (b1932)
Columbian
Presidente
Signed and dated 81, watercolour
on paper
71½ x 44in (182 x 112cm)
£110,000-130,000 *S(NY)*

*So popular are Botero's works
with collectors that according to
the Wall Street Journal there are
now three separate groups of
forgers, in Miami, Caracas and
Paris, who specialise in producing
Botero paintings. At Christie's
Latin American sale in New York
in May 1993, a Botero estimated
at $500,000 (£333,333) and
illustrated on the front cover of a
separate Botero catalogue was
pronounced by the artist himself
to be a 'very vulgar copy', and was
withdrawn from sale just in time.*

William Gropper (1897-1977)
American
Waiter
Signed, oil on panel
12in (30.5cm) square
£1,700-2,200 *S(NY)*

Kees van Dongen (1877-1968)
French
Portrait de Monsieur de Camoen
Signed, painted in 1920, oil on
canvas
39½ x 32in (100.5 x 81cm)
£20,000-30,000 *S*

Peter Griffin (b1947)
British
The Smoker
Oil on canvas
42 x 30in (106.5 x 76cm)
£3,250-3,500 *MAA*

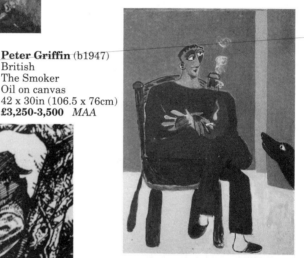

Gerald Gardiner (b1902)
British
Jesse and the Mice
Signed with initials and dated
1944, pen and ink
4 x 5in (10 x 12.5cm)
£300-350 *CBL*

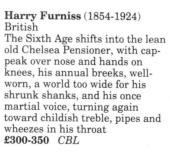

Harry Furniss (1854-1924)
British
The Sixth Age shifts into the lean
old Chelsea Pensioner, with cap-
peak over nose and hands on
knees, his annual breeks, well-
worn, a world too wide for his
shrunk shanks, and his once
martial voice, turning again
toward childish treble, pipes and
wheezes in his throat
£300-350 *CBL*

Conrad Felixmüller (b1897)
German
Fabrikarbeiter (Arbeitsinvalide)
Signed in pencil and inscribed,
1921, woodcut
19 x 11⅝in (48.6 x 29.4cm)
£1,200-1,600 *S*

Edward S. Harper
(1878-1951)
British
Portrait study of Sir Robert
Simon
Signed with monogram and
dated, watercolour
26 x 29in (66 x 74cm)
£350-400 *BWe*

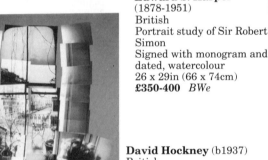

David Hockney (b1937)
British
Artist and Model
Signed and dated in pencil 1973-
4, etching
22½ x 17½in (57.4 x 44.2cm)
£5,000-6,000 *C*

David Hockney (b1937)
British
David Graves looking at
Bayswater
Signed and dated 1982,
photographic collage on green
paper
48 x 30½in (122 x 77.5cm)
£12,700-13,700 *C*

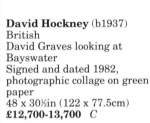

Frances Hodgkins (1869-1947)
British
Portrait of Lett Haines
Painted at Tréboul, Brittany, in
1927, oil on canvas
25 x 20¼in (63.5 x 51.5cm)
£17,500-19,000 *C*

*Arthur Lett Haines (1894-1978)
was the life-long friend and
companion of Cedric Morris
whom he met on Armistice Night.
He was a painter and sculptor
and co-founder with Morris of the
East Anglian School of Painting
and Drawing in 1937. The school
existed until the 1970s but its
heyday was during the 1940s
when it included Lucian Freud
amongst its many students.*

Philip Harris (20thC)
British
Self Portrait Blowing on the
Grass
Oil on canvas
14 x 12in (36 x 30cm)
£1,000-1,200 *Mer*

Alexandre Iacovleff
(1887-1939)
Russian
Portrait of Roger Faure
Signed and dated 1926, pencil,
sanguine and black chalk on
paper laid down on board
49¼ x 19¾in (125 x 50.2cm)
£3,800-4,500 S(NY)

Charles Loupot (1892-1971)
French
Man in Stove Pipe Hat, c1925
Signed, mixed media on paper
22¾ x 16¾in (58 x 42.5cm)
£7,000-8,000 S(NY)

Juan O'Gorman (1905-82)
Mexican
Autorretrato
Signed and dated 1963 in pencil,
lithograph
13½ x 9¼in (34.5 x 23.5cm)
£2,400-2,800 S(NY)

Sir William Nicholson
(1872-1949)
British
Rudyard Kipling
Signed, hand-coloured woodcut
13 x 10½in (33 x 26.5cm)
£1,250-1,450 CBL

Henry Meynell Rheam
(1859-1920)
British
Study of a Fisherman in Newlyn
Harbour
Signed and dated 1918, oil on
canvas
26 x 18in (66 x 46cm)
£3,500-4,000 *MAT*

Glyn Warren Philpot, R.A.
(1884-1937)
British
A Youth
Signed, oil on canvas
27 x 22in (69 x 56cm)
£4,400-5,400 *C*

John Bulloch Souter (20thC)
British
Goddess in Portland, a study of
Jacob Epstein in his studio
Signed, pastel
21½ x 18in (54.5 x 46cm)
£4,000-4,500 *S*

George Soper (1870-1942)
British
A Quiet Moment
Watercolour
11½ x 16in (29.5 x 41cm)
£1,250-1,450 *CSG*

Charles Spencelayh
(1865-1958)
British
Pensioner
Signed, oil
29½ x 19½in (75 x 49.5cm)
£3,000-3,500 *S(S)*

Leon Underwood (1890-1975)
British
The Egg Dealer
Signed and dated 1921, etching
10 x 7½in (25 x 19cm)
£350-400 *CSG*

Andy Warhol (1930-87)
American
Rebel Without a Cause (James
Dean)
Signed in pencil, silkscreen
printed in colours, 1985
38in (96.6cm) square
£4,700-6,000 *S*

Léon Zack (1892-1980)
Russian
Portrait d'Homme
Signed, oil on canvas
24 x 18in (61 x 46cm)
£850-1,200 *S*

Vladimir Sulyagin
(20thC)
Russian
Kasimir Malevich
Collage portrait
23⅝in (60cm) square
£500-600 *EW*

Andy Warhol (1930-87)
American
Mao
Signed in felt-tip, silkscreen
printed in purple and black, 1974
39½ x 29½in (100.5 x 75cm)
£1,500-2,000 *S*

Women
16th Century

Attributed to Francisco d'Antonio
(active 1412-after 1429)
Italian
A pair of paintings: Two Female Heads
Both fresco
14¾ x 10½in (38 x 26cm)
£3,000-4,000 *S(NY)*

Attributed to Lavinia Fontana
(1552-1614)
Italian
Portrait of a Lady
Oil on canvas
41 x 31in (104 x 79cm)
£9,000-10,000 *P*

After Titian (1477-1566)
Italian
La Bella
Oil on canvas
38¾ x 29¼in (98 x 74cm)
£1,300-1,600 *S(S)*

After Hans Maler (16thC)
Austrian
Portrait of Barbara Kiligerin, aged 20
Inscribed and dated 1530, oil on panel
13¾ x 10½in (35 x 26cm)
£1,300-1,800 *CSK*

**Circle of Francesco Ubertini, il
Bacchiacca** (1494-1557)
Italian
A Lady in Profile
Oil on panel
15¾ x 13in (40 x 33cm)
£1,500-1,800 *CSK*

17th Century

Jacques Callot (1592-1635)
French
La Noblesse
A set of 12 etchings
each 5½ x 3½in (14 x 9cm)
£3,000-3,600 *S*

**Giovanni Francesco Barbieri, il
Guercino** (1591-1666)
Italian
A Woman turned to Left, her Left Arm
Raised
Pen and brown ink
10¼ x 8in (26 x 21cm)
£20,000-30,000 *CNY*

Pieter Codde (1599-1678)
Dutch
A Lady, seen from behind, seated by a Table
holding a Letter
Oil on panel
15 x 10¾in (38 x 28cm)
£17,000-18,000 *C*

Justus van Egmont (1601-74)
Flemish
Portrait of a Lady holding Jasmine
Oil on canvas
51¼ x 38½in (130 x 98cm)
£10,500-11,500 *S*

Jacques de Fornazeris
(early 17thC)
French
Marie de Medicis, Reine de France
Engraving, c1610, printed in sepia
18¾ x 13¾in (48 x 35cm)
£400-500 *P*

Style of Gilbert Jackson (17thC)
British
Portrait of a Lady, aged 37, holding a pair of
Gloves and a Flower
Inscribed and dated 1627, oil on canvas
38 x 30in (96.5 x 76cm)
£3,300-3,800 *DN*

Follower of Wybrand de Geest
(1592-1659)
Dutch
Portrait of a Lady, holding a Book,
at a Table, with red curtain
background
Bears inscription, oil on canvas
70 x 44in (177.5 x 111.5cm)
£2,000-2,600 *CSK*

Attributed to Abraham Janssens
(1575-1632)   Flemish
A pair of paintings: Allegories of
Spring and Fall
Oil on panel
each 48¼ x 36¼in (123 x 92cm)
£23,000-30,000 *S(NY)*

Circle of Sir Godfrey Kneller (1646-1723)
British   Portrait of a Lady
Oil on canvas, in a carved wood frame
28½ x 23¾in (72 x 61cm)   **£2,000-2,500** *S(S)*

Cornelis Jonson (1593-1661)
British
Portrait of a Lady, Mary, Countess of
Pembroke
Signed and dated 1619, oil on panel
26¾ x 20in (68 x 51cm)
£14,000-15,000 *C*

Sir Peter Lely (1618-80)   British
Portrait of a Lady, Seated by a Classical
Column and brown drapery
Oil on canvas
50 x 40½in (127 x 102cm)
£6,700-7,700   *C*

*From the mid-17thC, Lely had the largest
practice of any portrait painter in the
kingdom. As van Dyck is associated with the
reign of Charles I, so Lely is indissolubly
connected with the Restoration, his portraits
encapsulating the sleepy voluptuousness
fashionable at the English court. He dressed
his sitters in browns and dull blues, that
cunningly set off the form and texture of a
sitter's body and skin. Horace Walpole
(writing 100 years later) was unimpressed by
these suggestive draperies. 'Lely supplied the
want of taste with clinquant; his nymphs trail
fringes and embroidery through purling
streams. Add, that van Dyck's habits are
those of the times; Lely's a sort of fantastic
nightgown fastened with a single pin. The
latter was in truth the ladies' painter.'
Horace Walpole, Anecdotes of Painting in
England (1762-80).*

Studio of Sir Peter Lely (1618-80)
British
Portrait of a Lady, standing in a Landscape
Oil on canvas
49¼ x 39¼in (125 x 100cm)
£3,500-4,000   *S*

Garret Morphey (active 1680-1716)
Irish
Portrait of Mrs Fortescue
Oil on canvas, in carved wood frame
24¾ x 29in (63 x 74cm)
£12,000-13,000   *S*

Circle of Sir Peter Lely (c1618-80)
British
Portrait of a Young Woman
Coloured chalks on copper
10¾ x 8¼in (27.5 x 21cm)
£1,700-2,200   *S*

Circle of Caspar Netscher (1639-84)
Dutch
A Lady seated in an Interior
Oil on panel
15¾ x 13in (40 x 33cm)
£8,000-9,000 *S*

Follower of Daniel Mytens (c1590-1647)
Dutch
Portrait of a Lady
Oil on canvas
78¼ x 46in (199 x 116.5cm)
£8,300-9,300 *S*

**Eglon Hendrik
van der Neer**
(1634-1703)
Dutch
Portrait of a Lady,
standing by a Fountain in
a Garden
Signed and dated 1671,
oil on canvas
45½ x 36½in (115 x 93cm)
£3,000-3,500 *C*

**Circle of Frans Pourbus the
Younger**
(1569-1622)
Flemish
A Portrait of Marie de Medici
Oil on canvas
25½ x 21¼in (65 x 54cm)
£1,500-2,000 *P*

**Attributed to Theodore Russell (After
Sir Anthony van Dyck)** (1614-89)
British
Portraits of Lady Clanbrassil; and Ann Carr
Duchess of Bedford
Both oil on panel, in replica Sunderland
frames
each 15½ x 11½in (39 x 29cm)
£3,200-3,800 *S*

North Italian School (early 17thC)
Portrait of a Lady holding Designs for Lace
Oil on canvas
50 x 38in (127 x 96.5cm)
£13,500-14,500 *S*

*The textile depicted in the painting shows
'blackwork' patterns of lace designs, probably
Genoese and datable to around 1610-20.
Textiles and carpets can often provide a clue
to dating a picture.*

Godfried Schalcken (1643-1706)
Dutch
A Boy offering a Basket of Grapes to a
Woman seated on a draped Terrace
Signed oil on panel
14 x 10½in (36 x 27cm)
£80,000-100,000 *C*

Venetian School (c1600)
A Woman
Pen and brown ink, red wash
heightened with white,
on blue paper, pricked
7½ x 5in (19 x 13cm)
£850-950 *C*

After Leonardo da Vinci
(Italian School, c1600)
The Mona Lisa
29¾ x 22in (76 x 56cm)
£3,600-4,000 *P*

*Based on the composition by Leonardo da
Vinci in the Musée du Louvre, Paris.*

18th Century

American School (18thC)
Portrait of a Lady in Blue
Oil on canvas
29¾ x 25in (76 x 64cm)
£400-450 *S(NY)*

Sir William Beechey, R.A. (1753-1839)
British
Portrait of Lady Knight standing by the
Coast, Ships beyond
Oil on canvas, in a carved wood frame
94 x 57¾in (238 x 146cm)
£5,800-6,800 *S*

*The sitter was the second wife of Admiral Sir
John Knight, hence the ship in the
background. According to his fellow artist
John Opie, 'Beechey's pictures were of that
mediocre quality as to taste and fashion, that
they seemed only fit for sea captains and
merchants.' Dull, competent and respectable,
Beechey built up a very solid practice, and
while his rival, the more flashy Hoppner,
appealed to the tastes of the Prince of Wales
(later George IV), Beechey was appointed
portrait painter to his mother, Queen
Charlotte.*

Thomas Beach (1738-1806)
British
Portrait of Mrs Boller
Signed and dated 1772, oil on canvas
29 x 24½in (74 x 62cm)
£9,000-10,000 *C*

*Beach was renowned for what the Morning
Chronicle referred to as 'his capital
likenesses'. His painterly exactitude could
lead to problems with some clients. On one
occasion, his nephew recalled, a less than
attractive lady returned her portrait to the
artist refusing either to pay him or to
acknowledge its likeness. Beach promptly
sent back the painting enclosing a letter
stating that any delay in payment would
result in judge and jury being asked to
compare the image with the original. His bill
was settled without further demur.*

Manner of François Boucher (1703-70)
French
A Young Woman
Oil on canvas
16 x 12¾in (41 x 32cm)
£1,500-1,800 *CSK*

Louis Carrogis, called Carmontelle
(1717-1806)
French
The Duchess of Chaulmes, as a Gardener in
an Allée
Inscribed 1771 and 327, black lead, red chalk,
watercolour
12½ x 7½in (32 x 19cm)
£36,000-45,000   C

*In 1758, at the age of 14, the sitter married
her cousin, the Duc de Chaulmes. Her
husband left for Egypt the day after the
wedding and stayed there for several years.
On his return he refused to see his wife and
consummate the marriage. He was convinced
that he would be thrown in jail by his family
as soon as he had an heir. His wife,
condemned to lifelong virginity, invariably
dressed in white. Mme. de Genlis was hard
on her: 'she was pretty but she lacked wit and
naturalness. She has thousands of ridiculous
pretentions. There was some pomposity in her
demeanour, her manners, her tone and in all
her speeches. However she was very well
behaved.' The statue of Diana in the temple
behind is evidently a subtle reference to her
virginity.*

Rosalba Carriera (1675-1757)
Italian
A Study of a Girl's Head with Flowers in her
Hair
Pastel
11⅔in (29.7cm) square
£7,000-8,000   P

Francis Cotes, R.A. (1726-70)
British
Portrait of Lady Mary Hay leaning against a
plinth
Oil on canvas
35½ x 27½in (90 x 70cm)
£15,000-17,000   S

Circle of Mason Chamberlin (1727-1827)
British
Portrait of Ann More with a Pekinese by her
side
15½ x 12¼in (39.5 x 32cm)
£700-800   S(S)

Gilles Demarteau, called Demarteau l'aîné (1729-76)   Flemish
Buste de jeune Femme penchée à droite; and
Buste de jeune Femme de trois-quart à gauche
Two chalk-manner etchings, with engraving
printed in black and sanguine
each 9½ x 6½in (24 x 16.5cm)
£1,800-2,200   *C*

After Pierre Falconet (1741-91)
French
Miss Moore
Mezzotint, 1777, by James Watson, a scratch
letter proof, Russell's second state of three
13¼ x 9¼in (34 x 23.5cm)
£200-250   *P*

John Downman (1750-1824)
British
Portrait of a Lady in a straw Bonnet with
white and blue Ribbons
Pencil, coloured chalks and watercolour
8½ x 7in (21 x 18cm)
£1,800-2,200   *C*

*Downman's pretty and elegant portraits in
chalks and watercolour were extremely
successful with his many clients, and though
he tried to break out into subject pictures, his
efforts invariably met with a very poor
reception. 'This is another attempt at
historical painting which moves our pity,'
commented the Morning Post disdainfully in
1797 when Downman exhibited a subject
painting at the Royal Academy. 'The artist
has long been known to society by his
portraits of persons of fashion which were
very neatly manufactured, and the ladies
were mightily pleased because he tinted every
cheek with a rosy effusion and washed every
bosom with a semblance of Olympian dew. In
the prosecution of such little likenesses he was
all perhaps that his employers desired, but
attempts at sublimity are above his powers.'*

English School (1707)
Portrait of a Lady
Oil on canvas
30 x 25in (76 x 64cm)
£2,000-2,200   *EG*

French School (c1770)
Portrait of a Lady holding a Torch
22½ x 19¼in (57 x 49cm)
£350-400 *Bon*

Thomas Gainsborough (1727-88)
British
Portrait of Caroline, 4th Duchess of
Marlborough
Pastel on grey paper, in original giltwood
frame
12½ x 9½in (32 x 24cm)
£55,000-65,000 *Bon*

*Gainsborough is known to have drawn only 7
pastel portraits all of which were executed in
the mid-1760s and early 1770s during his
years in Bath. The hairstyle of the sitter
dates this portrait to the late 1760s which
would make the Duchess of Marlborough
around 25 when the drawing was done.
Expert John Hayes, Director of the National
Portrait Gallery, described this as 'one of
Gainsborough's gentlest and most touching
portraits.' It appeared at auction at Bonhams
in November 1992, with an ideal provenance,
having remained in the hands of family
descendants since it was first produced, in
perfect condition and still in its original
giltwood frame. But although the portrait
met every saleroom criteria, it only managed
to sell just over its low estimate of £50,000 to
a London dealer, the result reflecting the
cautious mood of the times.*

Giovanni Antonio Guardi (1699-1760)
Italian
Portrait of the Empress Elisabeth Christine
of Austria in widow's weeds
Oil on canvas
28½ x 22in (72 x 55.5cm)
£9,000-10,000 *C*

*Painted for Field Marshal Count Johann
Matthias von der Schulenburg, who paid the
artist on 13 April 1745.*

Mauro Gandolfi (1764-1834)
Italian
Three Girls
Black and red chalk
7¼ x 9in (18 x 23cm)
£27,000-37,000 *CNY*

Joseph Highmore (1692-1780)
British
Portrait of a Lady, with her Dog
Oil on canvas, in a carved wood frame
29¼ x 24⅛in (74 x 61.5cm)
£1,500-2,000 *S*

Follower of Thomas Hudson (1701-79)
British
Portrait of a Lady wearing van Dyck
Costume
Oil on canvas
49 x 39in (124.5 x 99cm)
£3,000-3,500 *Bon*

Circle of Thomas Hudson (1701-79)
British
Portrait of a Lady
Oil on canvas
23¾ x 19¼in (59 x 49cm)
£500-600 *S(S)*

Charles Jervas (c1675-1739)
Irish
Portrait of a Lady holding a Mandolin
Oil on canvas
38¼ x 30¼in (97 x 77cm)
£3,500-4,000 *S*

Circle of Jens Juel (1745-1802)
Danish
A Portrait of a Lady holding a Fan
Oil on canvas
25 x 20¾in (64 x 52cm)
£900-1,200 *P*

Italian School (18thC)
Portrait of Italian Maiden
Oil on canvas
16 x 12in (41 x 31cm)
£1,300-1,500 *HI*

Nicolas de Launay (1739-92)
French
Les Hazards heureux de l'Escarpolette, af
Jean-Honoré Fragonard
Etching with engraving, 1782, published b
de Launay, Paris.
23½ x 17½in (59.4 x 44cm)
£4,700-5,700 *C*

Anthony Lee (d1769)
Irish
Portrait of Lady Paisley
Oil on canvas in carved frame
50 x 40¾in (127 x 103.5cm)
£3,800-4,500 *C(S)*

Elias Martin (1739-1818)
Swedish
A Milliner Holding a Hatbox
Watercolour over pencil
10 x 6¼in (25 x 16cm)
£2,400-3,000 *S*

Scottish School (18thC)
Portrait of Mary, Queen of Scots
Oil on canvas
29¾ x 25in (75.5 x 63.5cm)
£3,500-4,000 *C*

Thomas Stothard R.A. (1755-1834)
British
A Woman in Classical Dress
Inscribed, pen and brown ink and grey
washes
5 x 2in (13 x 5cm)
£380-450 *S*

Gerrit Zegelaar (1719-94)
Dutch
A Fishwife outside a Town House
Indistinctly signed, oil on panel
11 x 8¾in (28 x 22cm)
£3,300-3,800 *C*

*The artist, an imitator of Gerrit Dou,
was deaf and dumb.*

**Follower of Jacques-Antoine
Vallin**
(1760-1831)
French
A Young Woman
Oil on canvas
17½ x 14¼in (44.5 x 36cm)
£1,600-2,000 *CSK*

After John Opie (1761-1807)
British
A Winter's Tale
Mezzotint, 1785, engraved by Valentine
Green and published by Green, London
21 x 24¼in (53 x 61.7cm)
£400-500 *P*

19th Century

Edwin Austin Abbey (1852-1911)
American
Signed and dated 1879, watercolour and
gouache on paper
10 x 12in (25 x 31cm)
£13,000-14,000 *S(NY)*

Bernardo Amiconi (19thC)
Italian
A Study of a Young Girl
Signed and dated 1861, oil on canvas
37½ x 29½in (95 x 75cm)
£9,600-10,600 *HOK*

A.D. Bastin (active 1871-1900)
British
The Cottage Door
17¾ x 13¼in (45 x 34cm)
£800-1,000 *S(S)*

Adolfo Belimbau (19thC)
Italian
The Sound of Spring
Signed and inscribed, oil on canvas
24½ x 18in (62 x 46cm)
£800-1,000 *CSK*

Jules Frédéric Ballavoine
(1855-1901)
French
Portrait of a Lady with a Book
Signed, oil on panel
13¾ x 10¼in (35 x 26cm)
£4,000-5,000 *S*

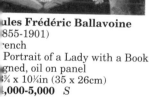

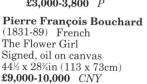

Eugène de Blaas (1843-1932)
Austrian
A Venetian Woman
Signed and dated 1870,
oil on canvas
31½ x 23¾in (80 x 61cm)
£3,000-3,800 *P*

Pierre François Bouchard
(1831-89) French
The Flower Girl
Signed, oil on canvas
44½ x 28¾in (113 x 73cm)
£9,000-10,000 *CNY*

Gaston Bouy (b1866)
French
Portraits of Ladies in Long Dresses
A pair, both signed, pastel
25½ x 10in (65 x 25cm)
£2,700-3,200 *S*

Clement Burlison
(active 1846-67)   British
Far Away Thoughts
Signed with initials and dated
1867, oil on canvas
20 x 16in (51 x 40.5cm)
£3,000-3,600   *C*

Theobold Chartran
(1849-1907)
French
Portrait of a Lady
Signed and dated 1897,
oil on canvas
29 x 24in (74 x 61cm)
£3,000-3,500   *DN*

Eliseo Fausto Coppini (b1870)
Italian
Rêverie
Signed and dated 17, oil on canvas
19½ x 14in (49.5 x 36cm)
£2,250-2,750   *S(NY)*

Guiseppe Castiglione (19thC)
Italian
A Restful Afternoon
Signed, oil on canvas
23 x 20in (59 x 51cm)
£9,200-9,700   *HFA*

Georges Croegaert (b1848)
French
An Absorbing Book
Signed and inscribed, oil on pane
8½ x 11¼in (21 x 28.5cm)
£3,500-4,000   *P*

School of Jacques-Louis David
(19thC) French
A Portrait of the Duchess of Orléans
Oil on canvas
24¾ x 21in (63 x 53cm)
£3,500-4,000   *S*

John Robert Dicksee
(1817-1905)   British
Florine
Signed, oil on canvas
15 x 12¾in (32.5 x 31cm)
£3,600-4,800   *C*

*Dicksee specialised in themes of
romance and chivalry.*

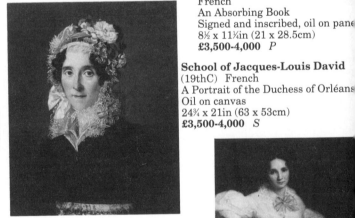

Christophe Thomas Degeorge
(1786-1854)   French
A Portrait of the Comtesse
Alice d'Audebaud
de Ferrussac
Signed and dated 1831, oil on canvas
45¾ x 35½in (116 x 90cm)
£4,000-4,500   *S*

Jacob Dooijewaard (1876-1969)
Dutch
Young Woman reading in an Interior
Oil on canvas
12¾ x 11in (32.5 x 28cm)
£1,400-1,800 *P*

Antoine Ducros (19thC)
French
Elegant Ladies in the Gardens of the Villa
Borghese, Rome
Signed and indistinctly dated, oil on canvas
21 x 13¾in (53 x 35cm)
£5,000-5,500 *S*

Thomas Faed, R.A. (1826-1900)
British
A Slight Difference - or A Tiff
Signed and dated 1867, oil on canvas
31½ x 21¾in (80 x 55cm)
£2,600-3,000 *C*

'In his notes for 1867, Faed gave the picture this title and recorded that he sold it to the famous dealer, Gambart, for £300. It has all the artist's hallmarks, including the 'wag at the wa' clock, the teapot on the side, and the debris on the floor, not to mention his unmistakeable characterisation.'

Delphin Enjolras (1857-1945)
French
The Letter
Signed, pastel on paper
28¾ x 21½in (73 x 54cm)
£5,000-6,000 *C*

Eduardo Léon Garrido (1856-1949)
Spanish
A Song for the Lady
Signed, oil on panel
21¾ x 17¾in (55.2 x 45cm)
£11,000-12,000 *CNY*

F. Girard (19thC)
French
Making Posies
Signed, oil on panel
9½ x 11¼in
(24.5 x 28.5cm)
£1,700-2,200 *P*

Charles Green
(1840-98)
British
The Scent of Flowers
Signed and dated 1869,
water and bodycolour
6 x 4¼in (15 x 11cm)
£600-700 *Bon*

Sir James Guthrie (1859-1930)
British
Portrait of a Woman
Signed and indistinctly dated 90, pastel on
green paper
12½ x 10¼in (32 x 26cm)
£7,200-8,200 *C(S)*

H. Gillard Glindoni (1852-1913)
British
Prying Eyes
Signed and dated 1901, watercolour
£1,700-2,200 *BWe*

George Henry R.A. (c1858-1943)
British
A Portrait of the Artist's Wife
Signed, oil on canvas
50 x 40in (127 x 101.5cm)
£12,500-13,500 *S*

Edwin Harris (1855-1906)
British
The Newlyn Girl
Signed, oil on panel, painted c1895
8¼ x 6in (21 x 15cm)
£2,800-3,500 *C*

George Hitchcock
(1850-1913)
American
A Dutch Flower Girl
Signed, oil on canvas
21½ x 17in
(54 x 43cm)
£5,500-6,500 *Bon*

ir Hubert von Herkomer, R.A.
.849-1914)
ritish School
ortrait of a Lady
igned with initials and dated 1905, oil on
anvas
3 x 51in (210.5 x 129.5cm)
,000-3,600 *C*

Paul César Helleu (1859-1927)
French
Le Visage Encadré
Signed, drypoint printed in colours, c1900, on
wove paper
11 x 16in (28 x 40.5cm)
£2,700-3,200 *C*

Hubertus van Hove (1814-65)
Dutch
Serving Maid presenting a Plate of Fruit to a
Lady
Signed with monogram, oil on canvas
28 x 24¾in (71 x 63cm)
£7,000-8,000 *P*

*** **Huber** (19thC)
Austrian
Double Portrait of Two Sisters
Signed, inscribed and dated 1840, oil on
canvas
35 x 28in (89 x 71.5cm)
£3,200-3,800 *P*

Gustave Jean Jacquet
(1846-1909)
French
La Belle Epoque
Signed, oil on canvas
24 x 19¾in (61 x 50cm)
£2,800-3,200 *C*

Sidney Kenderick (1874-1955)
British
Picking flowers
Signed, oil on canvas
36 x 24in (92 x 61cm)
£10,500-11,000 *HFA*

Robert Kemm (active 1874-85)
British
A Spanish Gypsy
Signed, oil on canvas
36 x 28in (92 x 71cm)
£1,800-2,300 *S*

George Goodwin Kilburne (1839-1924)
British
On the River Bank
Signed, watercolour heightened with white
9¾ x 13¾in (25 x 35cm)
£2,000-2,600 *S*

Friedrich Emil Klein (1845-1912)
German
Portrait of a Lady with a Falcon
Signed and dated 1876, oil on canvas
35 x 28½in (89 x 72cm)
£2,500-3,000 *Bon*

R. Klausner (late 19thC)
Continental
The Letter
Signed, oil on panel
15½ x 11¾in (39 x 30cm)
£2,000-2,500 *Bon*

**George Goodwin
Kilburne**
(1839-1924)
British
Reading
Signed, watercolour
7 x 10in (18 x 25cm)
£4,700-5,500 *S*

Sir John Lavery, R.A. (1856-1941)
British
Her First Disappointment
Signed and dated 1880, oil on canvas
27 x 20in (69 x 51cm)
£4,000-4,500 *C*

*'Lavery's first works show no particular
commitment to any specific genre' writes K.
McConkey. 'By producing a variety of
costume pieces, sentimental pictures, head
studies and landscapes, he hoped to identify a
clientele. Amongst his first supporters was
the Glasgow photographer, Terence Stevenson
who, at the end of November 1880, purchased
'Her First Disappointment'. The model for the
work was a gaiety skipping rope dancer,
Connie Gilchrist (1865-1946). In 1892 she
was to marry the 7th Earl of Orkney.'*

Victor Lecomte (1856-1920)
French
Une Jeune Femme lisant sur son Lit
Signed, oil on panel
7½ x 9½in (19 x 24cm)
£4,000-5,000 *C*

Lucien Lévy-Dhurmer (1865-1953)
French
La Bourrasque (The Gust of Wind)
Signed with initials, painted c1896, oil on
canvas
39½ x 26in (100 x 66cm)
£77,000-90,000 *S(NY)*

Frederic, Lord Leighton (1830-96)
British
Study of a Girl's Head wreathed in Laurel
Oil on canvas laid down on board
10 x 7in (25 x 18cm)
£8,000-9,000 *C*

ohn Frederick Lewis R.A. (1805-76)
British
Study of a Neapolitan Girl
Watercolour and bodycolour over pencil
4¾ x 11¼in (38 x 29cm)
7,500-8,500 *S*

Wilhelm von Lindenschmit (1829-95)
German
Sunday Reading in the Frauenkirche in
Munich
Signed and inscribed, oil on panel
20 x 14¼in (51 x 37cm)
£8,500-10,000 *S*

ter Jean-Etienne Liotard (late 19thC)
Tasse du Chocolat
scribed, oil on canvas
¾ x 21¾in (85.7 x 55.3cm)
,000-8,000 *C*

Sir John Everett Millais, P.R.A. (1829-96)
Oh! that a dream so sweet, so long enjoy'd,
Should be so sadly, cruelly destroy'd. Moore's
'Lalla Rookh'
Signed, inscribed and dated 1872, oil on
canvas
50 x 33in (127 x 84cm)
£50,000-60,000 *C*

Edvard Munch (1863-1944)
Norwegian
Mondschein
Signed and dated 1896, woodcut printed in
five colours
15¾ x 8½in (40 x 46.8cm)
£60,000-80,000 *C*

Stephen Reid (1873-1948)
British
Making Pot-Pourri
Signed and dated 1931, oil on canvas
30 x 50in (76 x 127cm)
£14,500-15,500 *S*

Sir William Charles Ross, R.A.
(1794-1860)
British
The Ladies Catherine, Selina and Louisa
Jenkinson in an Interior
Signed and dated 1824, pencil and
watercolour
18 x 13½in (46 x 34.3cm)
£4,700-5,700 *C*

Sir William Orpen, R.A. (1878-1931)
British
A Woman in Grey (The artist's wife, Grace)
Signed, oil on canvas, painted 1908
74½ x 49in (189 x 124.5cm)
£125,000-150,000 *C*

*Grace Knewstub and Orpen had met on a
painting holiday at Vattetot near Etretat
during the summer of 1899 and they were
married in 1901. She was the subject of
several portraits by her husband, but his
success as a portrait painter necessitated long
absences from his growing family and by
1909 the couple were beginning to drift apart.
Orpen began to spend more and more time in
Ireland with his mistress, the wealthy
American socialite, Mrs St. George, and Grace
remained in London with their young
daughters. The affair began after Mrs St.
George commissioned a striking full length
portrait in 1906, and lasted until 1921.*

John Phillip, R.A. (1817-67)
British
He loves me, he loves me not
Signed and dated 1864, oil on panel
20 x 16in (51 x 40.6cm)
£2,700-3,200 *C(S)*

Eisman Semenowski (19thC)
French
Portraits of Ladies in Hats
A pair, one signed, the other signed and
dated 1888, oil on panel
14 x 10in (35 x 25cm)
£5,500-6,500 *S*

Emma Sandys (active 1868-1874)
British
Buttercup
Signed and dated 1873,
watercolour and
crayon
18 x 14in (46 x 36cm)
£1,300-1,500 *EG*

**Attributed to
Joseph Karl Stieler**
(1781-1858)
German
Portrait of Amalie von Schintling
Oil on canvas
49½ x 37in (125 x 94cm)
£4,000-5,000 *C*

**Charles Joseph Frédéric
Soulacroix** (1825-79)
French
Writing the Letter
Signed, oil on canvas
15¼ x 10⅞in (38.5 x 27.5cm)
£9,500-10,500 *S*

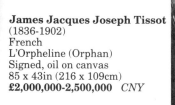

Alfred Stevens (1823-1906)
Belgian
L'Etude du rôle
Signed and dated '88,
oil on canvas
37 x 23½in (94 x 59cm)
£114,000-130,000 *CNY*

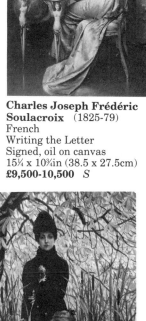

James Jacques Joseph Tissot
(1836-1902)
French
L'Orpheline (Orphan)
Signed, oil on canvas
85 x 43in (216 x 109cm)
£2,000,000-2,500,000 *CNY*

James Jacques Joseph Tissot
(1836-1902)
French
Sans Dot (Without Dowry)
Signed, oil on canvas
57¾ x 41½in (146.7 x 105.4cm)
£600,000-700,000 *S(NY)*

Ralph Todd (active 1880-93)
British
Cottage Interior with Old Lady arranging a
Vase of Daffodils
Signed, oil
11 x 15in (28 x 38cm)
£2,700-3,200 *TAY*

Edouardo Tofano (1838-1920)
Italian
Summer Refreshment
Signed, watercolour on paper
26 x 19in (66 x 48.2cm)
£6,000-7,000 *CNY*

Harry Watrous (1857-1940)
American
Solitaire
Signed, oil on canvas
23¾ x 18in (60.3 x 45.7cm)
£6,000-7,000 *S(NY)*

Florent Willems (1823-1905)
Belgian
La Liseuse
Signed and dated '58, oil on panel
31¾ x 25in (80.7 x 63.8cm)
£12,700-13,700 *C*

Charles Haigh Wood (active 1874-1904)
British
Fair Deceivers
Signed and dated '97, oil on canvas
30 x 41½in (76.2 x 105.4cm)
£22,000-28,000 *Bon*

20th Century

Peter Behrens (1868-1940)
German
Der Kuss (The Kiss)
Monogrammed, coloured
woodcut on paper
7¾ x 6in (19.7 x 15.2cm)
£750-850 *S(NY)*

Antonio Barone (1889-1971)
Italian
Beach Scene with Grazia
Watercolour on paper, painted c1914
10 x 13¼in (25.4 x 33.7cm)
£4,500-5,500 *S(NY)*

B. Berman (20thC)
Czechoslovakian (?)
Portrait of a Girl
Signed, pastel, painted c1940
31 x 22in (79 x 56cm)
£600-800 *ARE*

Emile Bernard (1868-1941)
French
La Coquette
Signed and dated 1929, oil on canvas
41 x 32in (104 x 81.5cm)
£1,600-1,800 *Cae*

Boyd and Evans (b1944 and 1945)
Sleeping Sea 1986
Signed, inscribed and dated, acrylic on canvas
24in (61cm) square
£2,600-3,000 *C*

Jean-Pierre Cassigneul (b1935)
French (?)
L'Aigrette Bleue
Signed, dated 1974, numbered 18/150,
lithograph printed in colours
21 x 17½in (53.5 x 44.8cm)
£1,200-1,600   *C*

Gerald Leslie Brockhurst (1890-1978)
British
Dorette (Kathleen Nancy Woodward)
Signed, dated 1932, etching
9¼ x 7¼in (23.4 x 18.4cm)
£700-800   *P*

*The model Dorette Woodward was the subject
of many of Brockhurst's pictures and she
became his mistress and second wife.*

Paul Delvaux (b1898)
Belgian
The Secret
Signed, dated 1966, numbered 29/7?
lithograph
25½ x 21½in (65 x 55cm)
£2,800-3,500   *S*

Otto Dix (1891-1969)
German
Schwangere Frau
Signed, dated 1921, pencil on paper
17¼ x 12½in (43.8 x 31.8cm)
£5,500-6,500   *S(NY)*

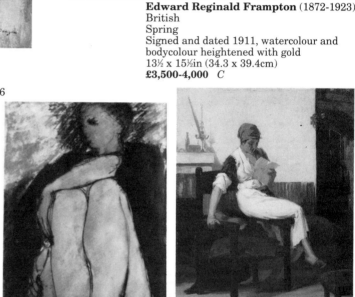

Edward Reginald Frampton (1872-1923)
British
Spring
Signed and dated 1911, watercolour and
bodycolour heightened with gold
13½ x 15½in (34.3 x 39.4cm)
£3,500-4,000 *C*

Kees Van Dongen (1877-1968)
French
Le Maillot Blanc (La Lutteuse)
Signed, oil on canvas, painted 1906
32 x 21¼in (81 x 54cm)
£45,000-60,000 *S*

John Emanuel (b1930)
British
Girl with the Red Dress
Gouache
12 x 24in (31 x 62cm)
£300-350 *G6*

Apostolos Geralis (1886-1983)
Greek
The Love Letter
Signed, oil on canvas
33 x 25½in (84 x 65cm)
£12,000-13,000 *S*

Stephen Goddard (20thC)
British
Valerie
Oil on canvas
14 x 7in (36 x 18cm)
£900-980 *PHG*

Goddard was painting portraits before
reaching his tenth birthday, encouraged by
his mother who was working as an illustrator
with EMI at the time. Having left school he
worked professionally as a designer and
illustrator for ICI, EMI and Readers Digest.
1982 was the first year that one of his
paintings was selected to hang in the Summer
Exhibition at the Royal Academy, since when
he has been a regular exhibitor at this and
many other exhibitions.

Imre Goth (1893-1982)
Hungarian, active in Britain
Portrait
Dated 1948, oil on canvas
20 x 16in (51 x 41cm)
£400-450 *JD*

Martin Grover (b1962)
British
Two Slightly Anxious Sisters, 1992
Acrylic on canvas
41 x 64in (104 x 163cm)
£1,600-1,800 *Mer*

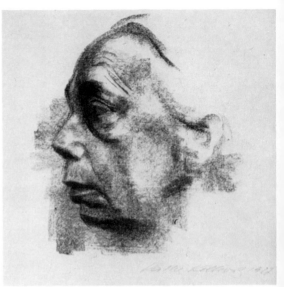

Käthe Kollwitz (1867-1945)
German
Selbstbildnis im Profil
Signed and dated 1927, lithograph
13½ x 11½in (32.5 x 29.5cm)
£1,800-2,200 *C*

Augustus John, R.A. (1878-1961)
British
Head of a Young Woman
Pencil, painted c1900
9 x 5½in (22.8 x 14cm)
£3,300-4,000 *C*

*John was renowned as perhaps the greatest
draughtsman of his generation and was one
of the most prominent artistic personalities of
his day, famous for his Bohemianism,
womanising and wild artistic temperament.
'When I think of him, I often feel that the only
thing to do is to chuck up everything and
make a dash for some such safe secluded
office-stool as is pressed by Maynard
(Keynes's) bottom. The dangers of freedom
are appalling! In the meantime it seems to
me that one had better buy up every drawing
by him that's on the market. For surely he's
bound to fizzle out; and then the prices!'
Lytton Strachey, letter to Duncan Grant,
1907.*

Gordon King (b1939)
British
Ascot
Signed, watercolour
21 x 14in (53 x 36cm)
£1,450-1,650 *Dr*

Peter Kuhfeld (20thC)
British
Summer Interior
Oil on board
27½ x 19⅓in (70 x 49cm)
£900-1,200 *Wa*

Sonia Lawson (b1934)
British
The Friends
Mixed media
18 x 29in (46 x 74cm)
£1,000-1,200 *BRG*

In 1993, Lawson's entry was selected for the poster of the Royal Academy Summer Exhibition. 'Sonia Lawson is going to be very big,' predicts John Brandler of Brandler Galleries, who submitted this work. 'She is one of our leading academic painters. At only 59, she still has a long career ahead of her and her works are figurative and very stylish. Over the past four years she has been very quiet because she has been looking after a sick relative, but now she is back at work and I think she is going to be seen as one of the major British artists of her generation. She is certainly one of my tips for the future.'

Derwent Lees
(1885-1931)
Australian
Girl in a Landscape
Signed, oil on canvas
30 x 19¼in (76.5 x 49cm)
£4,500-5,500 *C*

Tamara de Lempicka (1898-1980)
Polish
Woman at the Theatre
Oil on canvas
16¼ x 13in (41.3 x 33cm)
£8,000-9,000 *S(NY)*

Roy Lichtenstein (b1923)
American
Girl with Piano
Signed and dated 63,
magna on canvas
68 x 48in (172.7 x 122cm)
£1,250,000-1,500,000 *S(NY)*

Girl with Piano is an early example of Lichtenstein's famous cartoon paintings which are recognized as major landmarks in American Pop Art. Like other Pop artists such as Andy Warhol and Claes Oldenburg, Lichtenstein emphasised the transformation of everyday objects into art and employed a style related to the media of the time. The inspiration to work with comic strips, however, did not come from his famous contemporaries, but his own family. One of his children asserted that his father could no draw as cartoonists did, and unable to resist the challenge, Lichtenstein based his first cartoon picture in 1961 on his children's Mickey Mouse bubble gum wrappers, thus heralding the beginning of his mature style and most celebrated series of works.

Dora Leigh (20thC)
British
The Artist's Model Waiting
Signed, oil on canvas
19½ x 13½in (49 x 34cm)
£1,500-2,000 *BRG*

Konstantyn Lomykin (b1924)
Russian
Girl Washing
Signed and dated 1956, oil on board
19 x 20in (48 x 51cm)
£1,200-1,400 *CE*

Martin Lewis (20thC)
American
Night in New York
Signed, dated 1932,
drypoint on cream laid
paper
8½ x 9in (21.4 x 22.6cm)
£1,800-2,200 *S(NY)*

Qin Long (20thC)
Chinese
Figure with Mask
Contemporary rich
colour painting
36 x 36½in (92 x 93cm)
£1,200-2,000 *SAV*

Alfred H. Maurer (1868-1932)
American
Head of a Woman
Signed, gouache on paper
21½ x 18in (54.6 x 45.7cm)
£20,000-25,000 *S(NY)*

Sir Cedric Morris, Bt.
(1889-1982)   British
Milly Gomersall
Signed, inscribed and dated 36,
oil on canvas
28 x 24in (71 x 61cm)
£20,000-30,000 *C*

Albert Lynch (b1851)
Peruvian
A Lady with a Fan
Signed, pastel on canvas
42 x 34in (106.7 x 86.4cm)
£5,500-6,500 *S(NY)*

Dora Meeson (1869-1955)
Australian
A Chelsea Balcony
Signed and dated 1912, oil on canvas
36½ x 31in (92.7 x 78.8cm)
£13,500-15,000 *Bon*

Burton Silverman (b1928)
American
Woman in a Beach Hat
Signed and dated 82,
watercolour, gouache
and pencil on board
23½ x 14¼in (59.7 x 36.2cm)
£2,500-3,500 *S(NY)*

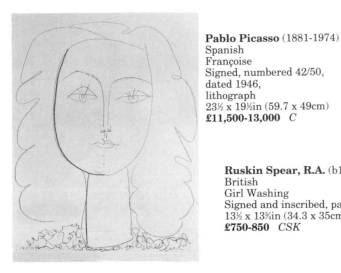

Pablo Picasso (1881-1974)
Spanish
Françoise
Signed, numbered 42/50,
dated 1946,
lithograph
23½ x 19½in (59.7 x 49cm)
£11,500-13,000 *C*

Ruskin Spear, R.A. (b1911)
British
Girl Washing
Signed and inscribed, pastel
13½ x 13¾in (34.3 x 35cm)
£750-850 *CSK*

Gilbert Spencer (1892-1979)
British
Study of a young girl
Signed and dated 1920, pencil
12½ x 10¼in (31.6 x 26cm)
£400-500   *CSK*

Philip Sutton (b1928)
British
Portrait
Oil on canvas
40in (101.5cm) square
£1,550-1,750   *BRG*

Mario Szantho (b1898)
Hungarian
The Gipsy Violinist
Signed, oil on canvas
28 x 39in (71.2 x 99.2cm)
£700-800   *CSK*

Colin Vincent (b1965)
British
Kate
Oil on canvas
24 x 20in (61 x 51cm)
£400-450   *A*

Fernand Toussaint (1873-1955)
Belgian
Dame au Parapluie
Signed, oil on board
17¾ x 14in (45 x 36cm)
£4,200-5,000   *S*

Dame Ethel Walker (1861-1951)
British
The Blue Dress, German Girl
Signed and inscribed, oil on canvas
40 x 30in (101.5 x 77cm)
£6,000-6,500 *BSG*

Andy Warhol (1930-87)
American
Round Jackie
Stamped with artist's signature and
authenticated, silkscreen ink and synthetic
polymer on canvas
18in (45.7cm) diam
£45,000-60,000 *S(NY)*

Walter Ernest Webster (1878-1959)
British
A Coquette
Signed, oil on canvas
21½ x 25in (54.5 x 63.5cm)
£6,500-7,500 *C*

Andy Warhol (1930-87)
American
Marilyn
Signed and stamp numbered 14/250, dated
1967, screenprint in colours
36in (91.4cm) square
£4,200-5,000 *C*

Gerda Wegener
(1885-1942)
Portrait of a Lady
Signed, pencil and
watercolour heightened
with white on paper
40 x 32¼in (101.6 x 82cm)
£2,300-3,000 *C*

Lawson Wood
(1878-1957)
British
Manoeuvring
Signed and dated 1912,
watercolour and
bodycolour
7 x 5in (17.5 x 12.5cm)
£1,600-1,800 *JA*

Nicolas de Largillière (1656-1746) French
Portrait of Joachim Delelée; Portrait of Brigitte Ansart
A pair, oil on panel
31¾ x 25½in (80.5 x 64.7cm)
£56,000-66,000 *C*

David Vinckboons (1578-1629)
Flemish
An Elegant Gentleman and a
Woman in a Garden
Oil on panel
9 x 6½in (23 x 16.5cm)
£11,000-12,000 *C*

After Thomas de Keyser (1596-1667)
Dutch
A Group Portrait of a Dutch Couple and a
Spaniel in a Wooded Landscape
Oil on Panel
30 x 24½in (76.2 x 61.5cm)
£2,700-3,500 *C(S)*

François Boucher (1703-70)
French
L'Oiseau Mal Défendu: A Shepherd and a
Shepherdess in dalliance in a wooded landscape
Signed and dated 1761, in a Louis XV carved and
gilded frame
30¾ x 25¾in (78 x 65.5cm)
£290,000-340,000 *C*

Arthur Devis (1708-87)
British
Portrait of Mr Starkie and his Wife
Oil on canvas,
29 x 24in (73.5 x 61cm)
£20,000-25,000 *S*

Ludolf Verworner (1867-1927)
German
A Young Couple Playing Draughts
Signed and dated '91, oil on canvas
21¾ x 30⅜in (55 x 78cm)
£4,200-5,000 *S*

Cameron Galt (b1964)
British
Ceremony 1991-92
Oil on canvas
50 x 32in (127 x 81.5cm)
£7,000-7,500 *Hou*

Kal (Kevin Kallaugher)
(b1955)
British
The Press Sharks with
Charles and Diana
Signed and dated, pen,
ink, watercolour, coloured
pencil and bodycolour
24 x 16½in (61 x 42cm)
£900-950 *CBL*

Alfred W. Elmore R.A. (1815-81)
British
Lucrezia Borgia
Signed and dated 1863, oil on canvas
35 x 23in (89 x 58.4cm)
£18,000-22,000 *C*

Phillippa Clayden (20thC)
British
Pathfinders
Oil and collage on board
48in (122cm) square
£4,500-4,700 *Bou*

Attributed to Alessandro di Cristofano Allori
(1535-1607)
Italian
Recto: A Boy; Verso: A Girl
Oil on copper, set in a stand
3¼in (8.7cm) diam.
£18,500-20,000 *S*

Jan van Rossum
(1630-73)
Dutch
A Portrait of a Young
Girl
Signed, dated 1671
Oil on canvas
56½ x 40½in (143.5 x
103cm)
£4,600-5,600 *P*

Cornelis Jonson (1593-1661)
Dutch
A Portrait of Two Children
Signed with initials, dated 1648, oil on canvas
52½ x 46½in (133.4 x 118.2cm)
£15,000-16,000 *C*

Follower of William Scrots
(active 1537-53)
Dutch
Portrait of Edward VI
Inscribed, oil on panel
13¼ x 10¾in (33.5 x 27.5cm)
£6,500-7,500 *S*

German School (16thC)
Portrait of a Young Girl Holding A Rattle
Inscribed, oil on panel
23½ x 17¼in (59.7 x 43.8cm)
£12,500-14,000 *S(NY)*

Petrus Troueil (active 1630s)
Portrait of two Boys of the Cotes family,
aged 10 and 8
Inscribed and dated 1639
24¾ x 30in (63 x 76cm)
£10,500-11,500 *C*

Nathan Theodore Fielding (1747-1814)
British
Two Children Seated on a Black Pony
Signed, oil on canvas
40 x 46in (101.6 x 117cm)
£42,000-50,000 *C*

After Richard Westall (1765-1836)
British
A Boy Angling; and another, a pair
Colour printed stipple engraving by Nutter and
Gaugain, published by J. Boydell, London, 1802
£2,650-2,850 *OG*

Bartholomew Dandridge
(1691-1755)
British
Portrait of Master Barton
Oil on canvas
48 x 38¼in (122 x 97cm)
£9,000-10,000 *S*

Nathaniel Hone (1718-84)
British
The Whitefoord Children in a Wood
Oil on canvas
40½ x 50½in (103.2 x 128.3cm)
£42,000-50,000 *C*

Jean-François Clermont, called Ganif (1717-1807)
French
Children Fishing on a Riverbank
28 x 40in (70.8 x 102cm)
£12,200-14,000 *C*

John Opie, R.A. (1761-1807)
British
A Boy in a dark suit with a Spaniel, chasing a
cat up a tree
51¾ x 41¼in (131.4 x 105cm)
£9,500-10,500 *C*

Miss Jane M. Dealy (Lady Lewis)
(active 1879-1931), British
'And she went to Market, All on a Market Day'
Signed and inscribed, oil on canvas
40 x 50in (101.6 x 127.6cm)
£17,500-20,000 *C*

Chevalier Louis-William Desanges
(active 1846-87) British
Portrait of the Hon Amias Lucien Orde-Powlett
Signed with monogram, dated 1858, oil on canvas
36in (91.5cm) diam
£5,500-6,500 *C*

Pierre Edouard Frère (1819-86)
French
Winding the Wool
Signed, oil on panel
14 x 11in (35.5 x 28cm)
£8,500-9,000 *HFA*

William Adolphe Bouguereau
(1825-1905)
French
Petites Maraudeuses
Signed and dated 1872, oil on
canvas
79 x 43in (200.7 x 109.2cm)
£153,000-170,000 *S(NY)*

Edmund Adler (1871-1957)
Austrian
Preparing for the Festival
Signed, oil on canvas
22 x 27in (56 x 68.5cm)
£13,500-14,000 *HFA*

Emile Vernon (late 19th/early 20thC)
British
Waiting for the Vet
Signed and dated 1919, oil on canvas
25 x 20in (63.5 x 51cm)
£23,000-30,000 *C*

Marie Anne Robiquet (b1864)
French
Le Chapeau Rose
Signed and dated 1910, oil on canvas
37 x 29in (94 x 74cm)
£19,000-20,000 *HFA*

Georg Jakobides
(1853-1932)
Greek
The Smoker
Signed, oil on canvas
35¾ x 25in
(91 x 64cm)
£60,000-70,000 *S*

Felice Zennaro (1833-1926)
Italian
Caring for the Chimney Sweep
Signed and dated 1898, oil on canvas
38½ x 54in (98 x 137cm)
£7,500-8,500 *S*

Anders Zorn (1860-1920)
Swedish
A Portrait of Maud Cassel, aged seven
Signed and dated '87, watercolour
heightened with white bodycolour
39 x 23¼in (99 x 59cm)
£100,000-120,000 *S*

Mabel Lucie Attwell (1879-1964)
British
Portrait of an English Lady Never Saying Die!
Inscribed, watercolour with bodycolour
6½ x 10¼in (16.5 x 26cm)
£1,650-1,750 *CBL*

English School (c1910)
Portrait of a Young Girl With Her Teddy
Inscribed on stretcher 'by N. M'Carthy', oil on
canvas
17¼ x 13½in (44 x 34cm)
£900-1,000 *ALL*

Peter Formichev (1896-1975)
Russian
The Young Apprentice
Oil on canvas, painted 1949
43 x 35in (109 x 89cm)
£5,000-6,000 *RMG*

Egon Schiele (1890-1918)
Austrian
Knabe in Matrosenanzug
Signed and dated 1914, gouache, watercolour,
coloured crayon and pencil
18¾ x 12¼in (47.8 x 31.2cm)
£43,000-50,000 *S*

Gordon Nicolic (20thC)
British
Untitled
Dated 1990, crayon and pastel
27½ x 39½in (70 x 100cm)
£1,500-1,600 *EW*

Thomas Sully (1783-1872) British
Mother with her Children
Signed with monogram, dated 1831, watercolour
on paper
11in (28cm) square
£5,600-6,600 *S(NY)*

English School (1635)
Portrait of a Lady and a
young Boy, perhaps Anne
Bonham and her son,
Hugh
Inscribed and dated 1635
71½ x 47½in
(181.5 x 121cm)
£8,700-10,000 *C*

Georges François Paul Laugee (b1853)
French
The First Born
Signed and dated 1883, oil on canvas
52 x 34in (132 x 86cm)
£17,000-18,000 *HFA*

Sir Thomas Lawrence, P.R.A. (1769-1830)
British
Priscilla, Lady Burghesh, holding her son the Hon
George Fane
Bears old label on reverse dated 1820
19 x 17in (48 x 43cm)
£40,000-50,000 *C*

Louis Carrogis, called Carmontelle
(1717-1806)
French
The Princess of Salm seated with her son
the Prince of Salm, by a Chinese pavilion
Inscribed and dated 1770, black lead, red
chalk, watercolour
12¾ x 7⅝in (32.5 x 19.4cm)
£32,000-40,000 *C*

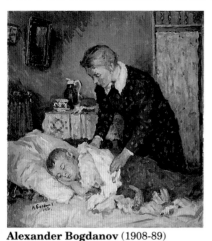

Alexander Bogdanov (1908-89)
Russian
Tucking In
Oil on canvas, painted 1950
17 x 16in (43 x 40.5cm)
£1,800-2,200 *RMG*

Emiliano di Cavalcanti (1897-1976)
Brazilian
Maternidad
Signed, oil and gouache on paper mounted on panel
20½ x 29½in (52.4 x 75cm)
£22,000-30,000 *S(NY)*

Jean Arnoald Heyermans (b1837)
Dutch
Grandfather's Watch
Oil on canvas
29 x 23½in (73.4 x 60cm)
£2,000-2,250 *JD*

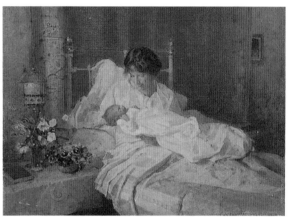

Carlton Alfred Smith (1853-1946)
British
A Mother with her Baby
Signed and dated 1916, pencil and watercolour
9 x 12in (23 x 30.3cm)
£9,000-10,000 *C*

Robert Gemmel Hutchison (1889-1970)
British
Bedtime
Signed, oil on canvas
17½ x 29½in (44 x 75cm)
£6,000-6,500 *BSG*

Hector Caffieri (1847-1932)
British
Motherhood
Signed, watercolour
14 x 24in (36 x 61.5cm)
£6,500-7,000 *MJA*

Harold Dearden (1888-1962)
British
A Summer Idyll
Signed, oil on canvas
33 x 36in (84 x 92cm)
£4,000-4,500 *NZ*

Arthur Devis (1708-87) British
A Group Portrait of John Cotes of Woodcote and
his sons in the park at Woodcote, painted c1745
Oil on canvas
39¾ x 49½in (101 x 126.7cm)
£90,000-100,000 *C*

English School (c1680)
A Group Portrait of Henry Chorley of Preston, and
family
Inscribed with names of the sitters, oil on canvas
53¼ x 71½in (135.2 x 181.6cm)
£18,000-20,000 *CNY*

Caspar Netscher (1639-84)
Dutch
Portrait of a Couple with their
children in a garden
Oil on canvas
20½ x 23½in (52 x 59.7cm)
£40,000-50,000 *S(NY)*

Sir Francis Grant, P.R.A. (1810-78)
British
A Group Portrait of the Artist's Children in a Highland landscape
Signed, oil on canvas
44 x 57in (111.5 x 144.5cm)
£28,000-38,000 *C(S)*

Alexander Ivanov (b1950)
Russian
Weekend
Mixed media on paper,
etching, watercolour and
inks
18in (46cm) square
£450-500 *Mer*

Follower of Joachim Beuckelaer (16thC)
Flemish
A Fish Stall
Oil on canvas
41 x 61in (104 x 154.5cm)
£6,700-7,700 *S*

After Jan Havicksz. Steen (17thC)
Dutch
A Family Merrymaking in an Interior
With signature JSteen (JS linked), oil on
panel
23½ x 19¼in (60 x 49.2cm)
£9,000-10,000 *C*

*After the picture in the Musée Fabre,
Montpellier*

Manner of Nicholas Lancret (18thC)
French
The Repast of the Hunting Party
Oil on canvas
37½ x 41¾in (95 x 106cm)
£4,700-5,700 *C(S)*

Dirck Hals (1591-1656)
Dutch
Merry Company in an
Interior
Bears initials PS, oil on
panel
12¾ x 20¾in (32.5 x 53cm)
£40,000-50,000 *S*

Sir Peter Paul Rubens
(1577-1640)
Flemish
The Marriages of
Constantine and Fausta
and of Constantia and
Licinius
Oil on panel
18½ x 25¼in
(47.3 x 64.4cm)
£750,000-850,000 *C*

Percy Craft (1856-1934)
British
The Regatta at the Cambridge Mays
Oil on panel
8¾ x 12¼in (22 x 32cm)
£3,000-3,200 *BSG*

Henry Charles Bryant (1840-1920)
British
Market Day, Malmesbury
Signed and dated 1858, oil on canvas
25 x 31in (64 x 79cm)
£11,500-12,000 *FAO*

Indulis Zarins (20thC)
Russian
The Apéritif
Oil on Canvas
39½ x 20in (100 x 51cm)
£3,000-4,000 *Ce*

Frank Moss Bennett (1874-1953)
British
At the Sportman's Arms
Signed and dated 1937, oil on canvas
23½ x 29½in (60 x 75cm)
£26,000-35,000 *Bon*

Michael Coulter (b1937)
British
Swanage Pier
Watercolour
16½ x 22in (42 x 56.5cm)
£900-1,000 *PHG*

George Large (20thC)
British
Blue and White
Watercolour
19½ x 27in (50 x 69cm)
£1,000-1,125 *LA*

Jean-Léon Gérôme (1824-1904)
French
Louis XVI et Molière
Signed and dated MDCCCLXII, oil on
panel
17½ x 30in (44.5 x 76.2cm)
£70,000-80,000 *S(NY)*

Frank William Warwick Topham
(1838-1924)
British
Home After Service
Signed and dated 1879, oil on canvas
50½ x 80⅓in (128.3 x 204.5cm)
£47,000-60,000 *S(NY)*

Eugenio Alvarez-Dumont (1864-1927)
Spanish
En La Tarde en Biarritz
Signed and dated 1909, oil on canvas
35 x 45in (89 x 114cm)
£55,000-70,000 *S(NY)*

Ludwig Karsten (1876-1926)
Norwegian
The Winter Garden at Julebaek
Signed and dated '18, oil on canvas
55½ x 58in (141 x 147cm)
£40,000-50,000 *S*

James Drummond (1816-77)
British
Armourer's Shop in the time of
Charles I
Signed and dated 1874, oil on
canvas
34 x 46in (86 x 116.5cm)
£23,000-24,000 *HFA*

David Vinckboons (1576-1629/32)
Flemish
Peasant Feast
Signed with monogram and dated 1606, oil on panel
9¾ x 12½in (24.8 x 32cm)
£93,000-115,000 *S(NY)*

English School (c1770)
Peasants resting at the foot of an Escarpment
with Cattle, Goats and Sheep
41 x 34⅜in (104 x 88.6cm)
£7,000-8,000 *C*

Luigi Bechi
(1830-1919)
Italian
Courting on the Porch
Signed, oil on canvas
38 x 29in (96.5 x 74cm)
£18,000-20,000 *S*

David Ryckaert III
(1612-61)
Flemish
A Peasant seated at a table
eating gruel
Oil on panel
15½ x 11½in (39 x 29cm)
£4,000-5,000 *P*

**Pieter Brueghel the
Younger** (c1564-1637)
Flemish
Village Wedding Dance
Oil on panel
16½ x 22½in (42 x 57cm)
£267,000-300,000 *S(NY)*

William Bromley (active 1835-88)
British
Watching the Float
Signed, oil on canvas
14 x 18in (36 x 46cm)
£8,500-9,000 *FAO*

James Clark Hook, R.A. (active 1867-71)
British
Landing the Catch
Oil on canvas
24 x 32in (61 x 81.5cm)
£11,500-12,000 *FAO*

Theodor von der Beek (b1838)
German
Hide and Seek
Signed and dated 1884, oil on canvas
43 x 31in (109 x 79cm)
£9,000-10,000 *S*

Alfred Glendening, Jnr (1862-1907)
British
Country Cousins
Signed with monogram and dated 1896, watercolour
20 x 30in (51 x 76cm)
£8,000-8,500 *HFA*

Sir James Guthrie
(1859-1930)
British
To Pastures New
Signed and dated 83, oil
on canvas
13 x 22in (33 x 56cm)
£78,000-90,000 *C(S)*

Carlton Alfred Smith (1853-1946)
British
Blowing Bubbles
Signed, watercolour
15½ x 20⅓in (39 x 52cm)
£11,500-12,000 *MJA*

Thomas Mackay (1851-1909)
British
By the River
Signed, watercolour
7 x 9¾in (18 x 24cm)
£3,300-3,500 *MJA*

Nikolai Obriynba (20thC)
Russian
Before the Rains
Oil on canvas, painted 1955
60 x 102in (152.4 x 259cm)
£30,000-32,000 *Ce*

Arthur Maderson (b1942)
British
Harvest Time, 1992
Oil
17½ x 23in (44.5 x 59cm)
£1,700-1,850 *A*

John E. Costigan (1888-1972)
American
Milking the Cow
signed, watercolour on paper,
painted c1930
22 x 29in (56 x 73.7cm)
£1,700-2,200 *S(NY)*

Floris van Schooten (c1585-1656)   Dutch
A Still Life of Fruit and Vegetables on a Table, with two
Kitchen Maids
Oil on canvas
42½ x 59in (108 x 149.5cm)
£40,000-50,000   S

Pieter Cornelisz. van Slingelandt
(1640-91)   Dutch
A Girl paring Parsnips in a Kitchen
Indistinctly signed with initials, oil on
panel, 9½ x 8½in (24 x 21cm)
£11,500-13,000   C

Victor Emile Janssen
(active 1807-45)   German
Preparing the Evening Meal
Signed, oil on panel
17 x 14in (43 x 36cm)
£5,400-5,800   HFA

Hendrick Martensz. Sorgh (1611-70)
Dutch
A Kitchen with a Bittern hanging from
a Poultry Ring
Signed, oil on panel, 18¾ x 25in
(48 x 64cm). £28,000-35,000   C

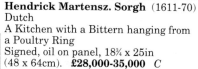

Apostolos Geralis (1886-1983)
Greek
Preparing the Bread
Signed, oil on canvas
27½ x 35½in (70.2 x 90.2cm)
£21,000-25,000   C

Isidor Kaufmann
(1853-1921)
Austrian
A Helping Hand
Signed, oil on panel
14¾ x 11¾in (37.5 x 29.8cm)
£8,000-10,000   Bon

James McNeill Whistler (1834-1903)
British
The Sands, Dieppe
Signed, watercolour on paper
8½ x 5in (21 x 13cm)
£35,000-45,000 *S(NY)*

Robert Gemmell Hutchison (1855-1936)
British
Nymph of the Shore
Signed and inscribed, oil on board
14 x 10in (35.5 x 25.3)
£3,000-4,000 *C(S)*

Alexander M. Rossi (active 1870-1905)
British
The Young Bathers
Signed, watercolour
12 x 20in (31 x 51cm)
£2,300-2,500 *EG*

Guillermo Gomez y Gil (19thC)
Spanish
Gipsies at the Beach
Signed, oil on canvas laid down on board
41¼ x 55½in (105 x 141cm)
£16,000-18,000 *S*

William Marshall Brown, R.W.S. (1863-1936)
British
When the Tide is out
Signed, oil on canvas
10 x 14in (25 x 36.5cm)
£3,500-4,500 *C(S)*

August Schiott (1823-95)
Danish
A group of boys on Aalsgaarde Beach
Signed, oil on canvas
67 x 78½in (172 x 200cm)
£7,200-8,500 *S*

Mary Jackson (20thC)
British
Deckchairs
Oil on canvas
9¾ x 13¾in (24 x 35cm)
£350-550 *BSG*

Dorothea Sharp (1874-1955)
British
Climbing the Rocks
Oil on canvas
23 x 17in (59 x 43cm)
£11,000-11,500 *Dr*

Harry Wingfield (b1910)
British
Peter and Jane at the
Seaside
Signed, gouache
11 x 8in (28 x 20cm)
£350-375 *Dr*

*Original for Ladybird
Keywords Series*

Laurie Taylor (active 1920-30s)
Australian
Meeting the Boats, Cadgwith Cove, Cornwall
Signed, oil on canvas
16 x 12in (41 x 31cm)
£1,000-1,200 *NZ*

John Mackie (b1953)
Scottish
Beach at Sanary
Oil on canvas
16 x 20in (141 x 51cm)
£750-800 *WG*

John Cameron (b1872)
British
Battle Scene
Signed, watercolour with
bodycolour
11½ x 9½in (29 x 24cm)
£2,650-2,750 *CBL*

James William Glass (1825-57)
British
Richard, Coeur de Lion, on his way to Jerusalem
Signed and dated 1854, oil on canvas
69¼ x 95in (176 x 241cm)
£50,000-60,000 *S(NY)*

José Cusachs y Cusachs (1851-1908)
Spanish
Soldiers on Horseback
Signed and dated 1905, oil on canvas
21¾ x 18in (55.5 x 46cm)
£26,000-35,000 *CNY*

William Holmes Sullivan (active 1870-d1908)
British
Capture of the Eagle, Waterloo
Signed, inscribed and dated 1898
Oil on canvas
24 x 36½in (61 x 92cm)
£9,000-10,000 *C*

Anton Strassgschwandtner (active 1826-81)
Austrian
The Young Emperor Franz Joseph awarding Medals
Signed and dated 1850, oil on canvas,
28¾ x 40in (73 x 102cm)
£53,000-65,000 *S*

José Clemente Orozco (20thC) Mexican
Acordada (Caballos y Zapatistas)
Signed, oil on canvas, 26 x 32½in (66 x 82cm)
£250,000-280,000 *S(NY)*

Jean Carolus (19thC)
Belgian
Gentlemen playing Billiards
Signed, oil on canvas
28 x 36½ (71 x 93cm)
£8,000-9,000 *S*

John Haskins (b1943)
British
Village Cricket Match
Signed, oil on canvas
16 x 24in (41 x 61cm)
£1,200-1,400 *Dr*

Daphne Rowles (20thC)
British
Tennis Players
Gouache, painted c1940
18 x 15in (46 x 38cm)
£400-450 *JD*

Attributed to Joseph Francis Nollekens (1702-47)
Flemish
The Card Game
Oil on canvas
25¼ x 30in (64 x 76cm)
£5,600-6,600 *C*

Edgar Bundy (1862-1922)
British
A Hand to Beat
Signed, watercolour
16 x 22in (41 x 56cm)
£3,600-3,800 *HFA*

Joaquin Agrasot y Juan (1837-1919)
Spanish
Before the Bullfight
Signed, inscribed and dated 1872, oil
on panel
12½ x 9¼in (31.5 x 23.5cm)
£4,000-6,000 *P*

Robert A. Wade (b1945)
Australian
Concert in St. James's Park
Watercolour
14 x 21in (36 x 53.5cm)
£1,000-1,250 *OSG*

Marc Chagall (1887-1985)
French
Danseuse et Musicien
Signed, gouache, watercolour and
coloured crayons, executed c1972
28½ x 20in (72.5 x 51cm)
£232,000-250,000 *S*

Hendrick Bloemaert (1601-72)
Dutch
A Boy Playing the Flute
Signed, oil on canvas
29 x 26in (74 x 66cm)
£47,000-60,000 *S(NY)*

Sir Peter Lely (1618-80)
British
A Girl playing a Theorbo-Lute
Oil on canvas
57 x 37¼in (144.7 x 94.6cm)
£400,000-450,000 *C*

Anders Zorn (1860-1920)
Swedish
Italian Street Musicians
Signed and dated '82, watercolour
heightened with bodycolour
14¾ x 10in (37.5 x 25cm)
£26,000-35,000 *P*

Amadeo, 5th Count Preziosi (d1882)
Italian
Dervishes dancing in a Mosque
Pencil and watercolour
13¾ x 10in (35 x 25cm)
£2,000-3,000 *Bon*

Pedro Figari (20thC)
Latin American
Baile
Signed and numbered, oil on board
15½ x 13in (39.4 x 33cm)
£18,000-22,000 *S(NY)*

Donald Hamilton Fraser
(b1929)
British
Dancer with a Red Sash
Silkscreen
21 x 17in (53.5 x 43.5cm)
£225-250 *CCA*

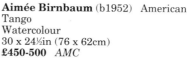

Pierre Carrier-Belleuse (1851-1933)
French
La Danseuse
Signed and dated 1897, pastel on canvas
64 x 38½in (162.6 x 97.8cm)
£13,500-15,000 *S(NY)*

Aimée Birnbaum (b1952) American
Tango
Watercolour
30 x 24½in (76 x 62cm)
£450-500 *AMC*

Georges Croegaert (1848-1923)
French
A Time for Tea
Signed, oil on panel
17 x 13¾in (43 x 35cm)
£3,000-4,000 *C*

François Brunery (late 19thC)
French
The Chef's Choice
Signed, oil on canvas
24¼ x 19¾in (61.6 x 50.2cm)
£11,000-12,000 *C*

Edgar Bundy (1862-1922)
British
The Novice
Watercolour
14 x 20½in (35.5 x 52cm)
£2,000-2,200 *HO*

Adolphe Alexandre Lesrel
(b1839)
French
Les Chevaliers
Signed and dated 1897, oil on
panel
24¼ x 20½in
(61.5 x 52cm)
£4,700-5,700 *C*

Gaetano Bellei (1857-1922)
Italian
The Winning Hand
Signed and inscribed, oil on
canvas
£16,500-18,000 *S(NY)*

Ettore Forti (late 19thC)
Italian
Dall'Antiquario, Pompei
Signed and inscribed, oil on canvas
19¼ x 30½in (49 x 77.5cm)
£16,600-19,000 *C*

William Adolphe Bouguereau (1825-1905)
French
Canéphore
Signed, oil on canvas
96 x 69¼in (244 x 176cm)
£140,000-170,000 *CNY*

Frederic, Lord Leighton (1830-96)
British
The Bracelet
Oil on canvas
60¼ x 23½in (152 x 60cm)
£420,000-500,000 *C*

John William Godward (1861-1922)
British
The Last Bunch
Signed and dated 1912, oil on canvas
39in (99cm) diam
£85,000-89,000 *HFA*

Sir Lawrence Alma-Tadema, R.A. (1836-1912)
British
A Picture Gallery
Signed and inscribed, c1873, oil on panel
0½ x 23¼in (77.5 x 59cm)
£160,000-200,000 *S(NY)*

Ulpiano Checa y Sanz (1860-1916)
Spanish
Course de Chars à Rome
Signed and dated 1890, oil on canvas
19¾ x 33½in (50 x 85cm)
£15,500-17,500 *S*

Paolo Etienne (1874-1960)
French
Arab Women in a Harem
Signed and dated 1912, oil on canvas
27¼ x 41¾in (69 x 106cm)
£10,500-12,000 *S*

William Gale (1823-1909)
British
In a Middle Eastern Garden
Signed with monogram, oil on
canvas
50½ x 40in (128.3 x 101.6cm)
£9,000-10,000 *C*

Robert Dowling (1827-86)
British
The Slave Dealer
Signed and dated 1880, oil on canvas
£18,200-22,000 *C*

Rudolph Ernst (1854-1932)
Austrian
The Opium Smoker
Signed, oil on panel
16 x 10½in (41 x 27cm)
£29,000-40,000 *S*

Sir Frank Dicksee (1853-1928)
British
The Mirror
Signed and dated 1896, oil on
canvas
37½ x 46½in (95.3 x 118cm)
£550,000-650,000 *S(NY)*

Albert Pasini (1826-99)
Italian
The Fruit Market
Signed and dated 1886, oil on canvas
11¾ x 9in (30 x 23cm)
£47,000-60,000 *S(NY)*

Daniel Israel (1859-1901)
Austrian
Entertaining the Harem
Signed and inscribed, oil on panel
16¾ x 21⅛in (42.5 x 54cm)
£16,000-18,000 *P*

Henri Emilien Rousseau (1875-1933)
French
Desert Chieftain
Signed, oil on canvas
21¾ x 18in (55 x 46cm)
£5,300-6,300 *P*

José Villegas y Cordero
(1848-1922)
The Siesta
Signed and dated 1874, oil on
canvas
44 x 27½in (111.8 x 70cm)
£230,000-250,000 *S(NY)*

George Henry Laporte
(1799-1873)
German
A Barter among the Tribes of
the Desert
Oil on canvas
28¾ x 40½in (73 x 103cm)
£22,000-28,000 *S*

Benedetto Gennari (1633-1715)
Italian
Venus Embracing Cupid
Oil on canvas
73½ x 53⅓in (187 x 136cm)
£38,000-50,000 *S(NY)*

Marco Liberi (c1640-1700)
Italian
An Allegory of Peace
Oil on canvas, in carved and giltwood frame
43½ x 53⅓in (111 x 135.5cm)
£17,500-20,000 *S*

Jacques Dumont, called le Romain (1701-81)
French
Galatea
Oil on canvas
21 x 25½in (53.5 x 65cm)
£11,000-13,000 *C*

Circle of Hendrick van Balen
(1575-1632)
Flemish
Diana and Callisto
Executed c1640, on copper
19¼ x 16⅓in (49 x 42cm)
£10,000-11,000 *P*

Frans Francken, the Younger,
(1581-1642)
Flemish
The Misdeeds of Love
Executed c1625, on copper
19 x 24¾in (49 x 63cm)
£30,000-40,000 *P*

Guillaume Seignac (1870-1924)
French
L'Abandon
Signed, oil on canvas
37¾ x 69in (96 x 175cm)
£28,000-35,000 *S(NY)*

Oumbertos Argyros (1877-1963)
Greek
Getting Dressed
Signed, oil on canvas
30¼ x 25in (77 x 64cm)
£7,500-8,500 *S*

Jules-Frederic Ballavoine
(1855-1901)
French
A Naked Beauty
Signed, oil on canvas
32 x 21¼in (81 x 54cm)
£7,800-9,000 *C*

William Russell Flint
(1880-1969)
British
Trembling Leaves
Signed, watercolour
19 x 26in (48 x 66cm)
£40,000-42,000 *HFA*

**Léon Jean Basile
Perrault** (1832-1908)
French
La Baigneuse
Signed and dated 1875, oil
on canvas
55 x 78in (139.5 x 198cm)
£74,000-90,000 *S(NY)*

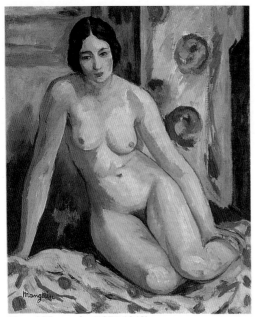

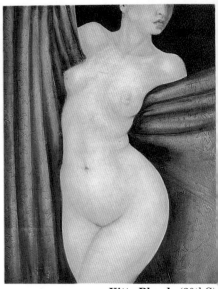

Henri Manguin (1874-1949)
French
'Grenouillette' Accroupie
Signed, executed 1921, oil on canvas
21½ x 18in (54 x 46cm)
£30,000-40,000 *S*

Kitty Blandy (20thC)
British
Nude With Blue
Drapes
Oil on canvas
28 x 22in (71 x 56cm)
£300-350 *AMC*

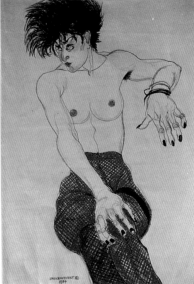

Jo Brocklehurst
(20thC)
British
Punk 1984
Signed, pastel on paper
36 x 24in (92 x 61cm)
£1,100-1,200 *JD*

Gerda Wegener (1885-1942)
Danish
La Danseuse
Signed and inscribed, oil on canvas
48½ x 31½in (123 x 80cm)
£4,000-5,000 *C*

Edward Wolfe R.A. (1897-1981)
British
The Dempster Boys - Portmeirion
Oil on canvas
49 x 37in (124.5 x 94cm)
£2,500-3,000 *CSK*

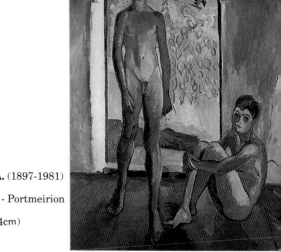

School of Fontainebleau (c1560)
Temperance
Oil on panel
28½ x 42¼in (72 x 107cm)
£30,000-35,000 *S*

**Circle of Tiziano Vecellio, called
Titian** (c1480-1575)
Italian
Nymph and Satyr
Oil on canvas
39 x 31¾in (99 x 80.5cm)
£12,600-13,600 *S(NY)*

*The pose of the nymph derives from
Titian's Salome, painted c1550, in
the Prado, Madrid.*

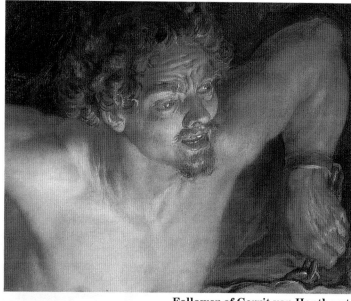

**The Master of the Kress
Landscapes** (active c1505-30)
Fortuna
Oil on panel
12 x 9½in (30 x 24cm)
£12,200-13,200 *C*

Follower of Gerrit van Honthorst
(17thC)
Dutch
Prometheus
Oil on canvas
21 x 25¼in (53 x 64cm)
£6,700-7,700 *S*

Paolo de Matteis (1662-1728)
Italian
Tancred and Erminia
Oil on canvas
71 x 91¾in (180 x 233cm)
£34,000-40,000 *S*

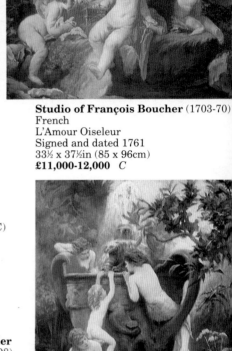

Studio of François Boucher (1703-70)
French
L'Amour Oiseleur
Signed and dated 1761
33½ x 37½in (85 x 96cm)
£11,000-12,000 *C*

Charles-Michel-Ange Challe (1718-78)
French
Venus and Cupid
Signed, oil on canvas
28¾ x 36in (73 x 92cm)
£11,000-12,000 *S*

l. **Brigid Marlin** (20thC)
British
Clockwork Leda
Mische technique
32 x 24in (81 x 61cm)
£3,000-3,250 *JBA*

r. **Charles Napier
Kennedy** (1852-98)
British
The Fountain of Youth
Signed and dated, oil on
canvas
71 x 45in (180 x 114cm)
£9,500-10,500 *C*

Mario Carreño (20thC)
Cuban
Mythological Rider
Signed and dated 43, oil on canvas laid down on
masonite
24 x 20in (61.5 x 51cm)
£25,000-30,000 *S(NY)*

Gaston Casimir Saint-Pierre (1833-1916)
French
Flore et Zephir
Signed, oil on canvas
29 x 37in (74 x 94cm)
£12,000-13,000 *C*

Couples
16th & 17th Centuries

Heinrich Aldegrever (1502-58)
German
The Set of Large Wedding Dancers
A set of 12 engravings, 1538
Each 4½ x 3in (11.8 x 8cm)
£2,800-3,500 *S*

Follower of Sir Anthony van Dyck
(1599-1641)
Flemish
Double Portrait of King Charles I and Queen
Henrietta Maria
Canvas laid down on board
22½ x 28½in (57.2 x 72.5cm)
£2,600-3,000 *C*

Manner of Pieter Balten (1525-98)
Flemish
Portraits of a Man and a Woman
A pair, oil on panel
Each 7¼ x 6in (18.5 x 15.5cm)
£950-1,200 *S(S)*

Attributed to Gerard Donck (1627-40)
Flemish
A Portrait of a Burgomaster and his Wife in a
Landscape
Bears signature of A. Cuyp
Oil on panel
42 x 35in (107 x 89cm)
£4,200-5,000 *P*

> **Miller's is a price
> GUIDE not a price
> LIST**

Gerard Hoet (1648-1733)
Dutch
A young woman at a window holding a bunch
of grapes aloft which she has selected from a
basket of assorted fruit being held by a youth
Signed, oil on canvas
15½ x 12¾in (39.5 x 32.5cm)
£17,500-18,500 *P*

18th Century

Tim Bobbin (18thC)
British
Trouble and Strife
Oil on canvas
25¼ x 36in (64.5 x 91.5cm)
£350-450 *S*

Johann Daniel Bager (1734-1815)
German
A woman washing in her bedchamber; and A
seated cavalry officer pulling on his boots
A pair, signed with initial B and dated 1771,
oil on panel
17½ x 14in (45 x 35.5cm)
£6,500-7,500 *P*

Attributed to Felice Giani (1760-1823)
Italian
Paolo and Francesca
Black chalk, pen and brown ink, brown wash,
watermark fleur-de-lys above an ornate
shield and van der Ley
18½ x 23½in (47 x 60cm)
£3,000-3,500 *CNY*

Thomas Hickey (1741-1824)
British
Portrait of a Gentleman and his Wife
Signed and dated 1781, oil on canvas
20¼ x 16½in (51.5 x 42cm)
£4,700-5,700 *S*

German School (mid-18thC)
Portraits of Emperor Franz I and Empress
Maria Theresa
A pair, oil on canvas
50 x 34¾in (127.5 x 88cm)
£3,800-4,500 *S(S)*

Painted to celebrate their marriage in 1740, Ramsay's Portrait of Sir Edward and Lady Turner doubled its lower estimate of £250,000 at Christie's in April 1993, and set a new auction record for the artist. Ramsay, court painter to George III, was one of the leading European portrait painters of the 18thC. This work typifies the charm of his informal style - 'It would be difficult to point to a more sensitive expression of conjugal affection in British portraiture of the 18thC,' wrote Professor Smart in the catalogue to the 1992 exhibition of Ramsay's work, held at the National Portrait Galleries in Edinburgh and London. The portrait had been in the possession of the family until it appeared at auction and was in a generally good condition. Christie's expert, Rupert Burgess, said that nothing like it by Ramsay had been seen on the market before and he was delighted with the price. It seems somehow fitting that this intimate and personal picture sold to a private British collector, bidding against the London trade.

Allan Ramsay (1713-84)
British
Portrait of Sir Edward and Lady Turner
Signed and dated 1740
42½in (108cm) square
£560,000-600,000 C

Pietro Antonio Rotari (1707-62)
Italian
A Russian Girl; and A Boy
A pair, oil on canvas
17¾ x 13½in (45 x 34.7cm)
£35,000-45,000 C

Francis Wheatley, R.A. (1747-1801)
British
A Lover's Anger
Inscribed and dated on label 1786, pencil, pen and grey ink and watercolour
12½ x 10in (31.4 x 25.4cm)
£11,000-12,000 C

Wheatley worked in the genre of literary subjects throughout his career. The majority of his themes were taken from English literature and many of the books which he chose to illustrate are still famous today. 'A Lover's Anger' was written by Matthew Prior (1664-1721).

Giuseppe Zais (1709-84)
Italian
A Maid and a Traveller in a Landscape
Inscribed verso, pen and brown ink with grey wash
14¼ x 10⅜in (36.4 x 27.3cm)
£900-1,000 P

19th Century

Giuseppe Aureli (b1858)
Italian
The Proposal
Signed and inscribed Roma, pencil and
watercolour
20 x 13½in (50.8 x 34.3cm)
£700-800 *CSK*

Helen Allingham, R.W.S. (1848-1926)
British
The Boy's Likeness
Signed, watercolour
12¾ x 10½in (32.5 x 26.5cm)
£4,700-5,500 *S*

Marie-Jean Caire (19thC)
French
A Young Couple in a Barn
Signed and dated 1889, oil on canvas
50¾ x 37¾in (129 x 96cm)
£3,000-3,500 *S*

Zedekiah Belknap (1781-1858)
American
A pair of portraits of Mr and Mrs Jonathan
Richardson
Inscribed and dated 1829, oil on scored panel
27 x 22¾in (68.5 x 58cm)
£14,500-15,500 *CNY*

*A curious detail is that on the back of the
male portrait is inscribed Mr Richardson's
weight, 237lbs. Surely very few sitters
throughout history have cared to have their
exact weight recorded for posterity, a
distinction more usually reserved for portraits
of prize pigs and other favourite animals.*

James Bamborough (active 1866-85)
British
The Friendly Critic
Signed and dated 1864, watercolour
9 x 7¼in (22.8 x 18.5cm)
£900-1,100 *C(S)*

Circle of Gustave Courbet (1819-77)
French
Déjeuner sur l'herbe
Oil on panel
7 x 20½in (17.8 x 51.8cm)
£12,000-13,000 *CNY*

This painting is in the tradition of the déjeuner sur l'herbe subjects of Manet and Monet from the mid-1860s, as well as being stylistically similar to Courbet. Country leisure, with activities such as picnicking and swimming, had provided new subjects for many modern painters at a time when escape from city life to the country - the seashore or woods - had become increasingly popular.

E. Fiore (19thC)
Italian
The Rejected Suitor
Signed, inscribed Roma and dated '76, oil on canvas
19¾ x 27¾in (50 x 70.5cm)
£4,300-5,300 *P*

Edward John Cobbett (1815-99)
British
Letter From Afar
Signed, oil on canvas
36 x 28in (91.5 x 71cm)
£7,500-8,000 *HFA*

Jean-Louis Forain (1852-1931)
French
Le Divan
Stamped with signature, India ink, watercolour and charcoal on paper laid down on paper
10 x 9¼in (25 x 23.5cm)
£1,500-2,000 *S(NY)*

George Goodwin Kilburne (1839-1924)
British
A Quiet Stroll
Signed, watercolour, c1900
9 x 12in (23 x 31cm)
£2,500-3,000 *AdG*

Pompeo Massani (1850-1920)
Italian
Momenti Felici
Signed, oil on canvas
19¾ x 25¼in (50 x 64cm)
£4,500-5,500 *C*

Fortunino Matania (b1881)
Italian
Cupid's Tricks
Signed, watercolour
18 x 14in (46 x 36cm)
£1,900-2,100 *Dr*

Ammi Phillips (1788-1865)
American
A pair of portraits of a dark-eyed young
woman and a dark haired gentleman
Oil on canvas, painted c1815
30 x 25in (76.2 x 63.5cm)
£11,000-12,000 *S(NY)*

Erskine Nicol (1825-1904)
British
Attired for the Day
Signed and dated 1867, oil on canvas
40 x 31⅛in (102 x 80cm)
£9,000-9,500 *WL*

Albert Friedrich Schroder (1854-1939)
German
The Duet
Signed, inscribed and dated LXXXVI, oil on
panel
11¾ x 15¾in (30 x 40cm)
£1,900-2,400 *P*

Henri Pierre Picou (1824-95)
French
Romeo and Juliet
Signed, oil on canvas
19 x 23½in (48 x 60cm)
£2,800-3,500 *S*

Jean-François Raffaëlli (1850-1924)
French
L'Heure du Thé
Signed, oil on panel
12½ x 10⅓in (31.4 x 26.7cm)
£21,000-25,000 *S(NY)*

Attilio Simonetti (1843-1925)
Italian
The Flirtation
Signed and dated '95, watercolour
24 x 18¾in (61 x 47.5cm)
£1,400-1,800 *S*

Jules Worms (1832-1924)
French
Flirtation
Signed, oil on panel
14¾ x 11in (37.5 x 28cm)
£2,000-3,000 *C*

Henri de Toulouse-Lautrec (1864-1901)
French
Lucien Guitry et Jeanne Granier
Stamped with monogram, peinture à l'essence on board
25½ x 20½in (65 x 52cm)
£620,000-700,000 *S*

Lautrec's interest in theatrical subjects intensified towards the end of 1893, when the newspaper L'Escarmouche employed him to prepare illustratons of current stage successes. At the same time he began to collaborate with acquaintances at the avant-garde Théâtre Libre, for whom he designed programmes and occasionally worked on sets. This picture, an extraordinary example of Lautrec's economical methods of characterisation, shows the actors Lucien Guitry and Jeanne Granier who played opposite each other in Maurice Donnay's 'Les Amants' in 1895, a sophisticated comedy about the frustration of adulterous passion.

20th Century

George Frederick Arthur Belcher
(1875-1947)
British
'Do you believe in love at first sight?'
'Do I! I've got to - I'm only down here for the weekend!'
Signed, watercolour with bodycolour
7¾ x 6in (19 x 15cm)
£800-850 *CBL*

Anthony Green (b1937)
British
The 16th Wedding Anniversary/Our Carpet
1977
Signed and titled on reverse, oil on
hardboard, shaped
94 x 78in (238 x 198cm) max
£16,000-16,500 *BRG*

Sholto Douglas (1871-1958)
British
The Meeting
Watercolour and charcoal
9 x 11in (22.5 x 28cm)
£200-235 *TFA*

R. O. Lenkewicz (20thC)
Painter with Patti Avery, Temptation of St
Anthony, Project 18, Painter with Woman
Study, c1990
Oil on board
25in (64cm) square
£4,000-6,000 *SAV*

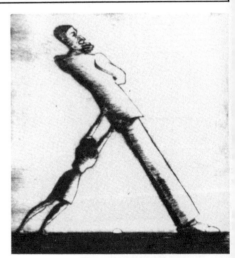

Peter Peri (1899-1967)
British
Supporting Her Husband, 1946
Etching
8 x 7⅛in (20 x 18.2cm)
£275-300 *BLD*

Children

'Children are always an immensely popular subject,' says Dr. Allan Smith of Fine Art of Oakham, dealers in 19thC pictures. Many of the works in this section come from the Victorian period including both traditional portraits and decorative genre pictures, showing rosy cheeked peasant lads and lasses, and children at play. Blowing bubbles seems to be one of the most frequently portrayed juvenile pursuits, an image that is not only realistic, but sentimentally symbolic, signifying the transcience of childhood pleasures.

With these pictures, as in all areas of the 19thC market, the best examples have more than held their own throughout the recession. 'Good quality pictures are becoming increasingly difficult to find and have usually exceeded their top estimate at auction,' explains Dr. Smith, 'though poorer pictures might do all right in a bull market, great paintings will always do well. Good is always good and second rate is always second rate, and in this climate it is the top quality works that are in demand.'

However charming and innocent the final result might appear, painting children can be one of the most testing jobs for the artist. With younger children the major problem is making them sit still. 'In the past artists used to use head clamps,' portrait painter Tom Coates explains wistfully, 'and sometimes they would use inanimate models dressed up in the sitter's clothes.' Modern day portrait painters resort to story tapes, videos and above all, speed of execution. 'You want to get in there, do the job and get out again as soon as you can,' advises Coates with the voice of painful experience.

Both out of artistic belief and practical necessity, Coates is a firm believer in allowing movement into a child's portrait: 'Kids are going to be busy. They're always on the move, so why not let your drawings be on the move? If I were commissioning someone myself I would get them to come and spend the weekend and let them follow the sprog around. Perhaps you can catch them when they're asleep or draw them in the bath. It doesn't have to be a formal sit-in-front-of-the-camera type of portrait.'

Throughout history, however, the ultimate person the portrait painter has to please is not the child but the commissioning adults, a difficult task given the natural tendency of parents to regard their offspring as, possibly, the most beautiful creature in the world. 'I think the perfect portrayer of children has got to be a liar, deceitful and everything,' concludes Coates cynically. 'You've got to give the people what they want.'

arel de Moor (1656-1738)
utch
hree Peasant Children Eating
gned Carolo Morello, oil on canvas
4½ x 41½in (138.5 x 105.4cm)
7,000-8,000 C

he present work was formerly attributed to e enormously popular Spanish artist urillo, and belonged to the Earl of odolphin (1698-1787), who swapped the cture with his grandson in exchange for the al of a celebrated Arabian horse.

Circle of Jacob Gerritsz Cuyp (1594-1644)
Dutch
A Portrait of a Young Girl
Oil on panel
39 x 29½in (99 x 75cm)
£3,200-4,000 P

Nicolaes Maes (1634-93)
Dutch
Portrait of a Girl
Signed and dated 1675, oil on canvas
22 x 17¾in (56 x 45.5cm)
£15,000-17,000 *C*

Jan Albertsz Rootius (1615-74)
Dutch
Portrait of a Young Girl
Inscribed, traces of signature, oil on panel
27¼ x 21¼in (69.5 x 54cm)
£30,000-35,000 *P*

18th Century

British School (late 18thC)
Portrait of a Young Girl with her Dog
Oil on canvas
50 x 40in (127 x 101.6cm)
£5,500-6,500 *S(NY)*

Circle of Jacopo Amigoni
(1675-1752)
Italian
A Portrait of a Young Boy
Bears a coat-of-arms, oil on canvas
13¼ x 10¼in (33.5 x 26cm)
£2,500-3,000 *P*

**Giacomo Francesco
Cipper, called Il
Todeschini**
(active 1706-36)
Italian
A Laughing Boy
Inscribed, oil on canvas
28½ x 23½in (72.4 x 59.7cm)
£8,000-9,000 *S(NY)*

**Attributed to Jean-Baptiste
Charpentier I** (1728-1806)
French
Allegories of Lost Innocence
and Vanity: Children playing
with a Pet Bird; and A young
Mother blowing bubbles at
Casements
A pair, oil on canvas
18¼ x 15in (46 x 38cm)
£8,000-9,000 *C*

Johann Georg von Dillis (1759-1841)
German
A Portrait of the Hon. Henry Temple with his
youngest sister Elizabeth
Watercolour over traces of pencil, executed in
Munich in 1794
13 x 9in (33 x 23cm)
£5,000-6,000 *S*

*Henry Temple (1784-1865), later Lord
Palmerston, was one of the dominant figures
of the 19thC British politics, finally becoming
Prime Minister at the age of 71 and
retaining the position until his 80th year.
According to Benjamin Disraeli's
reminiscences, one of the most remarkable
features of the aged Prime Minister, was his
appetite.*

Jean François Clermont, called Ganif
(1717-1807)
French
Children Playing by Wooded Pools
A pair, oil on canvas
42 x 35in (106 x 89cm)
£29,000-35,000 *C*

*Sold by Christie's in November 1992, this
decorative pair of pictures exceeded its
£6,000-8,000 estimate. Though children
might be the subject of the works, their
activities are extremely adult, namely
hunting, drinking and romantic dalliance,
the children providing a mirror image of
grown-up pursuits, in a manner that
delighted an 18thC audience.*

Bartholomew Dandridge (1691-1755) British
Portrait of a Small Boy
Oil on canvas
50 x 40in (127 x 101.6cm)
£10,000-11,000 *DN*

Attributed to Thomas Gibson (1680-1751)
British
Portrait of William King, aged 10
dated 1720, oil on canvas
78 x 51in (198 x 129.5cm)
£15,000-16,000 *C*

Daniel Gardner (1750-1805)
British
Portrait of Charles Cornwallis, Viscount
Brome, Lady Mary Cornwallis and Miss
Caroline Townshend as children
Inscribed, signed and dated March 1780,
pastel
29½ x 37½in (75 x 95cm)
£10,000-11,000 *C*

Follower of Jean-Baptiste Greuze
(1725-1805)
French
A Young Girl with a Dove
Oil on canvas
20 x 15¼in (51 x 39cm)
£800-1,000 *CSK*

John Camillus Hone (1759-1846)
Irish
Portrait of a Young Girl
Signed, inscribed and dated 1776, oil on
canvas
20½ x 15¾in (52 x 40cm)
£4,200-5,000 *S*

*The Artist was the son of Nathaniel Hone. He
went to Calcutta in about 1780, and returned
to Dublin c1790.*

Robert Lefèvre (1755-1830)
French
A Portrait of Napoléon Junot
Signed and dated 1811, oil on canvas
44½ x 33in (113 x 84.5cm)
£4,700-5,700 *S*

*Napoléon Junot (1807-51) second Duc
d'Abrantès, was the eldest son of Andoche
Junot, a divisional general in the Naploeonic
armies, and Laure Permon who wrote
Souvenirs historiques de Napoléon (1831-35).
He pursued a diplomatic career for some time,
but his eccentric nature, the ill health of his
finances and the court cases which resulted,
forced him to resign. Taking the example
from his mother he looked for solace in
writing letters, collaborated on several
literary magazines and published several
novels.*

Circle of Nicolas-Bernard Lépicié
(1735-84)
French
A young boy playing with marionettes while
two children and their mother look on
Oil on canvas
17¾ x 14½in (45 x 36.8cm)
£3,800-4,500 *S(NY)*

Martin Maingaud (active early 18thC)
French
The Three Daughters of George I
Oil on canvas
37 x 47½in (94 x 120.5cm)
£15,000-17,000 *S*

The sitters are Anne (b1709), Amelia Sophia Eleonora (b1711) and Elizabeth Carolina (b1713). Princess Anne, who possessed a somewhat strident character, was described as being '...vain without cause, imperious without being dignified, and ambitious without the means of gratifying the passion.' When a young child she told her mother that she wished she had no brothers so that she might succeed to the throne, stating that she would die tomorrow to be queen today.' In order to satisfy this ambition she married in 1734 the unattractive Prince of Orange, having declared that she would do so even if he were a baboon. 'Well then' said the King, 'there is baboon enough for you.'

Enoch Seeman (1694-1745)
Polish
A Portrait Group of six Children and their Mother and two Dogs in a Landscape
Oil on canvas
70¼ x 93¼in (178.4 x 237cm)
£6,500-7,500 *C*

John Vanderbank (1694-1739)
British
Study of Children and Dogs
Pen and brown ink over pencil
8½ x 12in (21.5 x 31cm)
£1,800-2,200 *S*

Follower of Antoine Vestier (1740-1824)
French
Portrait of Two Girls
Oil on canvas, in a Louis XIII carved and gilded frame
27¼ x 23¾in (69 x 60cm)
£3,000-4,000 *C*

Johann Eleazar Schenau
(c1737-1806)
German
Three Girls watching a Boy playing with a toy windmill
Signed, oil on canvas
12 x 9in (30.5 x 23cm)
£4,500-5,500 *S(NY)*

19th Century

Walter A. Anderson (active 1856-86)
British
Blowing Bubbles
Oil on canvas
12 x 10½in (30.5 x 26cm)
£3,900-4,500 *C*

Sophie Anderson (1823-1903)
British
It's my turn to play Mother
Signed with initials, oil on canvas
24 x 20in (61 x 50.8cm)
£2,100-2,600 *C*

This husband and wife team specialised ir genre and domestic pictures.

Thomas Jones Barker (1815-1882)
British
A Portrait William Hume as a boy in
Wicklow
Signed and dated 1869
48½ x 34in (123 x 86cm)
£4,000-5,000 *HOK*

Rose Maynard Barton, R.W.S. (1856-1929
Irish
A Young Child seated in a Park
Signed and dated 1897, pencil and
watercolour
12 x 7½in (30.5 x 19cm)
£2,600-3,000 *C*

David Bates (1841-1921)
British
Children by a Lock
Signed and dated 1891, oil on canvas
10 x 13in (25 x 33cm)
£2,700-2,900 *Dr*

'Consistently good in both oils and watercolours,' writes dealer David Gilbert, 'Bates was not inclined to overstatement; his pictures have a quiet fidelity as winning today as they were in his own lifetime.' His pale grey-greens, warm ochres and vibrant blues applied with an authoritative ease gave his pictures a particularly neat and attractive finish. Like Constable he showed a knowledgeable treatment of sky and cloud effect that makes his pictures both atmospheric and spacially interesting. A landscape of this period is more interesting if inhabited and Bates always obliged with one or more figures, chatting, idling or occupied in some rural activity.

Bates lived at Malvern and in the Birmingham area, and today many of his pictures are found in Worcestershire, Birmingham and the Midlands.

Carl Wilhelm Friedrich Bauerle
(1831-1912)
German
Among the Ferns
Signed and dated 77, oil on canvas
66¾ x 80½in (167 x 204.5cm)
£26,000-35,000 *C*

Francesco Bergamini (1815-83)
Italian
Caught in the Act
A pair, signed and inscribed, oil on canvas
13¾ x 20in (35 x 51cm)
£6,000-8,000 *P*

Nikolai Bogdanoff-Bjelski (1868-1945)
Russian
An Afternoon Fishing
Signed and dated 1917, oil on canvas
51 x 40in (129.5 x 101.6cm)
£14,000-15,000 *S(NY)*

I. Bonifazi
(late 19thC)
Italian
Il Pastorello
Signed and dated
1875,
oil on panel
8¾ x 7½in
(22 x 19cm)
£1,600-2,000 *C*

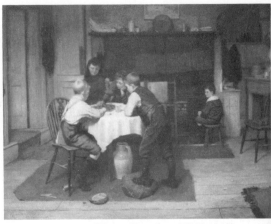

Harry Brooker (1848-1940)
British
A Close Game
Signed and dated 1894, oil on canvas
28 x 36in (71 x 92cm)
£17,500-20,000 *HFA*

Johann Georg Meyer von Bremen
(1813-86)
German
The New Doll
Signed and dated 1876, oil on panel
5¾ x 4½in (14.5 x 11.5cm)
£6,000-7,000 *CNY*

*The artist was nicknamed 'Kinder-Meyer',
because of his predilection for painting
children - unashamedly sentimental
portrayals which earned him a huge
following, particularly in the United States.
According to Hook and Poltimore (see Biblio.),
Meyer von Bremen perfected a number of
tricks to elicit the maximum emotional
response from the spectator - one of which was
to direct his pretty subject's gaze straight at
the audience, thus drawing them irresistibly
into the picture.*

John G. Brown (1831-1913)
American
The Study Hour
Signed and dated 1905, oil on canvas
30 x 25in (76 x 63.5cm)
£17,500-20,000 *S(NY)*

Adam Buck (1759-1833)
British
Portrait of William Gordon Coesvelt and his
sister Sarah Elizabeth
Signed and dated 1809, pencil and
watercolour
14 x 10¾in (35.5 x 27.3cm)
£2,200-2,600 *C*

George Washington Brownlow (19thC
British
The Newborn Lamb
Signed and dated 1863, oil on canvas
25 x 30in (63.5 x 76.5cm)
£3,800-4,500 *CNY*

T. C. Buttery (19thC)
British
The Young Artist
Oil on panel
12 x 9¾in (30.5 x 25.5cm)
£1,900-2,400 *S(S)*

James Charles (1851-1906)
British
Outside the Sweetshop
Signed, oil on canvas
32 x 29in (81 x 74cm)
£16,500-17,500 *HFA*

obert Crozier (active 1854-82)
ritish
eeding the Doves
igned and dated 1869, oil on canvas, in
riginal frame
1¾ x 16½in (55 x 42.5cm)
7,000-7,500 *CGa*

Giuseppe Costantini (b1850)
Italian
Playing Hide and Seek
Signed and dated 1884, oil on panel
14 x 9¾in (35.5 x 25cm)
£8,700-9,700 *S*

George Chinnery (1774-1852)
British
The Children of the Artist
Oil on canvas
42 x 45in (106.5 x 114cm)
£3,400-3,800 *WBS*

Etienne Dinet (1861-1929)
French
Gamines sautant à la Corde
Signed and dated 1888, oil on canvas
20 x 25¼in (50.8 x 64.2cm)
£14,500-16,000 *C*

Lawrence Duncan (active 1860-91)
British
Picking Blackberries
Signed, watercolour
12 x 9in (31 x 23cm)
£2,000-2,500 *TLG*

Franz Dvorak (b1862)
Austrian
Sisters
Signed and dated 1892,
oil on canvas
42 x 32in (106.5 x 81cm)
£13,000-14,000 *HFA*

François Alfred Delobbe
(1835-1920)
French
Feeding the Chicks
Signed and dated 1879,
oil on canvas
25¾ x 21½in (65 x 54cm)
£6,000-7,000 *CNY*

Edmund Eagles (active 1851-77)
British
Four in Hand
Inscribed, signed and dated 1874, oil on
canvas
27¾ x 49¾in (70.5 x 126.4cm)
£12,000-14,000 *Bon*

English Provincial School (c1800)
Portrait of a Young Boy with his Negro Page
Oil on canvas
32½ x 24in (82.5 x 61cm)
£4,000-4,500 S

Anonymous (19thC)
Portrait of a little girl
Pastel
13 x 15½in (33 x 39.5cm)
£400-450 MBA

Robert Farrier (1796-1879)
British
Preparing for War - Si vis pacem, para bellum
Signed and inscribed, oil on panel
23 x 24½in (59 x 62.5cm)
£2,300-2,800 Bon

Emily Farmer (1826-1905)
British
The Daisy Chain
Signed, watercolour
22 x 14in (56 x 36cm)
£2,000-3,000 TLG

German School (c1810)
Portrait of Duke William of Brunswick, when a boy
Inscribed, oil on canvas
19¼ x 16in (49 x 41cm)
£5,000-6,000 S

Myles Birket Foster (1825-99)
We're up here, at the top of the hill
Signed with monogram, watercolour
12¼ x 18in (31 x 46cm)
£23,000-24,000 *Pol*

Edouard Frère (1819-86)
French
Getting Up
Signed and dated 1878, oil on panel
10¼ x 8in (26 x 20cm)
£8,500-9,500 *S*

Frère specialised in the portrayal of children and enjoyed enormous international popularity. One of his greatest fans was the English critic John Ruskin who had a rather unfortunate predilection for portrayals of little girls and praised Frère's work with extravagant emotional passion that had more to do with the painter's choice of subject matter than his artistry: 'Who would have believed it possible to unite the depth of Wordsworth, the grace of Reynolds, and the holiness of Angelico?'

Victor Gabriel Gilbert (1847-1933)
French
Portrait de Jeune Fille
Signed and dated 1881, oil on canvas
58½ x 41¾in (149 x 106cm)
£8,000-9,000 *S(NY)*

Kate Greenaway (1846-1901)
British
The Young Gardeners
Signed, watercolour heightened with white
3¾ x 4in (8 x 10cm)
£1,000-1,500 *C(S)*

Arthur Hacker (1858-1919)
British
Posie for Grandma
Signed with initials, oil on canvas
14 x 7in (36 x 17.5cm)
£3,200-3,400 *HFA*

George Harcourt, R.A. (1868-1947)
British
Muriel, Cynthia and George (Perkins)
Signed and dated 1900-01, oil on canvas
71¾ x 90½in (182.2 x 230cm)
£26,000-30,000 S(NY)

Edward Atkinson Hornel (1864-1933)
British
Dancing Girls, c1900
Oil on canvas
24 x 29in (61.5 x 74cm)
£10,000-15,000 AdG

Edward Lamson Henry (1841-1913)
American
At the Well
Signed and dated '80, oil on panel
8¼ x 6¼in (21 x 16cm)
£11,000-12,000 S(NY)

Robert Inerarity Herdman, R.W.S.
(1829-88)
British
Spring Flowers
Signed and dated 1853, oil on canvas
18¾ x 14½in (47.5 x 37cm)
£3,900-4,500 S

Grace Carpenter Hudson (1865-1937)
American
Chu-Bome: The Orphan
Signed and dated '17, oil on canvas
19½ x 13½in (49.5 x 34.3cm)
£18,000-19,000 S(NY)

Charles Hunt (1803-1877)
British
A Willing Playmate
Monogrammed, oil on panel
11 x 8in (28 x 20cm)
£4,400-4,800 *Dr*

Robert Gemmell Hutchison, R.S.W.
(1855-1936)   British
Hallowe'en
Signed, oil on canvas
12¼ x 18in (31.5 x 46cm)
£5,500-6,500 *S*

Isidor Kaufmann (1853-1921)
Austrian
Portrait of a Young Chassidic Boy
Signed, oil on panel
14 x 10½in (35.6 x 26.7cm)
£53,000-60,000 *S(NY)*

*Isidor Kaufmann is the most important of the
Jewish genre painters. Born in Hungary,
trained in both Budapest and Vienna,
Kaufmann 'travelled throughout Eastern
Europe in search of material in Jewish
townships and villages, sketching as he went,'
painting 'shetl' paintings that 'are
characterised by an exhaustive attention to
detail and an acute sense of the psychological
authenticity of his models ...His brushwork is
so precise that it is visible often only under
magnification.' (Jay Weinstein, A Collector's
Guide to Judaica, London, 1985, p178).*

Carl Kronberger (1841-1921)
German
Children in a Snowstorm
A pair, both signed, oil on canvas
13¾ x 11¼in (35 x 28.5cm)
£18,000-20,000 *S*

George Goodwin Kilburne (1839-1924)
British
Getting Up
Signed and indistinctly dated, pencil and
watercolour
23¼ x 17¾in (60 x 45cm)
£6,700-7,700 *C*

Albert Ludovici (1820-94)
British
A Child in the Rain
Signed and dated 85, watercolour over pencil
heightened with bodycolour
13½ x 8in (34.5 x 20cm)
£4,500-5,000 *S*

SUSAN AND ROBERT BOTTING
Fine Watercolours and Paintings
West Sussex

John Stickland Goodall RI RBA   *"On The Beach"*
Watercolour   11" x 14"

A fine collection of works including M.B. Foster, C.A. Smith, H. Allingham, C.E. Wilson, J. Callow, J. Thors,
R.W. Macbeth, J.S. Goodall (6), W.W. Ball, R.W. Fraser, A.A. Fraser, W. Cruickshank, G. Shalders, A. Bouvard.

We exhibit at leading Antiques Fairs throughout the country, including the British International Antiques Fair
and August Fair at the NEC, the City Antiques Fair, West London Antiques Fairs and Chester,
Tatton Park and Manchester Fine Art Fair.

For complimentary tickets to Fairs and colour photographs, please telephone (0243) 584515

John McGhie (b1867)
British
Bringing Home the Supper
Signed, oil on canvas
20 x 24in (51 x 61cm)
£5,300-6,000 *S*

William Steward MacGeorge (1861-1931)
British
The Lily Pond
Oil on canvas
37½ x 33½in (95.2 x 85cm)
£4,700-5,700 *C(S)*

Sir William McTaggart (1835-1910)
British
Liberty
Signed and dated '64, oil on panel
11½ x 9¼in (29.3 x 23.5cm)
£6,000-7,000 *Bon*

Léo Malempré (late 19thC)
French
A Country Beauty
Signed and indistinctly dated 1886?, oil on
canvas
10¾ x 7½in (27 x 19cm)
£2,300-2,800 *C*

William Maliphant (b1862)
British
A Young Girl listening to a robin's song
Signed and dated 1906, oil on canvas
9½ x 13¾in (24 x 35cm)
£1,200-1,600 *AG*

William Henry Midwood (active 1867-71)
British
The Babysitter
Signed, oil on canvas
14 x 18in (36 x 46cm)
£2,800-3,500 *C*

Philip Monson (19thC)
Portrait of a young boy
Signed 1853, oil on canvas
47½ x 36⅛in (121 x 92cm)
£1,200-1,600 *S*

Louis Fairfax Muckley (active 1887-1901)
British
The Portrait
Signed and dated 1888, pencil and
watercolour
6¼ x 15in (15.5 x 37.8cm)
2,600-3,000 *C*

Arthur Rackham (1867-1939)
British
' 'Twas the Night Before Christmas'
Signed, pen, ink and watercolour
9 x 8in (23 x 20cm)
£6,000-6,500 *CBL*

*Arthur Rackham was one of the most
remarkable illustrators of his generation. As
the Chris Beetles Gallery notes, he first began
to illustrate books in 1894 and by the turn of
the century he had evolved his characteristic
style: enhancing the expressive linear quality
of his drawing with a perspectival use of a
muted colour range that could be well
reproduced. For some 15 years Rackham's
only serious rival as a fairy story and gift
book illustrator was Edmund Dulac. His
fertile and fantastic imagination combined
with his innovative technique have
established him as a seminal figure in the
development of children's book illustration in
Britain.*

Jonathan Pratt (1835-1911)
British
The Toy Basket
Signed and dated 1874, oil on board
12 x 10in (30.5 x 25.5cm)
2,000-2,400 *C*

Pierre-August Renoir (1841-1919)
French
Le Chapeau Epingle, 2e Planche
Lithograph printed in 11 colours, c1898
24 x 19in (61 x 48.5cm)
£45,000-55,000 *S*

Henri van Seben (1825-1913)
Belgian
Late for School
Signed and dated 1857, oil on canvas
35 x 27¼in (40 x 70cm)
£6,500-7,500 *C*

Paul Seignac (1826-1904)
French
Blind Man's Buff
Signed, oil on panel
22 x 30in (56 x 76cm)
£14,000-15,000 *HFA*

Antonio Rotta (1828-1903)
Italian
A Young Girl Eating Grapes; A Young
Shepherd
A pair, both signed, oil on panel
8¾ x 5½in (22 x 14cm)
£9,500-11,000 *S*

Lucy Kemp Welch (1869-1958)
British
Girl with Puppies
Signed, watercolour
8 x 8½in (21 x 22cm)
£3,250-3,500 *CAS*

Aurelio Zingoni (1853-1922)
Italian
The Chimney Sweep
Signed and dated 1881, oil on canvas
38¼ x 28¾in (97.5 x 73.5cm)
£7,500-8,500 *S*

20th Century

George Denholm Armour (1864-1949)
British
Companions
Signed, watercolour and bodycolour on linen
13½ x 15½in (34.5 x 40cm)
£2,800-3,500 *C*

Charles Edward Wilson
(active 1891-c1936)
British
A New Found Friend
Signed, watercolour
18 x 13in (46 x 33cm)
£9,500-10,000 *HFA*

Attributed to Alfred John Billinghurst
(1880-1963)
British
Muscles
44 x 34in (111.6 x 86.2cm)
£550-650 *CSK*

Sue Bradley (b c1943)
British
Summer Haze
Signed and dated 1992, watercolour and
pastel
14 x 18in (36 x 46cm)
£500-600 *HI*

Miguel Covarrubias (1904-57)
Mexican
Urchin
Signed, India ink and pencil
heightened with white on paper
11 x 7½in (28 x 19cm)
£550-650 *S(NY)*

Knud Edsberg (20thC)
Danish
A Captive Audience
Signed, inscribed and dated
'47, oil on canvas
17½ x 21½in (44.5 x 54.5cm)
£1,000-1,500 *S*

Giles (Carl Ronald Giles, OBE) (b1916)
'Mind that child ...'
Signed, inscribed and dated '56, pen, ink and
monochrome watercolour
10 x 21in (25 x 53cm)
£1,000-1,250 *CBL*

*While Victorian artists concentrated on the
endearing and often sickly sweetness of
children, contemporary cartoonists have often
celebrated the child's matchless ability to be
completely appalling. Giles uses the family as
his regular subject, and the children he
portrays are inventive, anarchic and
completely amoral - their almost uniformly
bland smiles in this example belying the
lethal actions in which they are happily and
destructively involved.*
*If 19thC painters show us an idealised dream
of children, 20thC illustrators such as Giles
exploit their nightmarish and humorous
potential.*

Mary Gallagher (20thC)
British
The Little Pink Bridesmaid
Oil on canvas
30 x 24in (76 x 61cm)
£1,200-1,400 *VCG*

Harrington Mann (1864-1937)
British
Cathleen and Annabel, the artist's daughters
Signed, oil on panel
11 x 15½in (28 x 39cm)
£4,000-4,500 *S*

Harold Harvey (1874-1941)
British
Fisher Boy
Signed and dated 04, oil on canvas
12 x 10in (31 x 25.5cm)
£9,500-10,500 *C*

Milton Kobayashi (b1950)
American
The Bathers
Signed and dated 1979, watercolour on board
17¼ x 27in (43.8 x 68.6cm)
£3,400-4,000 *S(NY)*

KILL SOKOLOV
Blue nue oil 62 x 46 cm

Gerard Hoffnung (1925-59)
British
'My first journey alone was spent
 with a label
tied to my coat'
Signed, pen, ink and monochrome
watercolour
9 x 4¾in (23 x 12cm)
£1,000-1,250 *CBL*

Walter Pemberton (active 1900-25)
British
Portrait of a Girl
Signed
10 x 12in (25 x 31cm)
£425-525 *SAV*

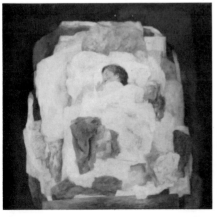

Lu Yun-Hua (b1960)
Chinese
White Harmony
Oil on canvas, painted 1990
48 x 51in (122 x 129.5cm)
£5,500-6,500 *RMG*

Dame Laura Knight (1877-1970)
British
Portrait of a Young Boy
Oil on canvas
35 x 30in (89 x 76cm)
£1,000-1,200 *ARE*

Will G. Penn (20thC)
British
Portrait of a Young Girl
Signed and dated 1921
37½ x 30in (95 x 76cm)
£3,500-4,000 *ARE*

Margaret Winifred Tarrant
(active 1914-34)
British
The Seasons Come and Go, Revealing
Nature's Glory As They Pass
Signed and inscribed, pencil and watercolour
8 x 18½in (20.5 x 47.5cm)
£5,300-6,300 *C*

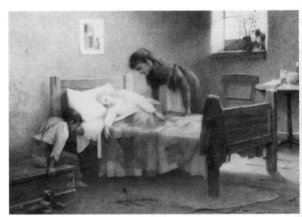

Charles Spencelayh (1865-1958)
British
A Ray of Hope
Signed and inscribed, watercolour
12¼ x 18¼in (31 x 46.2cm)
£1,700-2,000 *C*

Mothers and Children

The theme of mother and child is eternally popular and finds its ultimate sanctified expression in the endless portrayals of the Virgin and Child (see Religious pictures), to which many of the following works pay homage. This section also includes pictures devoted to fathers and their offspring, which generally speaking are more formal portrayals.

English School (17thC)
Portrait of Sarah Prideaux, wife of John Fortescue
Inscribed, oil
32¾ x 30in (83.2 x 76.2cm)
£3,500-4,000 *C*

François Boucher (1703-70)
French
A Young Mother and Two Children by the Fire
Pen and brown ink, over a black chalk counterproof
9 x 7⅛in (22.4 x 18.2cm)
£4,000-4,500 *C*

Ralph Earl (1751-1801)
American
Mrs Henry Channing and her Son, Henry William Channing
Signature rubbed, painted c1795, oil on canvas
42 x 32in (107 x 81.3cm)
£24,000-28,000 *S(NY)*

As a leading American painter of portraiture and landscape in the last quarter of the 18thC, Ralph Earl bridges the gap between being classified as a folk art or an academic painter. His work uniquely combines the directness of a provincial painting and the technical sophistication of academic painting.

Attributed to Robert Hunter
(active 1752-1803)
British
Portrait of a Gentleman with his Son
Oil on canvas
49 x 39in (124.5 x 99cm)
£1,200-1,500 *S*

19th Century

A. D. Bastin (active 1871-1900)
British
How's That?
Signed, inscribed with title in pencil on reverse
11 x 15¼in (28 x 38.5cm)
£700-800 *S(S)*

Nicholas Joseph Crowley (1813-57)
Irish
Portrait of a Mother and Child
Oil on canvas
80½ x 52¼in (204.5 x 132.7cm)
£6,500-7,500 *S(NY)*

Emma Chadwick (1855-1932)
Swedish
Maternity
Signed, oil on canvas
20¾ x 25¼in (53 x 64cm)
£4,500-5,500 *S*

Josef Büche (1848-1917)
Austrian
A Young Family
Signed, oil on canvas
23 x 18in (59 x 46cm)
£4,200-5,000 *S*

S. Campolmi (19thC)
Italian
The Happy Family
Signed and dated 1878, oil on canvas
21 x 24¾in (53 x 62.5cm)
£8,800-9,800 *CNY*

Paul Michel Dupuy (1869-1949)
French
A Mother and her Children in a Boat
Signed, oil on canvas
18 x 25in (45 x 64cm)
£13,000-14,000 *S*

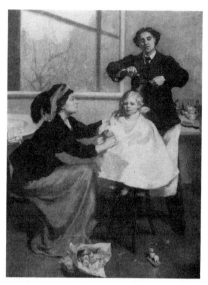

Mrs Betty Maud Christian Fagan (d1932)
British
The First Haircut
Signed, oil on canvas
38 x 29in (96.5 x 73.7cm)
£11,000-12,000 *C*

Vincenzo Irolli (1860-1949)
Italian
Consolazione
Signed, oil on canvas
21¼ x 18¼in (54 x 46.4cm)
£9,500-10,500 *C*

Julius Hans Gruder (1824-90)
German
A Woman with two Babies in a Classical
Landscape
Signed and dated 1854, oil on canvas
26in (65cm) diam
£4,400-5,400 *S*

Théodore Gérard (1829-95)
French
First Steps
Signed and dated 1876 and
Bruxelles 1880,
oil on panel
14½ x 11⅓in (37 x 29cm)
£2,400-2,800 *S*

Thomas James Lloyd (1849-1910)
British
The Lord of the Manor
Signed and inscribed verso, oil on panel
11½ x 21in (29 x 53cm)
£2,600-2,800 *CGa*

John Lucas (1807-74)
British
His Royal Highness Prince Albert, The
Princess Royal, and Eos
Inscribed, oil on canvas
17 x 14in (43 x 36cm)
£11,000-12,000 *S*

*Lucas's fame as a portrait painter brought
him many celebrated commissions and
several Royal sitters. In 1842, 2 years after
her marriage, Queen Victoria commissioned a
portrait of Prince Albert and in this work,
painted in 1843, the Prince is shown with
their eldest daughter, Victoria, and Eos, his
favourite dog, which he had brought with him
from Germany. Eos was not unused to
having his portrait painted. He was painted
several times by Landseer and a bronze
statuette of the dog was made for Victoria's
tomb.*

Giuseppe Magni (b1869)
Italian
Maternal Affection
Signed, oil on canvas laid down on board
23½ x 30½in (60 x 77.5cm)
£2,200-2,800 *P*

Giuseppe Mazzolani (1842-1916)
Italian
A Mother and Child at a Window
Signed, oil on canvas
24 x 19in (61 x 48cm)
£2,500-3,000 *S*

Frederick Morgan (1856-1927)
British
Grandpa's Favourite
Signed, oil on canvas
34 x 26in (86 x 66cm)
£20,000-22,000 *HFA*

Robert Morley (1857-1941)
British
Thoughts of Distant Lands
Signed and dated 1900, oil on canvas
34¼ x 44in (87 x 112cm)
£5,800-6,800 *S*

Bernard Pothast (1882-1966)
British
Motherhood
Signed, oil on canvas
25½ x 30½in (65 x 77.5cm)
£24,500-26,500 *BuP*

Circle of John Partridge (1790-1872)
British
Portrait of Emily Parsons and Her Son
24½ x 29½in (62.5 x 75cm)
£750-850 *S(S)*

Joseph Stallaert (1825-1903)
Belgian
Maternity
Signed, oil on canvas
49 x 37¾in (124.5 x 96cm)
£15,000-16,000 *S(NY)*

Publio de Tammasi (b1849)
Italian
Bath Time
Signed and inscribed,
watercolour
33 x 25½in (84 x 65cm)
£4,500-5,500 *S*

Johannes Weiland (1856-1909)
Dutch
The New Doll
Signed and dated 1901, oil on canvas
53 x 41¾in (134.6 x 106cm)
£7,000-8,000 *CNY*

Eugenio Zampighi (1859-1944)
Italian
Dinner Time
A pair, Signed, oil on canvas,
11½ x 16in (29 x 40.5cm)
£9,000-10,000 *P*

20th Century

Alfred Broge (b1870)
Danish
The Artist's Wife and Daughter
Signed and dated 1917, oil on canvas
30¾ x 24½in (78 x 62cm)
£2,800-3,500 *S*

Jane Camp (20thC) British
A Break on the Common
Signed, gouache
13½ x 14in (35 x 36cm)
£200-250 *Wyk*

Jean Charlot (b1898)
French
Madre con Hijo
Signed and dated 37, oil on canvas
24 x 20in (61 x 50.8cm)
£11,500-12,500 *S(NY)*

Amy Millicent Sowerby (1878-1967)
British
'The Warrior: I made myself a knight of old,
my aunt a lady fair - but just as I was going
to fight I tumbled off the chair. She did my
leg with bandages, which quite spoilt all my
joy - as if a knight of old could be an ordinary
boy!
Signed, watercolour with pen and ink
6 x 4½in (15 x 11.5cm)
£800-850 *CBL*

Charles Sims, R.A., R.W.S. (1873-1928)
British
Happy Motherhood
Signed, mixed medium on board
15½ x 21in (39.5 x 53.5cm)
£1,600-1,800 *S*

Family Portraits

Philip Reinagle, R.A. (1749-1833)
British
John Middleton with his family in his
drawing room
Oil on canvas
34½ x 43½in (87.5 x 110.5cm)
£7,000-8,000 *S*

*John Middleton was an artist's colourman,
who lived at 80 St Martin's Lane, London.
He is credited with inventing the solid tablets
of watercolour paint suitable for inclusion in
a travelling paint box.*

Follower of Gerrit van Honthorst
(1590-1656)
Dutch
Portrait of Frederick, Elector Palatine of the
Rhine with his wife, Elizabeth, Queen of
Bohemia, and their children
Oil on canvas
71¼ x 75½in (181 x 192cm)
£6,400-7,400 *S*

*Elizabeth was the daughter of James VI of
Scotland and James I of England. Her
husband Frederick accepted the crown of
Bohemia in 1619 only to lose it to the Catholic
Emperor Frederick II in November the
following year. The family were forced to flee
the country and spent the rest of their life in
exile. Elizabeth and Frederick had 13
children, 2 of whom died very young. Their
daughter, Sophia (1630-1714), became the
mother of King George I.*

John Watkins Chapman (19thC)
British
The Drawing Room
Signed and dated 1887, oil on canvas
20 x 24in (51 x 61cm)
£9,000-9,500 *EG*

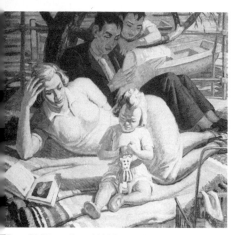

Harold Dearden (1888-1962)
British
Summer Idyll
Signed, oil on canvas
33 x 36¼in (84 x 93cm)
£750-850 *C*

David Hosie (20thC)
British
Sisters
Oil on canvas, painted 1992
72 x 60in (182.5 x 152cm)
£5,500-6,500 *JGG*

Figures and Groups
16th & 17th Century

Follower of Caravaggio (1562-1609)
Italian
Three Figures at a Table
Oil on canvas
37¼ x 46½in (95 x 118cm)
£120,000-140,000 *S*

*The gesture of the figure on the right suggests
that some dishonest transaction is taking
place. Genre pictures of this kind, often
involving card tricksters and pick-pockets,
were extremely popular in the circle of artists
associated with Caravaggio and Manfredi in
Rome. The present picture might well be by a
north Italian artist, and a Spanish origin has
also been suggested.*

Attributed to Hendrick Avercamp (1585-1634)
Dutch
Winter Landscape with Figures Skating
Oil on panel
9 x 15in (23 x 38cm)
£37,000-45,000 *S*

Circle of Joos van Craesbeeck
(1606-54)
Flemish
The Sense of Touch: a Doctor's
Surgery
Inscribed, oil on panel
19 x 25in (48.5 x 63.7cm)
£2,600-3,000 *C*

Pieter de Hooch (1629-84)
Dutch
The Courtyard of a House in Delft
Signed with initials and dated 1658, oil, with
gold on the keystone, on canvas laid down on panel
26½ x 22⅜in (67.8 x 57.5cm)
£4,500,000-5,000,000 *C*

**Hieronymus Janssens, called Der
Danser** (1624-93)
Flemish
Elegant Figures with a Lady and a
Gentleman dancing on a Terrace
Oil on canvas
45¾ x 33½in (116 x 85cm)
£16,500-17,500 *S*

Louis de Caullery (active c1600)
French/Flemish
Elegant Figures Promenading in the Gardens
of a Villa
Oil on panel
20 x 33¾in (51 x 86cm)
£70,000-80,000 *S*

Daniel van Heil (c1604-62)
Flemish
The Burning of Antwerp City Hall, 4
November 1576
Oil on panel
29 x 41½in (73.6 x 105cm)
£40,000-50,000 *C*

*The event depicted in the present picture was
of symbolic significance in the struggle to end
Spanish domination in the Netherlands. On
4 November 1576 the Spanish, deciding to
make an example of the rebellious city of
Antwerp, entered the city and set fire to the
newly built city hall. Two days of murder,
looting and inquisition followed, ending the
so-called 'Spanish Fury'.*

After Giulio Romano (1499-1546)
Italian
The Prison
Engraving, c1550
10¾ x 16¼in (27.4 x 41.8cm)
£5,300-6,300 *C*

Jan Havicksz. Steen
(1626-79)
Dutch
A Doctor taking a Lady's
Pulse in a Bedroom
Signed, oil on canvas
15¾ x 14in (39.7 x 35.8cm)
£27,000-32,000 *C*

David Vinckboons (1576-1632)
Flemish
The King of Spain receiving a
Distinguished Company
Pen and dark brown ink and grey wash
6½ x 9¾in (16 x 24.7cm)
£2,300-2,800 *S*

18th Century

Joseph van Aken (1709-49)
Flemish
An Elegant Lady Buying Vegetables at a
Stall
Oil on canvas
30 x 24½in (76 x 62.3cm)
£6,000-7,000 *P*

Circle of Nicolaes Verkolje (1673-1746)
Dutch
Interior with a Lady Refusing the Advances
of a Young Man, her Servant with a Parrot in
a Cage beside them
Oil on canvas
30¼ x 25in (76.5 x 63.3cm)
£6,000-7,000 *S*

Jean-Baptiste Greuze (1726-1805)
French
The Departure for the Wet-Nurse
Drawn with the point of the brush in black
and grey ink and wash over black chalk
15 x 20in (38.4 x 50.7cm)
£100,000-120,000 *S(NY)*

*This drawing is characteristic, both in
technique and in composition, of Greuze's
genre and moralising subjects. The subject of
wet-nurses and the raising of children was
much discussed in 18thC France. Diderot
devoted an article to it in his Encyclopédie,
and Greuze himself wrote the outline of a
story he intended to illustrate with a series of
paintings which described the lives of 2
youths brought up and educated in radically
different ways. This drawing shows the bad
child, Thibault, being given into the care of a
wet-nurse.*

Johann Georg Platzer (1704-61)
Austrian
An Elegant Company in a Wood, with a
Sleeping Hunter being robbed of his Purse
Oil on panel
13½ x 23¾in (34 x 60cm)
£35,000-40,000 *C*

Attributed to Lodovicus Rysbraeck
Flemish School (18thC)
A Banquet on a Terrace
Oil on copper
10 x 12in (25 x 31cm)
£2,100-2,600 *P*

Henry James Richter (1772-1857)
British
The Tight Shoe
Watercolour over traces of pencil
11¾ x 18in (30 x 46cm)
£3,300-3,800 *S*

Attributed to Pierre Alexandre Wille
(1748-1821)
French
Le Café du Caveau au Palais-Royal, Paris
Dated 1800, black chalk, pen and black ink,
grey wash, watercolour
13¾ x 19in (35 x 48.7cm)
£2,300-2,600 *CNY*

19th Century

Kazim Bienkowski (19th/20thC)
Polish
A Jewish Quarter in Poland
Signed and dated 1907, oil on canvas
14½ x 19in (37 x 48cm)
£3,500-4,000 *S*

Sam Bough, R.S.A., R.S.W. (1822-78)
British
The Philospher of San Souci
Oil on canvas
14¼ x 20½in (36 x 52cm)
£950-1,200 *S*

*The Philosopher of San Souci was Emperor
Frederick the Great. The picture celebrates
an incident in which judges who had ruled
against Frederick's wishes in a certain law
case were summoned before the Emperor who,
with scant regard for the impartiality of the
law, caned them, kicked them on the shins
and imprisoned them in the fortress of
Spandau. The painting was a result of a
wager between Bough and his friend and
fellow artist, Horatio Macculloch. Bough,
normally considered a landscape painter,
claimed that he would be able to paint a
historical picture and have it exhibited at the
Royal Scottish Academy. The stake was to be
a bottle of champagne to be presented to the
loser. When Bough demanded his prize
Macculloch pleaded no knowledge of the
original wager resulting in a rift between the
two friends.*

John Edmund Buckley (1820-84)
British
The Vanquished
Signed and dated 1862, watercolour and
bodycolour
13½ x 23¼in (34.3 x 59cm)
£950-1,200 *C*

Harold Arthur Burke, R.A., R.B.A.
(1852-1942)
British
Fish Market, Normandy
Signed, inscribed and dated 1891,
watercolour
5½ x 9in (14 x 23cm)
£600-640 *LH*

Edgar Bundy (1862-1922)
British
Antonio Stradivari
Signed and dated 1893, oil on panel
14 x 20⅓in (35.5 x 52cm)
£7,600-8,600 *Bon*

*Bundy's picture of the great violin maker
(offered at Bonhams in March 1993) attracted
huge interest on both sides of the Atlantic
from art dealers and violin dealers. It was
eventually sold to the Continental trade for
well over its £1,800-2,200 estimate, providing
a good example of a picture where subject
matter is by far the most important
consideration.*

A. Buzzi (19thC)
Italian
A Secret Admirer
Signed, pencil and watercolour
22½ x 16in (57 x 41cm)
£750-850 *CSK*

Luis Alvarez Catalá (1836-1901)
Spanish
La Boda
Signed, inscribed and dated 1889, oil on
paper laid down on canvas
9¾ x 18¼in (24.8 x 46.4cm)
£5,600-6,600 *C*

Consalve Carelli (1818-1900)
Italian
Figures in a Carriage
Signed and inscribed Napoli, watercolour
14¾ x 10½in (37.5 x 26.7cm)
£3,300-4,000 *DN*

*Estimated at £300-500, this painting sold for
ten times the lower figure at Dreweatt Neate's
sale in March 1993 to an Italian bidder -
emphasising the appeal of Italian pictures
(the drawing, by an Italian artist, shows a
Neapolitan street with a glimpse of Vesuvius
in the background) and the strength of the
Italian trade.*

Georges Jules Victor Clairin (1843-1919)
French
The Royal Entourage
Signed, oil on canvas
31½ x 51½in (80 x 130.8cm)
£22,000-27,000 *CNY*

After Léon Mathieu Cochereau (19thC)
French
In David's Studio
Oil on canvas
35 x 40in (89 x 102cm)
£3,000-4,000 *S*

This is a copy of Cochereau's most important work which is now in the Louvre. It depicts a class in the artist's studio in the Collège des Quatre Nations in Paris and includes portraits of David's students. Cochereau (1793-1817) painted the original when still only 21.

Giacomo di Chirico (1845-84)
Italian
The Christening
Signed, oil on canvas
38½ x 24¾in (98 x 63cm)
£23,000-28,000 *CNY*

Hermenegildo Daunas (1843-1903)
Spanish
Courting Couples
Signed and dated 77, oil on panel
14¾ x 18in (37.5 x 46cm)
£2,300-2,800 *C*

William Permeanus Cornish (active 1875-1904)
British
Saturday Night
Signed and dated 1898, watercolour
29¾ x 45⅛in (75.5 x 115.5cm)
£6,300-7,000 *S*

Théophile-Emmanuel Duverger (1821-86)
French
The Strolling Players
Signed, oil on panel
16½ x 24⅛in (42 x 61.6cm)
£6,700-8,000 *C*

Adolf Alexandre Dillens (1821-77)
Belgian
A Wedding Reception in Zeeland, Holland
Signed, oil on canvas
44½ x 66in (113 x 168cm)
£17,000-18,000 *S*

Attributed to Sir Charles Lock Eastlake
(1793-1865)
British
Courtship
Bears signature
28 x 41¾in (71 x 106cm)
£1,500-2,000 *S(S)*

Robert Farrier (1796-1879)
British
The Unexpected Return
Signed, oil on panel
32½ x 48in (83 x 122cm)
£4,000-5,000 *S*

Marie François Firmin-Girard
(1838-1921)
French
Verriers au Four
Signed, oil on canvas
29½ x 40½in (75 x 103cm)
£7,500-8,500 *CNY*

Benjamin Eugène Fichel (1826-95)
French
The Entertainer
Signed and dated 1884, oil on panel
15 x 21¾in (38 x 55cm)
£3,500-4,500 *P*

William Henry Fisk (1827-84)
British
Troublesome Days
Signed and inscribed, oil on canvas
35 x 51¼in (89 x 130cm)
£3,500-4,000 *C*

*On an old label on the reverse of this picture
is written: 'One hundred years ago / during
the great fire of London the / mob were
possessed with the idea that / the Roman
Catholics had set fire to / the city many of
them were murdered / in the streets some were
more fortunate / were rescued by the puritans
at / the hazard of their fortunes and
their / lives / Painted by W. H. Fisk / 11 North
Villas / Camden Square / England.'*

William Powell Frith R.A. (1819-1909)
British
Coming of Age in the Olden Time
Signed and dated 1889, oil on canvas
23 x 36¾in (58 x 93.5cm)
£8,000-9,000 *S*

*Historical genre was a popular 19thC subject,
and Frith was one of its great exponents.
Born in the same year as Queen Victoria and
dying in his 100th year, Frith was forced
against his will by his ambitious parents to
train as an artist and became one of the most
successful painters of the age, specialising in
historical genre, literary subjects and
panoramic scenes of Victorian life such as
'Derby Day' (Tate Gallery, London). A
brilliant and opportunistic businessman,
Frith recalled in his memoirs that it was a
toss-up as to whether he became an artist or a
businessman. Whistler, who had little respect
for this artist's bourgeois work, concluded
tartly that he must indeed have tossed up.*

Xaviero Della Gatta (b1777)
Italian
L'Acquaiolo
Signed and dated 1819, pencil and
watercolour
8 x 10in (20.3 x 25.6cm)
£3,000-3,600 *Bon*

Thomas Francis Hodgkins
(active 1835-1903)
British
The Annual Temperance Brotherhood
Festival, Hartwell Park, Aylesbury,
Buckinghamshire, July 19th 1859
Bears signature, oil on canvas
15¼ x 26¼in (38.5 x 66.5cm)
£1,200-1,700 *S*

Dr John Lee, who lived at Hartwell, stood for
Parliament five or six times for Aylesbury. A
firm believer in individual liberty and civil
rights, he was ridiculed for his support of the
right to vote for women. He was involved
with several national movements for the
improvement of society, particularly the
temperance movement, and held an annual
festival to Peace and Temperance at Hartwell
from 1841 for over 20 years.

Anton Kozakiewicz (b1841)
Polish
The Artist at Work
Signed and inscribed, oil on panel
14½ x 22½in (37 x 57cm)
£4,000-5,000 *S*

Ralph Hedley (1851-1913)
British
Christmas Market
Signed and dated 1909, oil on canvas
50¼ x 40¼in (127.6 x 101.6cm)
£6,400-7,400 *C*

John Adam Plimmer Houston (1812-84)
British
Columbus - The First Sight of Land
Signed and dated 1844, oil on canvas
30 x 25in (76 x 63.5cm)
£3,700-4,200 *S*

'Suddenly, about ten o'clock, he thought he
beheld a light glimmering at a distance.
Fearing that his eager hopes might deceive
him, he called to Piedro Gutierrez, gentleman
of the King's bedchamber, and enquired
whether he saw a light in that direction. The
latter replied in the affirmative.' Washington
Irving - Life and Voyages of Christopher
Columbus.

Thomas Musgrave Joy (1812-66)
British
The Barber of Seville
Signed and dated 1861, oil on canvas
28¼ x 36½in (71.8 x 92.7cm)
£3,000-4,000 *S(NY)*

Henry John Yeend King (1855-1924)
British
Flirtation
Signed, oil on canvas
31 x 43in (79 x 109cm)
£14,500-15,000 *HFA*

*'This London landscape and rustic genre
painter spent three years in a glassworks
before devoting his life to his art whence he
studied under William Bromley and also with
Bonnat and Cormon in Paris', writes Haynes
Fine Art. 'Yeend King was typical of many
late Victorian painters of rustic genre, often
painting garden scenes with pretty girls.
However, his robust 'plein air' technique and
bold palette were obviously the influence of
his Paris training.'*

Louis C. Moeller (1855-1930)
American
The Art Critics
Signed, oil on canvas
12 x 10in (30.5 x 25.4cm)
£15,000-16,000 *S(NY)*

Jules Massé (1825-97)
French
Une Matinée chez Barras
Signed and dated 1864, oil on canvas
41 x 56¾in (104 x 144cm)
£30,000-35,000 *S(NY)*

*Count Barras, the host, is situated in the
centre, between Mme. Grant and Mme.
Tallien; at the extreme right, Napoléon and
Joséphine Bonaparte; behind them Generals
Kleber, Murat and Lannes; Mmes de Staël
and Récamier sit conversing to Napoléon's
right; behind them, Messrs. Tallien, Jourdan
and Sieyes.*

Arturo Orselli (19thC)
Italian
La Balancelle
Signed, watercolour
26 x 38¼in (66 x 97cm)
£1,500-2,000 *S*

Adrien Moreau (1843-1906)
French
Le Bac
Signed and dated 1884, oil on canvas
51 x 79in (129 x 201cm)
£34,000-38,000 *S(NY)*

*The artist wrote the following description of
Le Bac in a letter to Knoedler & Co.: 'I
thought of painting that subject in order to
present a cross section of all the social classes
of the 17thC - noblemen, soldiers, peasants,
and beggars; at that time there existed few
bridges, so to cross from one bank to another
it was necessary to take the ferry. My study
for the landscape was made on the bank of the
Seine, close to the Forest of Fontainebleau.'*

Karel Frans Philippeau (1825-97)
Dutch
The Tea Party
Signed, oil on board
13½ x 18in (34 x 46cm)
£3,000-3,800 *B*

_aslett John Potts (1837-98)
_ritish
_ Woodland Courtship
-igned, oil on canvas
_5 x 28in (91.5 x 71cm)
_9,000-9,500 *HFA*

Victor Odescalchi (1833-80)
Austrian
Moriamur Pro Rege Nostro Maria Theresia
Signed, watercolour heightened with gum
arabic over traces of pencil
10½ x 12in (27 x 30cm)
£950-1,200 *S*

*This watercolour depicts the Empress Maria
Theresia showing her son, the future Emperor
Josef II, to the Hungarians in about 1840.*

Edwin Thomas Roberts (1840-1917)
British
The Fleet in the Bay, Naval Manoeuvres
Signed and inscribed, oil on canvas
28 x 36in (71 x 91.5cm)
£6,500-7,500 *S*

Frédéric Regamey (1849-1925)
French
Avant le Duel, Jeune Homme chez le Maître
d'Armes
Signed, oil on panel
15¾ x 13in (40 x 33cm)
£7,500-8,500 *S(NY)*

Charles Joseph Staniland (1838-1916)
British
At the Back of the Church
Signed and dated 76, pencil and watercolour
with touches of white heightening
20 x 36in (51 x 91.5cm)
£8,000-9,000 *C*

*Although Staniland painted historical
subjects, he is best known as a social realist
who focused on 3 main areas: the plight of the
London poor, shipwrecks and the lifeboat
service, and the hardships of mining
communities. Many of these subjects were
conceived as illustrations, notably for the
Graphic, which pioneered the field. By the
mid-1870s some of its leading artists - Luke
Fildes, Hubert von Herkomer, Charles Green
and William Small - had ceased to be regular
contributors, and Staniland, who had proved
himself working for the Illustrated London
News, particularly be reporting the Franco-
Prussian War of 1870, was one of those
brought in to fill the gap.*

John Sanderson Wells (active 1890-1940) British
A Street Scene with Figures, Horses and
Carriages
Signed, watercolour over traces of pencil,
heightened with touches of white
6¾ x 9¾in (17 x 25cm)
£2,000-2,500 *S(S)*

20th Century

Valerie Batchelor (20thC) British
Morning Coffee at Snells
Signed, watercolour
5 x 8in (13 x 20cm)
£150-175 *Wyk*

Edward Burra (1905-76)
British
Wednesday Night
Signed in pencil, etching, 1972, numbered
from edition of 75
12 x 10in (30.5 x 25cm)
£355-375 *WO*

Helen Bradley (1900-79)
British
'Come Children, the Shadows are Gathering'
Signed with a fly lower left, oil on board
20 x 24in (51 x 61cm)
£12,000-13,000 *C*

*At the age of 65, Helen Bradley began to paint
scenes of her childhood to show her
grandchildren what life had been like then.*

Terence Cuneo (b1907)
British
East African Market
Signed, oil
20 x 30in (51 x 76cm)
£6,250-6,750 *Dr*

John Steuart Curry (1897-1946)
American
Study for the Mississippi Flood
Signed and dated 1937, watercolour, gouache
and pencil on paper
13¾ x 10½in (35 x 26.7cm)
£10,500-11,500 *S(NY)*

*This work is one of several studies Curry
executed as illustrations of the flood of the
Ohio River which were requested by The
Saturday Evening Post, but never published.*

Laurence Stephen Lowry, R.A.
(1887-1976)
British
A Group of People
Signed and dated 1965, oil on canvas-board
19 x 14in (48 x 36cm)
£17,500-20,000 *C*

Bernard Dunstan (b1920)
British
The Turner Exhibition at the Royal Academy,
1974
Signed with monogram, oil on panel, painted
August 1989
11¾ x 15¼in (30 x 39cm)
£2,000-5,000 *BSG*

Martin Grover (b1962)
British
Harbour
Signed and dated 1991,
acrylic on canvas
37 x 73in (95 x 186cm)
£1,600-1,800 *Mer*

David Schneuer (1905-88)
German
Café Select
Signed, mixed media
20 x 18in (51 x 46cm)
£4,500-4,800 *TCG*

'David Schneuer's works are a unique and timeless testimony of Europe between the World Wars,' notes the Catto Gallery. The stylised, theatrical figures which inhabit the bars and cafés in his paintings are reminiscent of Munich and Paris of the 1920s. His works can be found in permanent collections throughout the world, and is one of the most collected artists that the Catto Gallery represents.

A. R. Penck (b1939)
German
Exekution
Signed with initials and dated 23 Juni, ink and wash on buff paper, painted c1957-58
8½ x 13in (21.7 x 33.2cm)
£1,500-2,000 *S*

Locate the Source

The source of each illustration in Miller's can be found by checking the code letters below each caption with the list of contributors.

Anselmo Miguel Nieto (1881-1964)
Au Café
Signed and dated 1904, oil on canvas
20 x 31½in (50.5 x 81cm)
£12,000-14,000 *C*

There is a drawing of the same subject with annotations to the identity of the sitters as, from right to left, Pablo Picasso, Stravinski, La Goulue and Guillaume Apollinaire in Le Moulin de la Galette.

Gill Watkiss (b1938)
British
Hayle Recreation Field
Signed and dated '86, oil on board
19 x 22in (48 x 59cm)
£900-950 *NZ*

Walter Richard Sickert (1860-1942)
British
Noctes Ambrosianae
Etching with aquatint, 1906
10¾ x 12in (27 x 30.8cm)
£1,900-2,200 *S*

Peasants and Country Life

The theme of peasants and agricultural labour has a long history in Western art. Medieval Books of Hours provided a religious calendar and illustrated the monthly cycle of toil in the fields. The Dutch and Flemish painters of the 17thC celebrated the earthy harshness and humour of peasant life and labour. 18thC painters in France and Italy transformed their country existence into a romantic rural idyll, while innumerable peasant genre painters in Victorian England created sentimental, sanitised and picturesque visions of country life. In the second half of the 19thC, a greater concern with realism spread across Europe - both stylistically, in terms of painting 'en plein air' and directly from the subject - and ideologically, showing increased social awareness in the portrayal of the agricultural labourer.

In our own century, country life is of far less appeal to artists, and the combine harvester and modern day farm worker lack the drawing power of the horse and plough and the rustic lads and lasses of the past. In the following section, modern day peasant pictures come from Russia and South America, from nations poor enough to have maintained their peasant population.

17th Century

Attributed to Pieter Quast (1606-47)
Dutch
A Soldier and Peasants smoking and drinking at a Table
Oil on panel
12½ x 15½in (31.4 x 39cm)
£8,700-9,700 *C*

Follower of Pieter Brueghel II
(1564-1637)
Flemish
Peasants Paying Tithes
Oil on copper
11½ x 14in (29 x 35.6cm)
£48,000-60,000 *C*

Giovanni Benedetto Castiglione, il Grechetto (1616-70)
Italian
Drovers by a Pool
Inscribed, black, brown and red chalk, watercolour and bodycolour
11 x 16½in (28.5 x 42cm)
£47,000-57,000 *C*

Manner of David Teniers the Younger
(1610-90)
Flemish
Peasants Revelling outside an Inn in a Landscape
Bears signature and date, oil on canvas
21¼ x 31½in (54 x 80cm)
£3,400-4,800 *S(S)*

Jan Baptist Lambrechts (1680-1731)
Flemish
A Young Sportsman carousing with a Serving Girl outside an Inn, skittle players beyond
Signed with initials
16¼ x 19in (41.2 x 48.6cm)
£6,700-7,700 *C*

18th Century

Attributed to Antonio Diziani
(1737-after 1797)
Italian
Peasants Dancing in a Mountainous
Landscape
Oil on canvas
58½ x 82in (148 x 208cm)
£13,500-14,500 *S*

Edward Bird (1772-1819)
British
The Mendicant
Signed with initials, oil on panel
7 x 6¼in (17.5 x 16cm)
£1,000-1,250 *CGa*

Philip-James de Loutherbourg, R.A.
(1740-1812)
French
A Rocky Landscape with Lovers surprised by boys
Signed, oil on canvas
27¼ x 35in (69 x 89cm)
£9,500-10,500 *C*

Jacob Buys (1724-1801)
Dutch
A Woman Selling Chickens
Signed, dated 1798, pencil, watercolour,
black ink framing lines, watermark
Whatman
16½ x 13in (42.5 x 33cm)
£1,500-2,000 *C(Am)*

Manner of Theobald Michau (1676-1765)
Flemish
Figures embarking from a ferry by a village
Oil on panel
9½ x 14¼in (24 x 36cm)
£1,200-1,800 *S(S)*

Johann Georg Pforr (1745-98)
German
Peasants celebrating the Vendage
outside a walled town
19 x 17¼in (48.3 x 43.8cm)
£6,500-7,500 *C*

William Marshall Brown (1863-1936)
British
Bringing Home the Catch
Oil
8¼ x 9⅜in (20 x 24cm)
£3,250-3,500 *McE*

Nicholas Condy (1793-1857)
British
The Cobbler's Shop
Signed, oil on panel
12½ x 17½in (32 x 44.5cm)
£3,300-3,800 *S*

R. Agresti (19thC)
Italian
Interior Scenes
Two, both signed, oil on canvas
22 x 30½ (56 x 77cm) and 21 x 29in (54 x
74cm)
£4,000-5,000 *S*

Victor Jean Baptiste Barthelemy Binet
(1849-1924)
French
Le Toît Rouge
Signed, oil on canvas
17¾ x 14½in (45 x 36.8cm)
£4,800-5,800 *S(NY)*

James Drummond (active 1870-1900)
British
Another Wee Dram
Signed and dated 98, oil on canvas
20 x 16in (51 x 41cm)
£2,600-2,800 *PaHG*

A de Dominicis (19thC)
Italian
Portrait of a young Italian peasant
boy beside a gate
Signed
13 x 9in (34 x 24cm)
£500-600 *HSS*

Henry Charles Fox (b1860)
British
Milking Time
Signed and dated 1906, watercolour
14 x 21in (35.5 x 53.5cm)
£1,500-1,750 *CG*

Stanhope Alexander Forbes, R.A.
(1857-1947)
British
A Country Lad
Signed, oil on canvas
18 x 12in (46 x 31cm)
£9,000-9,500 *CSG*

Henry Townley Green (1836-99)
British
An evening fishing with the family
Signed, oil on canvas
9 x 15in (22.5 x 38cm)
£10,000-11,000 *BW*

William Banks Fortescue (d1924)
British
The Fishergirl
Signed and dated 1885, oil
17¼ x 13¼in (44 x 34cm)
£950-1,200 *AH*

Alfred H. Green (active 1844-80)
British
The New Pet
Oil on panel
10 x 8in (25 x 20cm)
£3,600-3,800 *HFA*

Johannes Marinus Ten Kate (1859-96)
Dutch
Fisherfolk with their Catch
Signed, oil on canvas
23¾ x 31½in (60 x 79.7cm)
£7,500-8,500 *CNY*

Henry John Yeend King (1855-1924)
British
Gathering Firewood
Signed, oil on canvas
39½ x 29½in (125.7 x 100.5cm)
£4,600-5,600 *Bon*

Georgina Lara (19thC)
British
Village Life
Signed, oil on canvas
13 x 19in (33 x 48cm)
£3,000-3,250 *Dr*

Attributed to Charles James Lewis
(1830-92)
British
A Cottage Garden
Oil on canvas
10 x 12in (25.5 x 30.5cm)
£1,600-2,200 *Bon*

William Darling MacKay (1844-1924)
British
Stonebreakers, East Lothian
Signed and dated 1876, oil on canvas
19 x 27in (48.3 x 68.5cm)
£6,000-7,000 *C(S)*

Thomas Mackay (active 1893-1912)
British
The Stepping Stones, Homeward
Signed and dated 1911, watercolour
heightened with white
7¼ x 10½in (18.5 x 26.5cm)
£4,000-4,500 *JA*

Jean François de May (1798-1850)
French
Travellers on a Country Path
Oil on panel
7 x 9½in (18 x 24cm)
£1,300-1,800 *P*

Giuseppe Mazzolini (1806-76)
Italian
Fleeing the Storm
Signed, oil on canvas
24 x 19in (61 x 48.5cm)
£3,400-4,000 *S*

James Edwin Meadows (1828-88)
British
Near Wadhurst, Sussex
Signed and dated 1869, oil on canvas
24 x 40in (61 x 101.5cm)
£12,000-12,500 *HFA*

Adolf Ernst Meissner (1837-1902)
German
The Midday Rest
Signed and dated 1877, oil on canvas
26 x 40in (66 x 102cm)
£10,500-11,500 *P*

Jean-François Millet (1814-75)
French
Peasant Leaning on a Pitchfork
Signed, black crayon on paper
9¾ x 14¾in (24.7 x 37cm)
£86,000-100,000 *C*

'There are those who say that I deny the charms of the countryside. I find much more than mere charm - I find infinite glory,' wrote Millet to his friend Alfred Sensier in 1863. 'Peasant leaning on a Pitchfork (c1850-51) is a pivotal work in Millet's career. The artist had just fled from Paris to Barbizon, where he was to live the rest of his life, and the drawing hovers on the cusp between the controlled and more prettyfied rural visions of his early pictures and the robust and monumental power of his later works in which Millet imbues his humble peasant subjects with almost heroic stature and a religious significance, celebrating the eternal unity of man and land.

Alexander M. Rossi (active 1870-1903)
British
Anxious Moments
Signed and dated 1871, oil on canvas
28 x 36¼in (71.2 x 92cm)
£6,700-7,700 *C*

Richard Henry Nibbs (1816-93)
British
Off loading fishing boats on a Dutch beach
Signed and dated 86, watercolour
11½ x 25in (29 x 63cm)
£1,000-1,150 *LH*

Lucien Simon (1861-1945)
French
Les Bretonnes
Signed, oil on canvas
37¾ x 30in (96 x 76cm)
£5,300-6,300 *S*

Carlton Alfred Smith (1853-1946)
British
New Friends
Signed and dated 1881, oil on canvas
18 x 24¼in (45.7 x 61.6cm)
£4,500-5,500 *C*

Sophia Collingwood Smith (19thC)
British
Young Girls Picking Wild Flowers
Signed with initials and dated 87, pencil and
watercolour heightened with white
9½ x 15¼in (23.5 x 39cm)
£800-1,000 *CSK*

W. Underhill (active 1848-70)
British
After the Day's Shoot
Signed, oil on canvas, in elaborate gilt frame
30 x 25in (76 x 64cm)
£1,400-1,800 *BWe*

Alfred H. Vickers (active 1853-1907)
British
At Toulouse, France
Signed and dated 1894, oil on canvas
11¾ x 23¾in (30 x 60.5cm)
£1,200-1,500 *S*

Tommaso de Vivo (1790-1884)
Italian
Harvest Time
Signed, oil on canvas
22 x 35in (56 x 90cm)
£4,000-5,000 *S*

Jan Walraven (b1827)
Dutch
A Domestic Scene
Signed, oil on panel
19½ x 15in (49.5 x 38cm)
£5,200-6,000 *S*

Ernest Walbourn (active 1897-1904)
British
At a Country Gate
Signed, oil on canvas
15½ x 23½in (39.5 x 60cm)
£3,000-3,500 *S(S)*

20th Century

Thomas Hart Benton (1889-1975)
American
Loading Cotton
Signed and dated 44, oil on canvas board
12 x 16in (30.5 x 40.6cm)
£50,000-60,000 *S(NY)*

Reg Gammon (b1894)
British
Brittany Fisherwives
Oil on panel
15½ x 19in (39.5 x 48cm)
£2,250-2,500 *BRG*

Ivan Kirichenko (b1916)
Russian
In the Field
Oil on canvas
£400-450 *Tho*

Victor Nepyanov (20thC)
Russian
A Spring
Signed in Cyrillic and dated 1992
24¾ x 33in (63 x 84cm)
£300-400 *CSK*

George Soper (1870-1942)
British
Hop Picking
Signed and dated 1920, watercolour
8½ x 11¼in (21.5 x 29cm)
£1,300-1,400 *CSG*

George Large (20thC)
British
Summer Heat
Watercolour
13½ x 27½in (34 x 70cm)
£700-750 *LA*

Richard Sorrell, R.W.S.
(20thC)
British
Chickens
Oil
10 x 14⅝in (25 x 37cm)
£500-600 *AdG*

Frank Taylor (20thC)
British
Anatolian Women Washing Fleeces
Acrylic
18 x 36in (46 x 92cm)
£1,000-1,100 *PHG*

Garnet Ruskin Wolseley (1884-1967)
British
Mending Nets at Newlyn
Oil on canvas
50 x 30in (127 x 76cm)
£8,500-9,500 *VDG*

A. Vasychenko (20thC)
Russian
The Yard
Oil on board
£300-380 *Tho*

In The Kitchen

After Gerrard Dou (1613-75)
Dutch
An elderly couple in a kitchen seen through a casement
Oil on panel
14 x 12in (36 x 30.5cm)
£1,000-1,300 *CSK*

Johann Jacob Hoch (1750-1829)
Dutch
Interior Scene with peasants, poultry and kitchen utensils
Signed, oil on canvas
19½ x 27in (49.5 x 68.5cm)
£3,500-4,000 *S(S)*

Hermann Kern (1833-1912)
Hungarian
The Musician; and The Chef
A pair, both signed, oil on panel
19 x 12½in (48.2 x 31.8cm)
£8,000-9,000 *C*

Cornelis Bouter (1888-1966)
Dutch
Preparing a Meal
Signed, oil on canvas
29½ x 39½in (75 x 100.4cm)
£3,000-4,000 *Bon*

Percy Horton (1897-1970)
British
Mrs Edwards Peeling Potatoes
Signed, inscribed and dated
1931, charcoal and coloured chalks
11¼ x 9¾in (28.5 x 25cm)
£80-100 *CSK*

Hermann Werner
(1816-1905)
German
Feeding the Young Family
Signed, oil on canvas
15½ x 19½in (39 x 49.5cm)
£4,800-5,800 *S*

Sewing and Spinning

Though on the one hand pictures of women sewing and spinning represent the ultimate in gentle feminine and domestic virtues, the image can also carry a greater symbolic significance. In Greek and Roman mythology, the Three Fates who were believed to determine man's destiny, are generally depicted as hideous crones, spinning the thread of life, measuring it and ultimately cutting it off. Their attributes are the distaff, the spinning wheel, the spindle and the shears to snip the thread. The vocabulary of spinning has also passed into the English language to describe women's roles and positions, in phrases such as 'the distaff side' and the term 'spinster'.

Willem van Odekerken (d1677)
Dutch
A Peasant Woman at a Spinning Wheel
Signed, oil on panel
26½ x 21⅛in (67 x 54.6cm) **£5,500-6,500** *C*

Pierre Dierckx (b1855)
Belgian
A Family of Weavers in Flanders
Signed and dated 98, oil on canvas
35⅝ x 40¾in (90.5 x 103.5cm)
£3,000-3,500 *S*

Bernard de Hoog (1866-1943)
Dutch
Woman Sewing in an Interior
Signed, oil on canvas
29½ x 23¾in (75 x 60cm)
£2,700-3,500 *P*

Joseph Laurens Dyckmans (1811-70)
Belgian
The Old Lacemaker
Signed and dated 1844, oil on panel
19 x 15in (48 x 38cm) **£13,000-14,000** *HFA*

Etienne Jeaurat (1699-1789)
French
The Modest Woman; and The Frivolous Woman
A pair, oil on panel
11½ x 9in (29.2 x 23.2cm)
£32,000-40,000 *S(NY)*

John Arthur Lomax (1857-1923)
British
The Spinning Wheel
Signed, oil on canvas
24 x 18in (61 x 46cm)
£1,900-2,400 *S*

Alexander Max Koester (1864-1932)
German
Zwei Mädchen am Stickrahmen
Signed and inscribed, oil on canvas
28¾ x 36¾in (73 x 93.5cm)
£38,000-45,000 *CNY*

Wenzel Tornøe (1844-1907)
Danish
A Sleeping Seamstress
Signed, oil on panel
15¾ x 13¾in (40 x 35cm)
£4,700-5,700 *S*

Edward Portielje (1861-1949)
Belgian
Sewing by a Window
Signed, oil on canvas
24½ x 19¼in (62 x 49cm)
£7,200-8,000 *S*

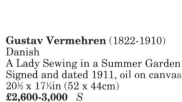

Gustav Vermehren (1822-1910)
Danish
A Lady Sewing in a Summer Garden
Signed and dated 1911, oil on canvas
20½ x 17¼in (52 x 44cm)
£2,600-3,000 *S*

Martin Bernat
(active 1469-97)
Saint Blaise Enthroned
Oil on panel
53¾ x 38¼in (136.5 x 97cm)
£90,000-120,000 *C*

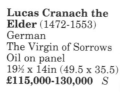

Lucas Cranach the Elder (1472-1553)
German
The Virgin of Sorrows
Oil on panel
19½ x 14in (49.5 x 35.5)
£115,000-130,000 *S*

School of the Upper Rhine (c1550)
The Legend of St. Ursula
Oil on Panel
39½ x 31½in (39.5 x 79.5cm)
£10,500-12,500 *P*

Studio of Juan de Flandes (c1540)
Spanish School
Julian the Hospitator
Oil on panel
49¼ x 35in (125 x 89cm)
£20,000-30,000 *P*

Goswyn van der Weyden (1465-1538)
Flemish
The Madonna and Child
Oil on panel
28½ x 25¼in
(72.5 x 64cm)
£70,000-85,000 *S*

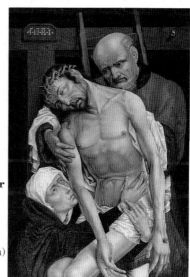

Workshop of Rogier van der Weyden
(c1400-46)
Flemish
The Deposition
Oil on panel
20½ x 14in (52 x 36cm)
£33,000-40,000 *P*

Elisabetta Sirani (1638-65)
Italian
Young Saint John the Baptist
Signed, oil on panel
27½ x 19in (70 x 48.3cm)
£30,000-40,000 *S(NY)*

Attributed to Bartolomé Roman (c1587-1647)
Spanish
The Archangel Uriel (?)
Oil on canvas
68 x 46½in (172.5 x 117.5cm)
£15,000-20,000 *S*

Philippe de Champaigne
(1602-74)
French
Saint Jerome in the Wilderness
Oil on canvas
30¾ x 24½in (78 x 62cm)
£86,000-100,000 *C*

Flemish School (17thC)
The Madonna and Child
Oil on panel
36½ x 25½in (93 x 64.5cm)
£6,000-7,000 *P*

Circle of Georges de la Tour
(1593-1652)
French
Saint Sebastian tended by Irene
Oil on canvas
41¼ x 55in (104.8 x 55cm)
£42,000-52,000 *S(NY)*

Attributed to Angelo Trevisani
(1669-1753 or later)
Italian
Hagar and Ishmael with the Angel
Oil on canvas
37¼ x 51½in (96 x 131cm)
£14,000-15,000 *S*

Louis-Jean-François Lagrenée (1725-1805)
French
Sarah presenting Hagar to Abraham
Oil on panel
12 x 14¾in (30.5 x 37.5cm)
£34,000-44,000 *S(NY)*

Nicolaes Verkolje (1673-1746)
Dutch
The Finding of Moses
Oil on Panel
13¾ x 16¾in (35 x 42.5cm)
£20,000-25,000 *S(NY)*

Gianbettino Cignaroli (1706-1770/2)
Italian
The Sacrifice of Isaac
Oil on canvas
50 x 40in (127 x 101cm)
£13,000-14,000 *C*

Attributed to Antonio Balestra (1666-1740)
Italian
King David Sleeping
Oil on canvas
46½ x 84¼in (118 x 214cm)
£28,000-35,000 *S*

Anonymous (18thC)
Cuzco School
Adoracion de los Reyes Magos
Oil on canvas
66¼ x 81¾in (168.3 x 207.6cm)
£23,000-28,000 *S(NY)*

Franz Dvorak (b1862)
Austrian
The Virgin Mary and Christ amongst Angels
Signed and dated 93, oil on canvas
26¾ x 37½in (68 x 95cm)
£7,000-8,000 *S*

Eugenio Lucas, called Lucas y Padilla
(1824-70) Spanish
The Mass of Purification
Oil on tin
12½ x 16in (31.7 x 40.5cm)
£11,500-12,500 *P*

Constantin Hansen (1804-80)
Danish
Saul throwing his spear at David
Signed, oil on canvas
56 x 78in (144 x 198cm)
£8,300-9,000 *S*

**Pierre Cecile Puvis de
Chavannes**
(1824-98)
French
Sainte Genevieve Enfant
en Prière
Signed and inscribed, oil
on vellum
53¾ x 30in
(136.5 x 76.2cm)
£280,000-350,000 *CNY*

Achille Leonaidi (19thC)
Italian
Signed, oil, c1852
104 x 41in (143.5 x 56.5cm)
£12,000-12,500 *JAP*

Richard Westall, R.A.
(1765-1836)
British
Satan Exulting
Pencil and watercolour
22¼ x 15¼in
(56.5 x 38.7cm)
£9,500-10,500 *C*

Doreen Baxter (b1910)
British
The Witch had just made a new spell!
Watercolour with bodycolour and pen
8¼ x 6in (21 x 15cm)
£400-450 *CBL*

Thomas Bromley Blacklock
(1863-1903)
British
In the Fairies' Wood
Signed and dated 1903, oil on
canvas
23½ x 28½in (60 x 72.5cm)
£8,500-9,500 *S*

Charles Sims, R.A. (1873-1928)
British
Titania's Awakening
Signed, inscribed and dated 96
Oil on canvas
27¼ x 14in (69 x 35.6cm)
£16,000-18,000 *C*

A. Duncan Carse (d1938)
British
Bother the Gnat
Signed, pen, ink and
watercolour
12 x 8in (31 x 20cm)
£3,000-3,250 *CBL*

l. **Arthur Rackham**
(1867-1939)
British
Of the Little People,
4 Goblin Thieves
Signed and dated 06,
pen, ink and
watercolour
14¾ x 11in
(37.5 x 28cm)
£26,000-27,000 *CBL*

r. **Margaret
Winifred Tarrant**
(1888-1959)
British
Fairies Midst Sweet
Peas
Signed and dated
1920
Watercolour and
bodycolour with
pencil
13 x 7½in
(33 x 19cm)
£5,000-5,500 *CBL*

Herman Henstenburgh (1667-1726)
Dutch
A Fruit Still Life
Signed, black lead, watercolour and bodycolour on vellum
13½ x 28in (24.7 x 28cm)
£8,000-9,000 C(Am)

Follower of Bartolomeo Bettera (17thC)
Italian
Still Life of Musical Instruments
Oil on canvas
34 x 48¼in (86.4 x 122.6cm)
£11,000-12,000 S(NY)

Antonio Gianlisi, the Younger (1677-1727)
Italian
Trompe L'Oeil Still Life with an Urn of Flowers
Signed, oil on canvas
39½ x 33½in (100 x 85cm)
£58,000-75,000 S(NY)

Juan de Arellano (1614-1676)
Spanish
Still Life of Flowers in a Glass Vase
Signed, oil on canvas
20¾ x 15¾in (52.4 x 40.3cm)
£120,000-150,000 S(NY)

Ambrosius Bosschaert II
(1609-45)
Flemish
Fruit in a Basket
Signed and dated 1631
Oil on panel
16½ x 21½in (41.7 x 54.3cm)
£320,000-350,000 C

Harmen van Steenwyck (1612-55)
Dutch
A Still Life of Fruit
Signed, oil on panel
12¾ x 16in (32.7 x 41cm)
£5,600-6,600 *P*

Abraham Mignon (1640-79)
German
Still Life of a Cockerel, a
Partridge, a Kingfisher and Song
Birds
Signed, oil on canvas
34¾ x 26¾in (88 x 68cm)
£108,000-125,000 *S(NY)*

Roman School (early 17thC)
Still Life with a Basket of
Fruit and two Children
Oil on canvas
32¼ x 49½in (82 x 126cm)
£240,000-280,000 *S*

Frans Snyders and Studio
(1579-1657)
Flemish
A Still Life of Fruit and Nuts
with a Monkey and a Squirrel
Oil on canvas
61 x 76¼in (155 x 193.5cm)
£90,000-110,000 *S*

Francesco Lavagna (active mid-18thC)
Italian
Still Life with Fruit and Flowers
Oil on canvas
28¾ x 39in (73 x 99cm)
£15,500-17,500 *S*

William Jones of Bath (active 1764-77)
British
Still Life of Fruit on a Ledge
Oil on canvas
24½ x 29¼in (62 x 74.5cm)
£3,500-4,000 *S*

Luis Meléndez (1716-80)
Italian
A Still Life of Sea Bream, Oranges, Garlic, a Cloth
and Kitchen Utensils on a Wooden Table
Signed, oil on canvas
16 x 24¾in (41 x 63cm)
£860,000-1,000,000 *Bon*

Jean-Louis Prévost the Younger
(1760-1810)
French
Still Life of Flowers in a Basket and a
Bird's Nest with Eggs on a Stone
Ledge
Signed and dated 1795, oil on canvas
16 x 12½in (40.6 x 39cm)
£40,000-50,000 *S(NY)*

Rachel Ruysch (1664/5-1750)
Dutch
A Carnation, Morning Glory and other
Flowers on a Stone Ledge with a Red Admiral
Signed, oil on panel
13½ x 10¾in (34.4 x 27.2cm)
£155,000-175,000 *C*

Joseph Lauer (1818-81)
Austrian
A Still Life with Fruit, Flowers and Dead
Game on a Ledge
Signed, oil on canvas
14¼ x 18in (36 x 45.5cm)
£4,700-5,700 *S*

Alceste Campriani (1848-1933)
Italian
Still Life with Grapes and Figs on a Draped Table
Signed, oil on canvas
11½ x 16½in (29 x 42cm)
£8,300-9,000 *CNY*

Anonymous (late 18th/early 19thC)
Mexican School
Cuatro Bodegones
Oil on canvas
25 x 20in (63.5 x 50.8cm)
£38,000-45,000 *S(NY)*

Edward Ladell (1812-86)
British
Still Life of Fruit and a Flask
Signed, oil on canvas
19½ x 16½in (49.5 x 42cm)
£12,200-13,200 *S(S)*

James Hardy, Jnr (1832-89)
British
The Day's Bag
Signed and dated 1862, watercolour and
bodycolour
19 x 25½in (48.3 x 64.3cm)
£4,400-5,000 *C*

Emile Preyer (1849-1930)
German
A Still Life of Fruit and a Knife on a Marble Ledge
Signed and dated 1879, oil on canvas
10½ x 14in (26.5 x 36cm)
£27,000-35,000 *S*

Thomas Worsey (1829-75)
British
Still Life
Signed and dated 1866, oil on canvas
10 x 8in (25 x 20cm)
£2,500-2,700 *HFA*

Eloise Harriet (E.H.) Stannard (c1828-1915)
British
Still Life
Oil on canvas, c1880
10 x 14in (25 x 36cm)
£4,000-5,000 *AdG*

John Nicolson (Exh 1885-1909)
British
A Corner of the Study
Watercolour with white heightening
19½ x 27½in (50 x 70cm)
£1,650-1,850 *PCA*

Joost Zeeman (c1776-1845)
Dutch
Still Life with Flowers in a Vase
Signed and dated 182(?), gouache
on paper mounted on board
26 x 20in (66 x 51cm)
£5,000-6,000 *S(NY)*

Gottfried Schultz (b1842)
German
Grapes, Peaches, Plums, Nuts and a Glass of Champagne on a marble
ledge
Signed and dated 1876, oil on canvas
13¾ x 17¾in (35 x 45cm)
£9,300-10,000 *C*

Barry Atherton (20thC)
British
Quing Ceramics, Burrell Collection
Pastel and watercolour
36 x 48in (92 x 122cm)
£6,000-6,500 *RB*

David Donaldson (20thC)
British
Still Life at St. Roman de Malegarde
Oil on canvas
28 x 26in (71 x 66cm)
17,000-18,000 *RB*

John G Boyd (20thC)
British
Many Happy Returns
Oil on canvas
36 x 40in (91.5 x 101.5cm)
3,000-3,500 *VCG*

Jane Corsellis (20thC)
British
Anniversary Dinner
Oil on canvas
40 x 30in (101.5 x 76cm)
£5,000-5,500 *BSG*

Roy Freer (20thC)
British
Apples/Cauliflower
Watercolour
25 x 30in (64 x 76.5cm)
£700-750 *KHG*

Mark Gertler (1892-1939)
British
Fish, Still Life
Signed, oil on board
22 x 31in (56 x 79cm)
£21,000-22,500 *CLB*

Andrew Hemingway (20thC)
British
Still Life with Tim's Shoes
Pastel on Rembrandt pastel board
6¾ x 6½in (17 x 16.5cm)
£1,000-3,000 *BSG*

Frederick Gore (b1913)
British
The Lily Enchantment
Signed, oil on canvas
40 x 30in (101.5 x 76cm)
£8,000-8,500 *Dr*

Edward Griffiths (20thC)
British
Chinese Lanterns
Egg tempera
14 x 12in (35.5 x 30.5cm)
£500-525 *FI*

Orlando Greenwood
(1892-1989)
British
Autumn Flowers
Oil on canvas
22 x 30in (55.5 x 76cm)
£3,250-3,500 *NZ*

Mary Jackson
(20thC)
British
Kitchen Windowsill
Oil
18 x 10in
(46 x 25cm)
£1,200-2,500 *BSG*

Annette Johnson
(20thC)
British
Early Morning
Etching
12½ x 9in
(32.4 x 22.5cm)
£75-85 *CCA*

Cecil Kennedy (b1905)
British
Virgo Rose
Signed
15½ x 11⅛in (39 x 29cm)
£4,000-4,500 *Bea*

John S. Ingle (b1933)
American
Still Life with Watermelon and Palm
Watercolour on paper
60 x 40in (152.4 x 101.6cm)
£30,000-40,000 *S(NY)*

Nikolai Khristolyubov (b1918)
Russian
Still Life with Lillies of the Valley
Dated 1991, oil on canvas
39 x 27in (99 x 69cm)
£6,000-7,000 *RMG*

Georgy Moroz (b1937) Russian
Still Life with Lilacs, oil on canvas, c1988
29 x 33in (74 x 84cm)
£5,000-6,000 *RMG*

l. **Pat Moran** (20thC) British
Summer Glory, oil on canvas
30 x 24in (76 x 61cm)
£3,500-3,800 *OM*

l. **Peter McLaren**
(20thC)
British
Still Life with
Poppies
Oil
33 x 36in (84 x
92cm)
£3,200-3,500
BSG

Gail Lilley (20thC)
British
Provençal Still Life
Pastel
18 x 19in (46 x 48cm)
£300-350 *A*

l. **Christine McArthur**
(20thC) British
Amaryllis and Sewing
Machine
Pastel on paper
38 x 29in (96.5 x 74cm)
£2,200-2,400 *RB*

Binny Mathews (20thC)
British
Poinsettia
Oil
35 x 40in (89 x 101.5cm)
£1,800-2,000 *AMC*

Shirley Trevela (20thC)
British
Red Pears
Watercolour and gouache
16 x 21in (41 x 53cm)
£750-850 *NBO*

Samuel John Peploe (1871-1935)
British
Still Life: Roses
Signed, oil on canvas
20 x 16in (50.8 x 40.6cm)
£46,000-60,000 *C(S)*

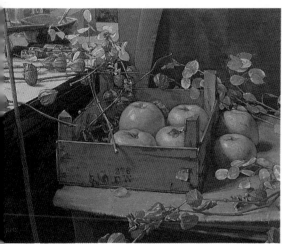

David Napp (20thC) British
Clarice Cliff and Moroccan fabric, chalk pastel
19 x 13in (48 x 33cm) **£1,250-1,450** *WG*

l. **Richard Smith** (1957) British
Still Life with Bramley Apples, oil on canvas
19½ x 24in (49 x 61.5cm)
£5,000-5,500 *BSG*

Carolyn Sergeant (20thC) British
Cherries, oil on canvas,
7 x 10in (18 x 25cm)
£650-700 *BSG*

r. **Peggy Somerville** (1918-75) British
Bowl of Peaches, oil on board
9 x 10in (22.5 x 25cm)
£3,450-3,650 *DM*

Graham Sutherland (1903-80)
Oranges
Signed and dated 63, gouache
24½ x 20¾in (62 x 52.5cm)
£2,300-3,000 *C*

Pieter Withoos (1654-93) Dutch
Studies of Five Butterflies and Three Flies
Signed and numbered, pen and grey and brown ink, watercolour
and bodycolour
9 x 14½in (22.7 x 36.3cm)
£2,000-2,400 *C(Am)*

Anglo Indian School (c1890)
An Album of Botanical Studies of Cultivated,
Ornamental and Tropical plants
All inscribed, the Album dated 90, pencil and
watercolour, 21 drawings on the pages of the album
11¼ x 12⅛in (28 x 30.5cm)
£6,400-7,500 *C*

Circle of Margarethe de Heer
(German School, active 1650)
A Thistle with insects including
Butterflies, a Dragonfly and a Grasshopper
Oil on vellum, laid down on panel
12¼ x 10½in (31 x 26.5cm)
£8,000-9,000 *P*

l. **Catherine
Warburton** (20thC)
British
Imperial Lilies and
Gerbera
Watercolour
36 x 26in (91 x 66cm)
£600-700 *AMC*

r. **David Alan
Redpath Michie**
(20thC)
British
Scabious
Signed, oil on canvas
34 x 40in
(86.5 x 102cm)
£2,700-3,200 *S*

On the Beach

According to the 18thC Brighton doctor, Richard Russell, sea water was an efficacious remedy for all kinds of complaints from tumours to gonorrhoea, whether bathed in, drunk, or mixed up with ingredients as unlikely as crab's eyes and woodlice. (See Biblio: Christopher Hibbert). Sea bathing was recommended as a cure in the 18thC, but by the Victorian age, it had also become a fashionable holiday pursuit. It was Royalty who initially popularised the seaside resorts. Each monarch had their own particular favourite. George III liked Weymouth, where a bathing machine was equipped with a band who played God Save the King to their swimming sovereign, George IV preferred Brighton, Queen Victoria holidayed in Ramsgate as a child and on the Isle of Wight with her own family. The advent of cheap public transport and the development of the railways made the coast accessible to the common people, seaside resorts grew rapidly in consequence and along with the visitors came the artists. Beach scenes and seaside promenades were a frequently painted subject in the second part of the 19thC and early 20thC, and as the following section shows, remain equally popular with the artists of today.

Charles Jean Auguste Escudier (b1848)
French
Enfants Pêchant
Signed, oil on canvas
25½ x 39¼in (65 x 99.7cm)
£10,000-11,000 *S(NY)*

John Wilson Carmichael (1800-68)
British
Bathing machines at Prior's Haven, Tynemouth
Signed and dated 1849, oil on canvas
11½ x 23½in (29 x 59.5cm)
£8,800-10,000 *AG*

Wilson Carmichael is a great favourite with North-Eastern collectors. When this painting was auctioned at Anderson & Garland's in Newcastle in March 1993, it was a local resident living just near the protrayed scene who paid substantially over the £1,500-2,500 estimate to obtain the picture. A highly decorative topographical work, with its fine view of Tynemouth Priory and Castle, the picture also provides a fascinating insight into Victorian bathing techniques, in particular the use of offshore floating bathing machines.

John F. Kensett (1816-72)
American
Beach at Newport
Signed and indistinctly dated, oil on canvas
10 x 17in (25.4 x 43.2cm)
£72,000-80,000 *S(NY)*

Attilio Pratella (1856-1932)
Italian
A Day at the Beach
Signed, oil on panel
8¾ x 13¾in (22.2 x 35cm)
£9,000-10,000 *CNY*

Michael Coote (20thC)
British
Paddling
Pastel
22 x 25in (56 x 54cm)
£600-800 *AdG*

Walter Frederick Osborne (1859-1963)
Irish
A Seaside Promenade
Oil on panel
5½ x 7½in (13.7 x 19cm)
£15,000-16,000 *C(D)*

This painting is most probably the promenade at Hastings painted c1891. It relates in composition and light to a larger oil painting in the National Gallery of Ireland entitled Punch and Judy on the Sands, Hastings.

Fred Cuming (b1930)
British
Bathers - Cap Ferrett
24in (61cm) square
Oil on board
£2,500-4,500   *BSG*

James Fitton, R.A. (1889-1982)
British
Seaside
Signed, oil on board
27 x 30in (69 x 76.5cm)
£2,100-2,600 *S*

François Gall (1912-45)
French
Figures on a Beach
Signed, oil on canvas
8¾ x 10¾in (22.2 x 27.3cm)
£2,500-3,000   *S(NY)*

Ken Howard (b1932)
British
Beach Scene
Oil on panel
6¼ x 8½in (15.2 x 21cm)
£8,000-10,000 *BRG*

Odette Dumaret (b1913)
French
La Plage, 1989
Oil on canvas
35 x 46in (89 x 116.5cm)
£4,000-4,500 *Ce*

Inna Grodetskaya (1914-72)
Russian
Swimming
Oil on board
£380-420 *Tho*

Peter Howson (20thC)
Venice Beach
Etching
13 x 18⅞in (33 x 47cm)
£250-300 *GPS*

*It takes an artist of Howson's vision,
originality and undeniably grim world view,
to produce a beach scene that is not uniquely
peopled by festive holiday makers.*

Leslie Hunter (1877-1931)
British
Plage à Juan les Pins
Watercolour, painted c1927
£5,500-6,000 *DMF*

James Kay (1858-1942)
British
On the Beach
Signed, oil on canvas
22½ x 36in (57.5 x 91.5cm)
£6,400-7,500 *S*

Mary Jackson (20thC)
British
Faithful Friend
Oil
9½ x 12in (24 x 30.8cm)
£450-750 *BSG*

Harry Wingfield (b1910)
British
The Last Fish
Signed, gouache
11 x 8in (28 x 20cm)
£325-375 *Dr*

Original illustration for the Ladybird 'Peter and Jane' books.

Harry Roseland (1867-1950)
American
Coney Island
Signed and dated 33, oil on canvas
28 x 40in (71 x 101.6cm)
£36,000-46,000 *S(NY)*

MILITARY

Artists have always painted battles, soldiers and great heroic leaders, and many have specialised in military subjects, but it was not until the First World War (and after photography had become the main means of reportage) that the British Government instigated the appointment of the Official War Artist, a tradition that carries on to the present day, and has resulted over the years in some major and moving portrayals of modern warfare.

Attributed to Jan van Huchtenburgh (1647-1723)
Dutch
Cavalrymen on a Road by a Forest, and a drawing of a cavalry battle
inscribed, black lead, pen and brown ink, grey wash
6¾ x 7¾in (17.4 x 19cm)
£700-800 *C(Am)*

Sebald Beham (1500-50)
German
A Standard Bearer
Dated 1519, bears initials verso, and attribution recto: Christof amberger, pen and black ink
7¼ x 3½in (18 x 9.5cm)
£12,000-13,000 *S(NY)*

Antonio Tempesta (c1555-1630)
Italian
A Mounted Turk attacking another Cavalryman
Inscribed, black chalk, pen and brown ink, brown wash
11¾ x 11in (30 x 28.2cm) **£2,000-2,500** *C*

French School (late 18thC)
Mounted Cavalier
black chalk and grey wash
18½ x 15½in (47 x 39cm)
1,500-1,800 *S*

Vincenz Georg Kininger (1767-1851)
Austrian
Polish Troops
Signed and dated 1807, watercolour and
bodycolour
17½ x 20½in (44.5 x 52cm)
£5,800-6,800 *C*

Siegfried Detler Bendixen (1786-1864)
German
Helen MacGregor in the Conflict at the Pass
of Loch Ard
Signed, inscribed and dated 1854, oil on
canvas
32¼ x 40¾in (82 x 103.5cm)
£9,000-10,000 *S*

Hubert Cornish (1757-1832)
British
Soldiers Marching in St. Helena
Inscribed, watercolour over pencil with
touches of bodycolour
17¼ x 18½in (43 x 47cm)
£700-800 *S*

Ernest Crofts (1847-1911)
Wellington at Waterloo
Signed and dated 1886, oil on canvas
37½ x 27½in (95.2 x 69.8cm)
£8,000-9,000 *Bon*

Paul Louis Grolleron (1848-1901)
French
The Attack
Signed, oil
13 x 16in (33 x 41cm)
£3,000-3,300 *Dr*

George Gascoyne (1863-1933)
British
Before the Battle
Etching
10¾ x 20½in (27.7 x 52.5cm)
£85-95 *CG*

Hermann Kauffmann (1808-89)
German
A Winter Landscape with Cavalry
Signed, oil on canvas
20 x 25½in (51 x 65cm)
£4,500-5,500 *C*

Jean Louis Ernest Meissonier (1815-91)
French
Soldiers on Patrol
Signed with monogram, oil on panel
13½ x 17½in (34.5 x 44.5cm)
£2,200-3,000 *S*

Marius Roy (b1833)
French
The Mess
Signed, oil on cradled panel
13 x 17¾in (33 x 45cm)
£3,500-4,500 *S(NY)*

Orlando Norie (1832-1901)
British
4th Dragoon Officer & Horse
Signed, watercolour
18 x 12½in (46 x 32cm)
£650-750 *LH*

Sir Frank William Brangwyn (François Guillaume) (1867-1956)
A French Soldier
Charcoal
14½ x 15½in (37 x 39cm)
£4,000-4,500 *CBL*

Richard Simkin (1850-1926)
British
1st Battalion Gordon Highlanders, 75th Foot
Signed, watercolour over pencil, heightened
with white
17¾ x 12in (45 x 31cm)
£700-800 *S*

"Once upon a time"

Charles Bruce Bairnsfather (1887-1959)
British
Once Upon a Time
Signed and inscribed, pastel and bodycolour
on tinted paper
30 x 21in (76 x 52cm)
£650-750 *CBL*

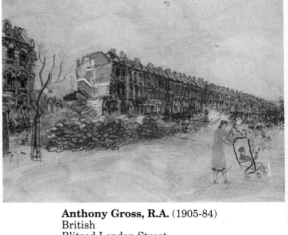

Anthony Gross, R.A. (1905-84)
British
Blitzed London Street
Signed and indistinctly dated 1940, pen and
blank ink with watercolour and gouache
14½ x 21in (37 x 53.5cm)
£1,500-1,800 *S*

*Anthony Gross began his career as a war
artist painting the effects of the Blitz on
London throughout 1940, before embarking in
December for Egypt on a troop ship. Painting
in the Western Desert and Syria, he made
several studies of dressing stations and field
hospitals, to which he gained access through
a doctor befriended on the outward voyage.
He finished the War painting the campaign
against the Japanese in the Arakan
Peninsula.*

Thomas Hennell, R.W.S. (1903-45)
British
Spitfires on an Airfield; a Dakota at
Mingaldon, 26th May 1945
Two, one signed, both pen and black ink and
watercolour
10¼ x 19½in (26 x 50cm) and 14¾ x 19½in
(37.5 x 50cm)
£1,400-1,800 *S*

*In 1943 Hennell was sent as an Official War
Artist to Iceland as a replacement for Eric
Ravilious, who had gone missing while on
patrol, and the following year was
commissioned as a Naval Lieutenant at
Portsmouth, in order to record the massing of
troops and equipment in Southern England
in Preparation for D-Day. By 15th June he
was in Normandy and followed the Allied
advance to the German border before being
called in June 1945 to Burma to record the
aftermath of Mountbatten's victories there.
He died in November 1945, ironically after
the War's end, at Surabaya in Eastern Java,
caught up in the hostilities between Dutch
colonists and Indonesian Nationalists, having
become one of the most travelled of all the war
artists.*

LE BAISER de la MÈRE PATRIE
1917

Louis Icart (20thC)
French
The Kiss of the Motherland
Signed and numbered 15/100, aquatint and
drypoint
19½ x 11½in (49 x 29cm)
£400-500 *CSK*

Ernest Howard Shepard (1879-1976)
British
Dig for Victory
Pen and ink with pencil
6¾ x 6in (17 x 15cm)
£600-650 *CBL*

Shepard gives one of the most famous slogans of wartime Britain a characteristically amusing twist. During World War II, cartoonists and illustrators such as Fougasse were employed to produce propaganda and convey official advice and instructions to the civilian population in a manner that was both memorable and palatable, using humour to reinforce their serious messages.

'Snaffles' (Charles Johnson Payne) (1884-1967)
British
An Officer of the Grenadier Guards in parade uniform and dressed for the Hunt
Signed, gouache over pencil
13½ x 10in (34.5 x 25cm)
£950-1,200 *AG*

Ronald Searle (b1920)
Souvenir of Changi
Signed and dated 1959, pen, ink and monochrome, watercolour
11¾ x 6½in (30 x 16cm)
£2,500-2,750 *CBL*

Bruce Marshall (20thC)
American
Charge of the Texas Rangers
Signed, oil on canvas
29¾ x 40in (75.6 x 101.6cm)
£400-500 *S(NY)*

Edmund Joseph Sullivan (1869-1933)
British
The Gentle German
Signed, inscribed and dated 1915, pen and ink
10½ x 7¼in (26 x 18cm)
£650-750 *CBL*

SPORTS & GAMES

This section includes board games and cards as well as more physical sporting pursuits. Though a number of different sports are illustrated, undoubtedly the most popular single sport in this year's category is golf - a pursuit enjoyed internationally and played by a lot of wealthy people and, as such, potential picture buyers. Golfing pictures are always in great demand, and as Atkinson Wells' 'Westwood Ho' (see page 429) demonstrates, the addition of a handful of golfers, no matter how sketchily drawn, can put up the price of an otherwise unexceptional landscape. More finished works, in particular those concentrating on famous courses or golfers, can command significantly high sums and have regularly gone way over their auction estimates in the past year. Golfing pictures appear to be recession proof. Golfing museums are being established across the world and as the sport grows ever more popular, so do the pictures that celebrate and record its history. The major sales of 'golfiana' take place in Scotland in July to coincide with the Open Championships.

Caran d'Ache (Emmanuel Poire)
(1858-1909)
Russian
Le Mal Necessaire
Signed, pen and ink
7 x 8½in (17.5 x 21cm)
£1,500-1,750 *CBL*

Edgar Bundy (1862-1922)
British
The Game of Cards
Signed, watercolour heightened with white
15¼ x 21¾in (38.7 x 55.3cm)
£1,000-1,400 *Bon*

John Strickland-Goodall (b1908)
British
The Tennis Match
Watercolour
£1,650-1,850 *THo*

I. Clark after Henry Alken (19thC)
British
A Prize Fight
National Sports of Great Britain
Aquatint published by T. McLean Janu.
1820
7½ x 11½in (19.7 x 29.6cm)
£400-450 *CG*

Carl Henrik Nordenberg (1857-1928)
Swedish
The Game of Checkers
Signed and inscribed, oil on canvas
31¾ x 25½in (81 x 64.5cm)
£13,500-15,000 *CNY*

For 19thC painters, a game of checkers or a hand of cards was often simply an excuse and a dramatic focus for a costume or romantic genre picture - a decorative symbol for the games of love and the tricks of fate.

Edward Jeffrey Irving Ardizzone, CBE
(1900-79)
The Vaulting Horse
Pen, ink and watercolour
8¼ x 11½in (20.5 x 28.5cm)
£2,000-2,250 *CBL*

Carl Wilhelm Anton Seiler (1846-1921)
German
The Winning Hand
Signed and dated 1890, oil on panel
9½ x 11½in (24 x 29.5cm)
£3,700-4,200 *P*

Milton Avery (1885-1965)
American
Pool Shark
Signed and dated 1955,
oil on canvas board
12 x 9in (30.5 x 23cm)
£14,500-16,000 *S(NY)*

Danny Byrne (20thC)
British
Best Odds Around, Mate
Oil
18½ x 27in (47 x 68.5cm)
£220-260 *EAG*

James Montgomery Flagg (1877-1960)
American
Study for a Boxing Mural
Signed with initials and dated Aug. 7/44,
watercolour, gouache and pencil on
paperboard
9¼ x 29¼in (23.5 x 74.3cm)
£5,000-6,000 *S(NY)*

*Flagg was one of the most prolific
caricaturists and illustrators of the first half
of this century. At the centre of New York
social life, he painted portraits for many of its
celebrities. For more than twenty years he
was staff artist for Life magazine, but he was*
*best known for a recruitment poster he did for
the government during World War I saying 'I
WANT YOU'. This work is a study for one of
several large murals commissioned by Jack
Dempsey for his restaurant in New York. The
murals depicted Dempsey's famous victories,
this one the Jack Dempsey-Jess Willard fight
held in Toledo on July 4, 1919. Flagg
completed the murals in the 1940s and they
hung for many years in the restaurant.*

Fougasse (Cyril Kenneth Bird)
(1887-1965)   British
Darts Player
Ink and watercolour
7¾ x 4¾in (19 x 12cm)
£325-375 *CBL*

William Heath Robinson (1872-1944)
British
Mrs Bloggs at the Football Match. Mrs.
Bloggs - well I'm blessed, after all this
traipsing about if they haven't been and lost
the ball
Signed and inscribed, pen, ink and pencil
with monochrome watercolour
12 x 10½in (30.5 x 26cm)
£3,250-3,500   *CBL*

J. Michael Brown (active 1880-1916)
British
Driving out of the Rough, The Royal
Liverpool Golf Club at Hoylake
Signed and inscribed, watercolour heightened
with bodycolour
7 x 10in (17.8 x 25.4cm)
£23,000-28,000   *C(S)*

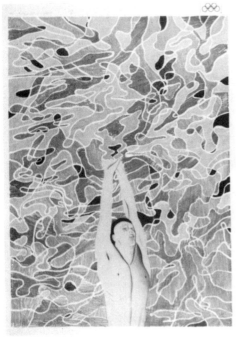

David Hockney (b1937)
British
Olympische Spiele München 1972
Signed, numbered 41/200, dated 1970,
lithograph printed in colours
34½ x 25¼in (87.5 x 64.5cm)
£1,500-1,800   *S(NY)*

J. Michael Brown (active 1880-1916)
British
Badly bunkered in the Cardinal, Prestwick
Signed, watercolour
£25,000-30,000   *P(Sc)*

Rudolph Scheffler (1884-1973)
German
Max Schmeling
Signed and dated 1929, oil on canvas
84 x 66in (213.4 x 167.6cm)
£13,500-15,000 *S(NY)*

McNeil McLeay (1829-78)
British
Members of the Royal Perth Golfing Society
playing on the North Inch, Perth, Scotland
Signed and dated 1866, oil on canvas
16¾ x 26¾in (42.5 x 58cm)
£34,000-45,000 *C(S)*

William Page Atkinson Wells (1872-1923)
British
Westward Ho
Signed, oil on panel
12 x 16in (30.5 x 40.6cm)
£6,800-7,200 *C(S)*

Charles Crombie (20thC)
The Rules of Golf
24 captioned plates, one leaf advertisement
for Perrier Water, c1908
£1,000-1,250 *DN*

Hugh Dodd (20thC)
Golf is a Four Letter Word
Signed, pencil, crayon and watercolour
13½ x 9¼in (34 x 23cm)
£600-700 *C(S)*

Scottish School (20thC)
A Fourball on a Links Course
Indistinctly signed and dated 46, oil on board
29in (73.7cm) square
£650-750 *C(S)*

MUSIC AND DANCE
16th and 17th Century

Circle of Ambrosius Benson
(Active 1519-50)
Flemish
A Music Party
Oil on panel
33 x 41½in (83.7 x 105.5cm)
£23,000-28,000 C

Flemish School (17thC)
A Rommelpot Player
Oil on canvas
23½ x 19¼in (60 x 49cm)
£2,600-3,200 P

Gerard van Kuijl (1604-73)
Dutch
A Music Party
Oil on canvas
49 x 71in (124.5 x 180cm)
£63,000-75,000 C

Attributed to Jacob Ochtevelt
(1635-1708)
Dutch
Two Musicians Playing to an Amorous
Couple
Oil on canvas
29 x 28¼in (73.7 x 72cm)
£5,600-7,000 P

Sir Peter Lely (1618-80)
British
A Man playing a Violin
Oil on canvas
57¼ x 37in (145.4 x 94cm)
£300,000-350,000 C

*In 1968, Lely's Portrait of a Man playing a
Violin fetched £18,000 at auction. In
November 1992 it was sold at Christie's for a
hammer price of £260,000, (£100,000 over its
top estimate), emphasising the strong demand
in today's market for quality Old Master
pictures. Its companion piece, Lely's Portrait
of a Girl playing a Theorbo-lute, sold for
£360,000 at the same sale, making by far the
highest price ever paid for a Lely at auction.*

18th Century

François Dequevauviller (1745-c1807)
French
L'Assemblée au Concert; and L'Assemblée au
Salon, after Nicolas Lavreince
A pair, dated1783, etchings with engravings,
published by Dequevauviller, Paris
15¾ x 19½in (40.3 x 49.7cm)
£3,400-4,000 *C*

François Guérin (active 1761-after 1791)
French
The Music Lesson (recto); A Girl, Sewing
(verso)
Oil on canvas
9 x 7¼in (23 x 18.2cm)
£9,500-11,000 *C*

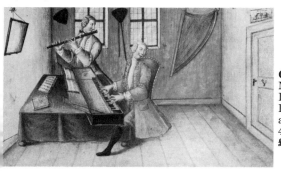

German School (c1740)
Musicians playing a Flute and a Spinet in an
Interior
Indistinctly inscribed, watercolour with pen
and black ink
4 x 6½in (10 x 16.5cm)
£5,000-6,000 *S*

19th Century

Richard Buckner (active 1830-97)
British
A Roman Piper
Signed, pencil and watercolour heightened
with white
20 x 13⅜in (51 x 34cm)
£280-350 *CSK*

Antonio Garcia y Mencia (b1850)
Spanish
The Musical Party
Signed and dated 1874, oil on canvas
29 x 23¼in (73.7 x 59cm)
£20,000-25,000 *S(NY)*

Francis Luis Mora (1874-1940)
American
A Family Party, Triana, Sevilla
Signed and dated 1908, oil on canvas
25 x 30in (63.5 x 76.2cm)
£6,500-7,500 *S(NY)*

Gaston Latouche (1854-1913)
French
Soirée chez un Artiste
Signed and inscribed, oil on cradled panel
30 x 31¼in (76 x 79cm)
£12,500-14,000 *S(NY)*

Alexis Vollon (b1865) French
A Pierrot playing a Guitar
Signed and dated 28 Juin 1898,
oil on canvas
13 x 10¼in (33 x 26cm)
£800-1,000 *CSK*

Francis Sidney Muschamp (d1929)
British
The Piano Lesson
Signed and dated 1879, oil on canvas
19¾ x 30in (50.2 x 76.2cm)
£20,000-25,000 *S(NY)*

Walter Richard Sickert, A.R.A.
(1860-1942)
British
The Pit at the Old Bedford
Signed, oil on panel
8 x 10in (20 x 25cm)
£44,000-55,000 *C*

Theodore Wores (1860-1939)
American
Afternoon Entertainment with Musicians
and Dancer
Signed and inscribed, oil on canvas, c1892
72 x 48in (183 x 122cm)
£38,000-45,000 *S(NY)*

20thCentury

Andrew Curtis (20thC)
British
All that Jazz
Oil on canvas
30 x 24in (76 x 61cm)
£600-675 *TFA*

Romare Bearden (b1914)
American
Kansas City
Signed, acrylic and paper collage laid down
on board, executed 1974
44½ x 51in (113 x 129.5cm)
£50,000-60,000 *S(NY)*

Sir William Russell Flint, R.A. (1880-1969)
British
Two Studies of Moira Shearer
Signed and inscribed, red chalk
9 x 13½in (23 x 34.2cm)
£1,900-2,400 *CSK*

Salvador Dali (1904-89)
Spanish
Danseurs de Flamenco
Signed and dated 1943, pen and brush and
Indian ink
38½ x 27½in (97 x 70cm)
£32,000-40,000 *S*

Sir William Russell Flint, R.A. (1880-1969)
British
Homage to Demeter, Provence
Signed, oil on canvas, executed 1939
36 x 62in (92 x 158cm)
£36,000-45,000 *C*

*At Christie's in November 1988 Flint's nubile
Provençal dancers sold for £45,000.
Reappearing there in March 1993, the picture
sold for a hammer price of £31,000 - an
undoubted drop in price but still a respectable
figure in the current market.*

Anthony Gross (b1905)
British
Las Sardanas, 1934
Signed, inscribed and numbered 38/50
7½ x 9¼in (19 x 23.5cm)
£800-900 *BLD*

Anonymous (c1900)
English
Design for marquetry decoration
Watercolour on card
12 x 18in (31 x 46cm)
£175-200 *JD*

August Leroux (1871-1954)
French
Danseuse
Signed, oil on canvas
18 x 13in (45.7 x 33.3cm)
£650-750 *DN*

Claude Weisbuch (b1927)
French
Serenade
Original engraving
19½ x 15½in (49.5 x 39cm)
£400-450 *TES*

Abraham Walkowitz (1880-1965)
Russian
Isadora Duncan Dancing
A group of 7 watercolours, each signed, India
ink and pencil on paper
7¾ x 2¾in (19.7 x 7cm)
£2,800-3,500 *S(NY)*

*'I beheld the dance I had always dreamed of,'
said American novelist Edith Wharton on
seeing Isadora Duncan perform, 'a flowing of
movement into movement, an endless
interweaving of motion and music satisfying
every sense as a flower does, or a phrase of
Mozart's.'*

Leon Underwood (b1890)
British
Dancing Figure with Ball
Signed and numbered 3/25, etching
6 x 4¼in (15 x 10.5cm)
£125-150 *BLD*

Konstantin Limikin (b1924)
Russian
The Rehearsal
Pastel, 1981
25 x 20in (64 x 51cm)
£7,000-8,000 *RMG*

CIRCUS, FAIRGROUND & ENTERTAINMENT

The themes of circus, clowns and pierrots have attracted many painters over the centuries from Watteau to Picasso. In art, as in literature, the clown is frequently presented as an outsider, and when deprived of his audience, his comic mask slips to reveal the potentially tragic figure beneath. For many 20thC artists, the circus provided an escape from reality and more traditional figurative fields, offering a world of colour and fantasy, without sacrificing human subjects and human feeling to abstraction: 'I have never liked realism,' declared Chagall who returned to the circus again and again in his work. 'My pictures were illogical and non-realistic long before Surrealism. What I wanted was a kind of realism, if you wish, but a psychic kind, and hence a quite different thing from the realism of objects and geometrical figures.'

Flaminio Allegrini (active 1625-35)
Italian
Gymnasts in classical costumes
Inscribed and dated 1529, black chalk, pen and brown ink, brown, blue and orange wash
13 x 10½in (33.2 x 26.5cm)
£6,500-7,500 *CNY*

Edgar Bundy (1862-1922)
British
Malvolio and Feste
Initialled and dated 1902, watercolour
13½ x 10½in (35 x 27cm)
£1,350-1,450 *Dr*

James Holland (1799-1870)
British
Country Fair
Signed and indistinctly inscribed, oil on canvas
16 x 25¾in (41 x 65cm)
£11,500-12,500 *C*

P. J. Crook (20thC)
British
The Fairground
Acrylic on wood
36 x 28in (92 x 71cm)
£2,500-2,750 *TFA*

Jean Dufy (1888-1964)
French
Au Cirque, Parade Equestre
Signed, oil on canvas
18¼ x 24in (46.4 x 61.3cm)
£20,000-25,000 *S(NY)*

Richard Ernest Eurich, R.A. (1903-92)
British
Circus Fragment
Signed and dated 1932, oil on board
14 x 10in (36.5 x 26.5cm)
£1,800-2,500 *Bon*

Walt Kuhn (1880-1949)
American
Clown with Drum
Signed and dated 1942, oil on canvas
60 x 40in (152.4 x 101.6cm)
£210,000-250,000 *S(NY)*

Dame Laura Knight (1877-1970)
British
Marba and Randy
Signed and inscribed, watercolour, black
crayon and pencil, painted 1930
10 x 14in (25.5 x 36cm)
£5,500-6,500 *C*

*Marba and Randy were clowns with Bertram
Mills Circus. They posed for Laura Knight at
intervals during the performances and appear
in two paintings from 1930.*

Willy James (b1920)
Swiss
Place de Foire aux Arbres Roses
Signed, oil on canvas
25 x 31½in (64 x 80cm)
£5,000-6,000 *S*

Lucy Kemp-Welch (1869-1958)
British
Grand Horses Entering the Ring
Signed, oil on canvas laid down on board
17½ x 23in (44 x 59cm)
£5,500-6,500 *P(L)*

George Large (20thC)
British
Fancy Dress
Watercolour
19 x 28in (48 x 71cm)
£900-950 *LA*

David Levine (b1926)
American
Joy Ride
Signed and dated 82, watercolour on pieced
paper
12½ x 9¾in (31.8 x 24.8cm)
£3,500-4,000 *S(NY)*

Walter Richard Sickert, A.R.A.
(1860-1942)
Brighton Pierrots
Signed and dated 1915, oil on canvas
25 x 30in (63.5 x 76cm)
£225,000-270,000 *C*

*Sickert was the guest of his painter friend
and patron, Walter Taylor, during August
and September 1915 at Brighton. Here he
concentrated on producing studies of the
concert-party of the Pierrots and Pierrottes on
Brighton Beach which he visited every night
for five weeks.*

*The resulting oil made an auction record for
Sickert in 1983, when purchased for £60,000
by the Fine Art Society. They sold it to a
client, who put it up for sale at Christie's in
March 1993, where it went way over its
£80,000-120,000 estimate, purchased for a
hammer price of £200,000 again by the Fine
Art Society. Works of art often seem to follow
a fairly circular path passing back and forth
between the same dealers and auction houses.*

Sir Robin Philipson (b1916)
British
The Same Old Game
Oil on panel
19½ x 23in (50 x 59cm)
£9,000-10,000 *RB*

Jack Butler Yeats, R.H.A. (1871-1957)
Irish
The Amateur Ventriloquist
Signed and inscribed, oil on canvas, painted
1945
18 x 24in (46 x 61cm)
£68,000-80,000 *C*

CAVALIERS

The 19thC saw the development of the historical novel as a popular literary form, and alongside this, the emergence of the historical picture. Cavaliers, with their debonair image of flamboyant costumes, were a favourite theme with both writers and painters of the period, immortalised by Dumas in 'The Three Musketeers', and portrayed by a host of artists throughout Europe.

George Henry Boughton (1833-1905)
American
New Year's Day in New Amsterdam
Signed and dated 1870, oil on canvas
40 x 64in (101.6 x 162.6cm)
£15,000-16,000 *S(NY)*

Frank Moss Bennett (1874-1953)
British
The Adventurers
Signed and dated 1938, oil on canvas
23½ x 29½in (59.7 x 75cm)
£25,000-35,000 *Bon*

Ferdinand Roybet (1840-1920)
French
Portrait of a Cavalier
Signed, oil on panel
32 x 25¼in (81.3 x 64cm)
£3,000-4,000 *S(NY)*

A. Petrocelli (19thC)
Italian
Cavaliers merry-making in a tavern interior
A pair, signed, oil on canvas
23½ x 35½in (59.7 x 90cm)
£3,800-4,800 *P*

Herman Ten Kate (1822-91)
Dutch
Soldiers in an Interior
Signed, oil on canvas
8¼ x 11½in (21 x 29.5cm)
£800-1,000 *AH*

MONKS & CARDINALS

Like cavaliers, monks, cardinals and priests were another popular 19thC subject, taking their place among the archetypes of contemporary genre painting. For all their religious costume, they are generally portrayed as a fairly self-indulgent crew, far more concerned with earthly pleasures than heavenly matters and frequently neglecting the holy spirit for an alcoholic one.

Victor Cacciarelli (19thC)
Italian
A Special Visitor
Signed, watercolour
14¾ in x 21½in (38 x 54cm)
£1,800-2,300 *Bea*

Pier Leone Ghezzi (1674-1755)
Italian
Portrait of a Venetian Cleric
Inscribed, black chalk, pen and brown ink
11¾ x 8¼in (29.5 x 21cm)
£2,500-3,500 *CNY*

Giuseppe Castiglione (1829-1908)
Italian
Sitting for his Portrait
Signed, oil on canvas
27 x 41in (68.6 x 104cm)
£15,000-16,000 *CNY*

Charles Baptiste Schreiber (d1903)
French
A Good Vintage
Signed, oil on panel
8¼ x 6in (21 x 15.2cm)
£1,500-2,000 *Bon*

A. Tamborini (b1843)
Italian
Two monks seated at a table reading Le Rire
Signed, oil on canvas
36 x 27½in (92 x 70cm)
£1,800-2,200 *P(S)*

VICTORIAN ROMANS: CLASSICAL GENRE

Alma-Tadema, perhaps the greatest of all Victorian classical genre painters, has dominated the market in this field over the past year. In May 1993 in New York, his spectacular picture 'The Baths of Caracalla' produced an auction record of $2.3 million (£1.5 million), equalled in London in June when Christie's sold 'The Roses of Heliogabus' for a hammer price of £1.5 million against a top estimate of £900,000. Though the artist has not always found favour with 20thC critics (one irritated commentator complaining that the marble he portrayed so lavishly looked exactly like gorgonzola cheese), his hedonistic Olympian visions, meticulously researched, beautifully painted and masterpieces of their genre, are enjoying as much success today as they first did 100 years ago with the wealthy patrons of the 19thC.

Alexandre Cabanel (1824-89)
French
Cléopâtre essayante des poisons sur des condamnes à mort
Signed, oil on canvas
34⅓ x 58¼in (87.6 x 148cm)
£310,000-400,000 *CNY*

Percy Anderson (1850-1928)
British
Dreamland
Signed and dated 1884, watercolour
39 x 52in (99 x 132cm)
£5,800-7,000 *S*

Sir Lawrence Alma-Tadema (1836-1912)
British
The Coliseum (A Roman Holiday)
Signed and inscribed, oil on panel
44 x 28⅓in (111.8 x 71.8cm)
£320,000-380,000 *CNY*

William Adolphe Bouguereau (1825-1905)
French
Idylle
Signed, oil on canvas
33¼ x 25in (84.5 x 63.5cm)
£75,000-100,000 *CNY*

Attributed to Marc Gabriel Charles Gleyre (1808-74)
Swiss
Le Soir ou Les Illusions Perdues
Oil on canvas
23¾ x 41½in (59 x 105.4cm)
£12,000-13,000 *S(NY)*

William Adolphe Bouguereau
(1825-1905)
French
Beauté Romane
Signed and dated 1904,
oil on canvas
71 x 32in (180.4 x 81.2cm)
£53,000-60,000 *CNY*

Emilio Vasarri (19thC)
Italian
At the Bazaar
Signed, oil on canvas
29¼ x 22⅜in (74.2 x 57.2cm)
£6,500-7,500 *C*

Robert Payton Reid (1859-1945)
British
Echo
Signed and dated 1906, oil on canvas
24 x 18in (61 x 45.7cm)
£3,700-4,700 *C*

Alfred C. Weatherstone (active 1888-1929)
British
Study of a classical girl seated on a terrace
Signed, watercolour
13 x 9in (34 x 24cm)
£650-750 *HSS*

William Henry Margetson (1861-1940)
British
Love's Talisman
Signed and inscribed, oil on canvas
34 x 22in (86.4 x 56.2cm)
£3,000-4,000 *C*

Albert Joseph Moore (1841-93)
British
Sea Shells
Signed with Greek anthemion
and dated 75,
oil on canvas
30¼ x 14in (79.5 3 36cm)
£150,000-180,000 *CNY*

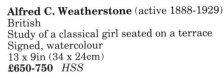

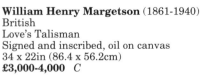

Frank William Warwick Topham
(1838-1924)
British
Refugees from Pompeii, AD 79
Signed and dated 1873, oil on canvas
48½ x 73⅜in (123 x 186.7cm)
£13,500-15,000 *C*

*Topham specialised in scenes of Italian life
and history. This example belongs to a long
tradition of interest in Pompeian subjects,
going back to the discovery of Herculaneum
and Pompeii in the mid-18thC, but
stimulated for the Victorians by the
publication of Bulwer-Lytton's novel The Las
Days of Pompeii in 1834.*

ORIENTALIST

Many artists travelled to the East in the 19thC, and even those who ventured little further than their London or Paris studios were still fascinated by Oriental themes and glamour, particularly when it concerned the hidden world of the harem and the possibility of portraying luxurious nudes lounging on silken cushions and gorgeous textiles. Originally painted to uncover the mysteries of the Orient for European clients, in our own age Arab genre pictures have long been purchased by Arabian and Middle Eastern collectors. Though the market has suffered during the recession, sales over the past year have suggested that Orientalist works are coming back into fashion with pictures making good prices at auction in both London and New York.

Frederick Arthur Bridgman (1847-1928)
American
Entrance to a Mosque
Signed, oil on canvas
21¾ x 18¼in (55.2 x 46.4cm)
£3,000-4,000 *S(NY)*

Georges Brétegnier (1863-92)
French
An Odalisque
Signed and dated 1889, oil on canvas
29¾ x 19¾in (75.5 x 50cm)
£18,000-20,000 *C*

After John Bagnold Burgess (1830-97)
British
East Meets West
Bears signature and date 1874
21 x 28½in (53.5 x 72cm)
£2,600-3,200 *P(L)*

Louis Devedeux (1820-74)
French
The Oriental Mother
Signed and inscribed, oil on board
13½ x 21¾in (34.3 x 55.3cm)
£3,500-4,500 *C*

Fabio Fabbi (1861-1946) Italian
Arab Dancing Girls
Signed, oil on canvas
27¾ x 16in (70.5 x 40.4cm)
£7,500-8,500 *C*

Jean-Léon Gérôme (1824-1904)
French
Marcus Botsaris
Signed, oil on canvas, painted 1874
27¾ x 21½in (70.2 x 54.6cm)
£185,000-225,000 *S(NY)*

*Marcus Botsaris (1788-1823) was a hero in
the early part of the Greek war of
independence, a struggle against the Turkish
government which began in April 1821. At
Missalonghi in 1823, Botsaris advanced
swiftly at the head of 1200 men, threw himself
on the vanguard in the night, and routed
them with great slaughter, capturing their
camp, standards, and a vast quantity of
baggage, and died in the arms of victory.
Botsaris' friend Lord Byron succeeded his
command upon his death at Missalonghi.*

Ferdinand Folchi (1822-83) Italian
The Barter
Signed, pencil and watercolour heightened
with white on paper
19¾ x 14in (50.2 x 35.6cm)
£6,500-7,500 *C*

Paul Joanovitch (b1859)
Austrian
The Snake Charmer
Signed and dated 87, oil on canvas
43 x 33in (109 x 84cm)
£35,000-45,000 *P*

Pollock S. Nisbet (1848-1922)
British
At an Algerian Well
Watercolour
8 x 13in (20.3 x 33cm)
£250-300 *L*

Arthur Melville (1858-1904)
British
An Arab Outside a Mosque
Signed, watercolour
27 x 20¼in (68.5 x 51.4cm)
£6,000-7,000 *L*

Hippolyte Lazerges (1817-87)
French
An Arab Girl by a Fountain
Signed and dated 1878, oil on panel
13¼ x 9½in (34 x 24cm)
£2,200-2,800 *S*

P. B. Pascal (19thC)
Continental
Meryem La Danseuse
Signed and dated 1887, oil on canvas
36¼ x 25¾in (92 x 65cm)
£5,500-6,500 *S(NY)*

Paul Dominique Philippoteaux (b1845)
French
Outside the Coffee House
Signed, oil on canvas
31½ x 27in (81 x 68.5cm)
£22,000-30,000 *C*

T. Puerto (late 19thC)
Italian
In the Harem
Signed and dated 87, pencil and watercolour
heightened with white and gum arabic
26½ x 40in (68 x 101.5cm)
£1,250-1,750 *CSK*

Georges Bertin Scott (b1873)
French
The Private Guard of Bachaga Ben Ghana in
a River Landscape
Signed and dated 1937, oil on canvas
32 x 25¾in (81 x 65cm)
£1,600-2,000 *P*

Giuseppe Signorini (1857-1932)
Italian
An Arab Café
Signed and inscribed, pencil and watercolour
on paper laid down on board
24¼ x 34in (61.6 x 86.4cm)
£13,500-14,500 *C*

Edouard Frédéric Wilhelm Richter
(1844-1913)
French
Harem Beauties
Signed and inscribed, oil on canvas
47½ x 32¼in (120.7 x 82cm)
£12,000-14,000 *S(NY)*

Ferdinand Roybet (1840-1920)
French
Young Arab
Signed, oil on panel
17 x 13½in (43 x 34in)
£7,000-8,000 *CNY*

Eisman Semenowsky (19thC)
French
The Harem Terrace
Signed and inscribed, oil on panel
14¾ x 21¾in (37.5 x 55.2cm)
£5,500-6,500 *S(NY)*

Niels Simonsen (1807-85)
Danish
Farewell to the Lover
Signed and dated 1875, oil on canvas
24½ x 19½in (62 x 49.5cm)
£4,000-5,000 *S*

Dudley Hardy (1867-1922)
British
Sailing West
Signed, bodycolour
10½ x 14½in (26.5 x 37cm)
£900-950 *CBL*

Georges Washington (1827-1910)
French
Arab Warriors
Signed, oil on canvas
24½ x 38in (62 x 97cm)
£7,500-8,500 *P*

NUDES

'There lives no man upon earth who can give a final judgment upon what the most beautiful shape of a man may be; God only knows that,' claimed Albrecht Dürer wisely in *Four Books of Human Proportions - 1528*. Over the centuries, ideals of human beauty change and fluctuate, and the rolling voluptuous nudes of Rubens and Boucher look positively obese to a modern generation brought up on a diet of waif-like super-models, and in a century when, as the Duchess of Windsor famously said, 'you can never be too rich or too thin.' In portraying the nude, artists have not only reflected the tastes of the times, but also their own personal preferences: 'Any great painter of the nude has always painted nudes that he liked,' states David Hockney, frankly. 'Renoir paints rather pretty plump young girls ... he was sexually attracted to them and thought they were beautiful so he painted them; and if some thin little girl came along he'd probably have thought, lousy model. Quite right. Michelangelo paints muscular marvellous young men; he thinks they're wonderful. In short, you get inspired.'

16th and 17th Centuries

Giovanni Francesco Cassioni
(1636-after 1706)
Italian
Flora Adorning a Term of Janus
Inscribed, pen and brown ink, on vellum
11 x 8in (28.2 x 20.8cm)
£2,000-2,500 *C*

Bolognese School (17thC)
Cleopatra
Oil on canvas
45¾ x 40in (116.2 x 101.6cm)
£8,000-10,000 *S(NY)*

The suicide of Cleopatra, bitten by an asp clasped to her breast, was a popular subject with 17thC Italian artists, providing a good historical excuse for the portrayal of the nude.

Giovanni Baglione (1570-1643)
Italian
Study of a Girl Sleeping with a Cat in her arms
Red and black chalk
4¾ x 7¼in (12 x 18.2cm)
£2,500-3,200 *S*

Giovanni Francesco Barbieri, called I Guercino (1591-1666)
Italian
Study of a Male Nude Lying on the Groun
Oiled charcoal heightened with white chal
on grey/buff paper
17½ x 13½in (44.3 x 35cm)
£78,000-100,000 *S(NY)*

Edward du Bois (1619-97)
Flemish
A Sheet of Studies of Nudes
Brown wash heightened with white
11⅛ x 8¼in (29.2 x 21cm)
£2,100-2,600 *C*

Marco Liberi (c1640-c1700)
Italian
An Allegory of Justice and Peace
Oil on canvas
39 x 52¾in (99 x 134cm)
£26,000-30,000 *S*

Johannes Sadeler I (1550-c1600)
Flemish
The Seasons
A set of four engravings, c1580
7 x 9in (17.5 x 22.5cm)
£2,000-2,500 *C*

Rembrandt Harmensz. van Rijn (1606-69)
Dutch
A Woman Sitting beside a Stove
Etching, 1658
8¾ x 7¼in (22.2 x 18.7cm)
£60,000-80,000 *C*

*Writing in 1718, Arnold Houbraken recalled
the following incident that occurred in
Rembrandt's studio with one of the artist's
models. 'Now it happened, on a warm
summer's day, that both the painter (one of
Rembrandt's pupils) and the model stripped
so as to be stark naked ... (Rembrandt) found
the doors closed, but, told about the thing, he
watched for a while their pranks through the
chink that had been made, until among other
words he also heard: 'Now we are exactly as
Adam and Eve in Paradise, for we are also
naked.' On this he knocked on the door with
his mahlstick and called out, to the terror of
both, 'But because you are naked you must get
out of Paradise.'*

Augustin Terwesten (1649-1711)
Dutch
Danae and the Shower of Gold
Oil on canvas
31 x 24¾in (79 x 63cm)
£3,000-4,000 *P*

Alessandro Turchi, called Orbetto
(1578-1649)
Italian
Diana and Actaeon
Oil on canvas
24 x 30½in (60.8 x 77cm)
£25,000-30,000 *P*

Circle of Joachim Wtewael (1566-1638)
Dutch
Women Bathing
Oil on copper
8 x 10¼in (20.3 x 26cm)
£13,000-14,000 *S(NY)*

18th Century

After François Boucher (1703-70)
French
Diana Resting after the Hunt
With signature, dated 1781, oil on panel
13 x 16in (33.3 x 41cm)
£6,500-7,500 *C*

Jacopo Amigoni (1675-1752)
Italian
Diana bathing with her Nymphs
Oil on canvas
36 x 28¼in (91.5 x 71.8cm)
£275,000-325,000 *Bon*

*Though Diana (or Artemis) was the Goddess
of chastity, this did not stop the virgin
huntress from being a favourite classical
subject with painters of the nude, and Diana
bathing with her Nymphs was a particularly
popular theme. Enthusiastic spectators,
however, should perhaps take heed of what
happened to Actaeon. While hunting in the
forest, the young prince stumbled accidentally
upon the grotto where the Goddess and her
companions were bathing. To punish him for
his glimpse of divine nudity, Diana turned
him into a stag and he was torn apart by his
own hounds. Amigoni's picture more than
trebled its £80,000 top estimate at Bonhams in
December 1992, combining quality painting,
with an attractive subject matter, added to
the fact that the work was fresh to the market
and had been in the possession of the same
family since the 1700s.*

Follower of Gennaro Greco (1663-1714)
Italian
Diana and her Nymphs bathing by a classical
ruin
23½ x 30¼in (59.8 x 76.8cm)
£8,000-9,000 *C*

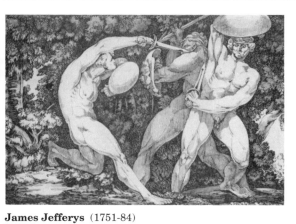

James Jefferys (1751-84)
British
Three male nudes fighting at the edge of a
wood
Pencil, pen and black ink, grey wash
14¾ x 21¾in (37.5 x 55.2cm)
£3,500-4,500 *C*

Anton Raphael Mengs (1728-79)
German
A Seated Nude
Inscribed, black and white chalk,
black lead on grey preparation
14½ x 9¾in (37 x 24.6cm)
£1,300-1,800 *C*

Noël Hallé (1711-81)
French
A Reclining Nude
Inscribed, black and white chalk on blue
paper
12½ x 19in (32 x 48.3cm)
£2,800-3,400 *C*

Berard Picart (1673-1733)
French
A Reclining Nude
Signed and dated 1730, red chalk
10 x 16½in (25.5 x 41.5cm)
£4,000-5,000 *CNY*

Pierre-Paul Prud'hon (1758-1823)
French
A Seated Female Nude
Black and white chalk, on blue paper
13 x 8½in (33.3 x 21.7cm)
£3,800-4,800 *C*

Attributed to Ignaz Stern, called Stella
(1679-1748)
German
Leda and the Swan
Oil on canvas
10½ x 14¼in (26.7 x 36.2cm)
£3,000-4,000 *S(NY)*

Circle of Jacques-Antoine Vallin
(1760-1831)
French
A Female Nude asleep on a Sofa
Oil on canvas
23½ x 28½in (59.7 x 72.3cm)
£2,800-3,200 *CSK*

19th Century

Alexandre Antigna (1817-78)
French
Scene d'Atelier
Signed, oil on panel
16 x 13in (40.3 x 32cm)
£6,500-7,500 *S(NY)*

The artist in this painting is a self-portrait

Modeste Carlier (1820-78)
Belgian
Diana, The Huntress
Signed, oil on canvas
30 x 20in (76.2 x 50.8cm)
£2,000-2,500 *CSK*

Louis-Robert Carrier-Belleuse
(1848-1913)
French
On the Beach
Signed and inscribed, pastel
36¼ x 28¾in (92 x 73cm)
£7,500-8,500 *CNY*

Paul Emile Jacobs (1802-66)
German
Diana and Nymphs bathing
Signed and dated 1846, oil on canvas
61 x 79⅜in (155 x 202.6cm)
£17,000-19,000 *C*

Harry Furniss (1854-1924)
British
Then the Nude Model, Sitting in Buff for
Hector or Apollo, Calderon from heel to
eyebrow
Monochrome watercolour
14½ x 10in (37.5 x 25cm)
£300-350 *CBL*

Edward Simmons (1852-1931)
American
A Female Nude playing the piano
Signed, oil on canvas
19¾ x 23½in (50 x 60cm)
£3,000-4,000 *S*

Wilhem Kray (1828-89)
German
The Bathers
Signed, oil on canvas
52 x 37¾in (132 x 96cm)
£5,600-6,600 *C*

Michel Richard Putz (19thC)
Continental
The Peacock Throne
Signed, oil on canvas
78¾ x 39¾in (200 x 100cm)
£8,000-9,000 *S(NY)*

Solomon Joseph Solomon (1860-1927)
British
Love's First Lesson
Signed and dated 1885, oil on canvas
46½ x 36in (118 x 91.5cm)
£8,500-10,000 *Bon*

Frederik Ludwig Storch (1805-83)
Danish
The Dream
Signed and dated 1870, oil on canvas
31 x 36in (78.2 x 91.4cm)
£5,000-6,000 *C*

Emile Vernon (19th/20thC)
French
Starlight
Signed, oil on canvas
35¾ x 24in (90.8 x 61cm)
£24,000-30,000 *S(NY)*

Vladimir Zupansky (1869-1928)
Czechoslovakian
A Nude in a Garden
Signed with monogram and dated 1897, oil
on canvas
43½ x 15¾in (111 x 40cm)
£5,000-6,000 *S*

20th Century

Cesare Bacchi (20thC)
Italian
Le Repos
Oil on canvas, 1939
79 x 60in (200 x 150cm)
£8,000-8,500 *JD*

*Bacchi's picture gives us some
idea of the discomfort faced
by the studio model.*

Ernest Berke (b1921)
American
Reclining Nude
Signed and dated 81, oil on canvasboard
12 x 16in (30.5 x 40.6cm)
£600-700 *S(NY)*

*Ernest Berke was born in Arizona and
specialises in scenes of the American West.*

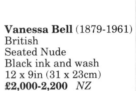

Vanessa Bell (1879-1961)
British
Seated Nude
Black ink and wash
12 x 9in (31 x 23cm)
£2,000-2,200 *NZ*

Stephen Bone (1904-68)
British
Young Girl at Toilette
Oil on canvas, c1950
30 x 25in (76 x 64cm)
£2,500-2,750 *CE*

Albert H. Collings (d1947)
British
A Reflection
Signed and dated 1919, oil on canvas
37¼ x 31¼in (94.5 x 79.3cm)
£4,000-5,000 *Bon*

Le Corbusier (Charles Edouard Jeanneret) (1887-1965)
French
Trois Personnages
Signed and dated 1933, pastel
8¼ x 12¼in (21 x 31cm)
£5,000-6,000 *P*

Charles Despiau (1874-1946)
French
Femme nue assise
Sanguine
14 x 10in (36 x 25cm)
£1,000-1,500 *S*

Richard Diebenkorn (b1922)
American
Reclining nude - pink stripe
Signed and dated 62, oil on canvas
31 x 25in (78.7 x 63.5cm)
£57,000-67,000 *S(NY)*

Frank Dobson (1888-1963)
British
Seated Nude
Crayon and chalk
18 x 12in (46 x 31cm)
£2,900-3,200 *NZ*

This picture was given by Frank Dobson to the artist and sculptor, Arthur Ayres.

Paul Delvaux (b1898)
Belgian
Night
Signed in pencil, lithograph, 1975
12½ x 10in (31.5 x 25cm)
£1,700-2,200 *S*

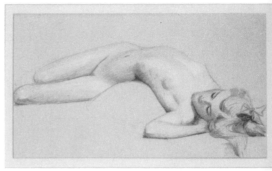

English School (20thC)
Draped Nude
Drawing
7½ x 11in (19 x 28cm)
£600-675 *BRG*

Bernard Dunstan, R.A. (b1920)
British
The Artist and his Model, '89 - '90
Linen laid on board
13¾ x 12in (35 x 31cm)
£2,000-5,000 *BSG*
*One of our most respected and much loved
painters, Dunstan was brought up in the
French/English tradition of 19th and early
20thC painting exemplified in the works of
Bonnard, Sickert, Vuillard and Degas.*

William Russell Flint (1880-1969)
British
Reclining Nude
Signed, coloured print
12 x 23in (30 x 58cm)
£600-700 *LANG*

*Even in a recession, and to the despair of
anyone with even vaguely feminist leanings,
Flint's works are always in demand - not on
the artist's watercolours and sketches, but
also prints and reproductions. Among the
most desirable of the mass-produced colour
reproductions are those produced by W. J.
Stacey and Frost & Reed. But beware, no
matter who the publisher, to command any
real price a Flint print should always be
signed in pencil and avoid faded prints and
the more common reproductions.*

Maryclare Foa (20thC)
British
Running with a blue tree, 1993
Oil on board
49 x 39in (124.5 x 99cm)
£850-950 *KG*

Ronald Ossory Dunlop (b1894)
British
Female Nude
Signed, oil on board
29 x 19in (74 x 48cm)
£900-980 *LH*

Duncan Grant (1885-1978)
British
Reclining Male Nude; Paul Roche
Signed with initials, black crayon
14 x 19½in (36 x 50cm)
£950-1,250 *C*

Alberto Giacometti (1901-66)
Swiss
Anette
Lithograph, 1965
10 x 7½in (25.5 x 19cm)
£150-160 *WO*

Steve Goddard (20thC)
British
Study of a Seated Nude
Oil on canvas
23 x 20in (59 x 51cm)
£900-1,200 *Wa*

Ernest Hyde (b1918)
British
Saucy Sally
Signed, gouache
16 x 12in (41 x 31cm)
£300-325 *Dr*

This is from the original Pin Up Calendar of 1958.

Philip Harris (b1965)
British
Two Figures Lying in a Shallow Stream
Signed and dated 1992, oil on canvas
72 x 42in (183 x 107cm)
£14,000-15,000 *Mer*

André Lhote (1885-1962)
French
Nu assis
Signed, watercolour
14½ x 10¾in (37 x 27cm)
£4,000-5,000 *S*

Paul McPhail (20thC)
British
Together
Dated 1992, oil on canvas
84 x 73in (215 x 184cm)
£5,000-5,250 *EW*

Edvard Munch (1863-1944)
Norwegian
Madonna
Lithograph and woodcut printed in 3 colours,
1896-1902
21¾ x 13¾in (55.5 x 34.8cm)
£35,000-45,000 *S*

Richard Edward Miller (1875-1943)
American
Bather
Signed, dated 1930, oil on board
36 x 38in (91.4 x 96.5cm)
£38,000-50,000 *S(NY)*

Henry Moore (1898-1986)
British
Reclining Woman on Beach
Signed in pencil,
lithograph printed in
colours, 1980-81
21¼ x 29in (54 x 73.5cm)
£1,900-2,500 *S*

Janet Owen (b1965)
British
Kiss
Signed and dated 1991, oil on board
10 x 8in (25 x 21cm)
£400-475 *Mer*

Mel Ramos (20thC)
American
Mysta of the Moon
Signed, titled and dated 1963, oil on canvas
50in (127cm) square
£17,500-19,000 *S(NY)*

Egon Schiele (1890-1918)
Austrian
Akt Studie in Pose
Signed and dated 1918, black crayon
11¾ x 17in (29.6 x 43.5cm)
£120,000-140,000 *S*

Philip Pearlstein (b1924)
American
Male and female models on Navajo blanket
Watercolour on paper
29 x 41in (73.7 x 104cm)
£7,000-8,000 *S(NY)*

Sir Matthew Smith (1879-1959)
British
Reclining Nude
Signed with initials, dated 1952, oil on canvas
25 x 30in (63.5 x 76cm)
£15,500-17,500 *C*

Kirill Sokolov (20thC) Russian
Blue Nude
Oil on board
25 x 18in (64 x 46cm)
£900-950 *VCG*

Leon Underwood (b1980)
British
Bathers, also known as Boys Bathing
Signed and inscribed, print
6½ x 4in (16.5 x 10.2cm)
£300-350 *BLD*

Kenneth Ross Welburn (b1911)
British
Nude Study
Signed, pen and watercolour
10 x 19in (25 x 48cm)
£100-120 *Dr*

John Ward (b1917)
British
Isabella
Signed, inscribed, oil on board
9 x 8in (23 x 20cm)
£800-900 *ALT*

Helen Jean Young (b1914)
British
The Bath
Signed, oil on board
13 x 9in (33 x 23cm)
£800-850 *NZ*

Hubert von Zwickle
(b1875)
Austrian
Eve
Signed and dated 1924,
oil on canvas
22 x 55½in (56 x 135cm)
£2,900-3,400 *C*

RELIGIOUS

In spite of troubled financial times worldwide, Old Master pictures have enjoyed some notable successes over the past season. Bonham's auction of Old Masters and British Pictures held in December 1992 was the auction house's most successful sale ever, raising a total of £1.28 million, thanks largely to two major Old Master pictures. 'Throughout the year,' Christie's told Millers, 'it has been the more traditional areas of the auction market which have shown the greatest resilience. Nowhere is this more evident than in the field of Old Master pictures. Over the last three years, worldwide sales of Old Master pictures at Christie's have remained consistently strong.' Writing in the *Financial Times*, Anthony Thorncroft agreed. 'The auction world has returned to its traditional ways where connoisseurs rule and established works of art hold pride of place.' Yet while the recession might not have halted the demand for Old Master pictures, it has certainly made buyers more selective and more careful. 'While most buyers have always looked primarily for quality,' notes Christie's,

'they now seem to place greater emphasis on acquiring works which are 'fresh' to the market, of sound condition and with a noteworthy provenance.'

Buying Old Master pictures and drawings requires a certain amount of knowledge, and not just about a work's provenance or condition. Many of the religious and mythological subjects portrayed are unfamiliar to our 20thC culture, as are the aesthetic and social mores that governed their depiction. The fact that such works might not be so immediately accessible as later, more decorative pictures, makes the market, according to dealer Tony Haynes, extremely under-valued: 'An Old Master picture that might have taken several years to paint can go for the same price as a decorative landscape by a Victorian artist who knocked out five canvasses a week,' explains Haynes. 'The works are commercially under-rated and very badly understood.' As such the field can offer a rich and fascinating mine to any collector prepared to do a little homework.

15th and 16th Centuries

Pieter Coeck van Aalst (1502-50)
Flemish
Triptych: The Holy Family
Oil on panel, shaped tops
46¾ x 64in (118.8 x 162.2cm)
£180,000-200,000 C

Mariotto Albertinelli (1474-1515)
Italian
Mary and Joseph Adoring the Christ Child
Oil on panel
34in (86cm) diam
£40,000-50,000 S(NY)

Follower of Jacopo Bassano (1515-92)
Italian
The Adoration of the Shepherds
Oil on canvas
21 x 29in (53.3 x 73.6cm)
£1,000-1,200 CSK

Nicolas Beatrizet (c1515-60)
The Conversion of Saint Paul, after Michelangelo
Engraving
17 x 21½in (43.4 x 54.7cm)
£800-1,000 C

Attributed to Filippo Bellini (1550-1604)
Italian
The Madonna of the Pillar appearing to Saint
James and the Apostles, with Saint
Christopher
Inscribed, black chalk, pen and brown ink,
brown wash, squared in black chalk
12½ x 60cm (31.8 x 23.5cm)
£2,000-2,500 *C*

Attributed to Lodovico Carracci
(1555-1619)
Italian
The Visitation
Inscribed, black chalk, pen and brown ink,
blue wash heightened with white
15½ x 11½in (39.5 x 29cm)
£5,500-6,500 *C*

Follower of Paul Bril (1554-1626)
Flemish
The Parable of the Tares
Oil on panel
18¾ x 25½in (47.8 x 64.5cm)
£10,500-11,500 *C*

**Attributed to Pieter Brueghel, the
Younger** (1564-1638)
Flemish
The Massacre of the Innocents
Oil on copper
18¾ x 26½in (47.5 x 67cm)
£450,000-550,000 *P*

*The lost original of this composition was
executed by Pieter Brueghel, the elder.*

After Pieter Brueghel the Elder
(1512-69)
Flemish
The Seven Vices
Complete set of 7 engravings, 1558
8¾ x 11½in (22.4 x 29.3cm)
£19,000-21,000 *S*

Giovanni Battista Cavalieri (1525-97)
Italian
Susanna and the Elders
Etching with engraving, 1566
13 x 18in (33 x 46cm)
£2,000-2,500 *C*

Francesco da Castello (b1540)
Flemish
Saint Sebastian
Oil on canvas
55½ x 41¾in (141 x 106cm)
£17,500-19,000 *S(NY)*

Follower of Lucas Cranach (16thC)
German
Judith with the head of Holofernes
Oil on panel
36½ x 32¾in (92.7 x 82.8cm)
£7,000-8,000 *C*

Vittore Crivelli (c1440-1501/2)
Italian
Saint Anthony of Padua
Tempera on gold ground panel, shaped top
28½ x 16¼in (72.5 x 41.4cm)
£15,500-17,000 *C*

Albrecht Dürer (1471-1528)
German
The Prodigal Son
Engraving
9¾ x 7½in (24.8 x 19cm)
£4,000-5,000 *S*

Flemish School (c1480)
The Entombment
Oil on panel
26½ x 15½in (67 x 39cm)
£50,000-60,000 *P*

Attributed to Giacomo Francia
(1486-1557)
Italian
Saint Petronius holding up a model of the
City of Bologna: a fragment
Oil on tempera on panel
12½ x 6¾in (31.8 x 17cm)
£10,500-11,500 *S(NY)*

Giacomo Francia (c1486-1557)
Italian
The Madonna and Child with the Infant
Saint John the Baptist
Oil on panel
24 x 19in (61 x 48.2cm)
£30,000-40,000 *C*

Bartolomeo Gagliardo, Il Spagnoletto
(1555-c1626)
Italian
Saint Francis in Prayer in front of a crucifix
(recto); An Evangelist writing at a desk
(verso)
Black chalk, pen and brown ink, brown wash
7 x 6¾in (18 x 16.6cm)
£1,500-2,000 *CNY*

Follower of Adriaen Isenbrandt (d1551)
Flemish
Virgin and Child in a landscape
Oil on panel laid on to another panel
17¼ x 12in (44 x 30cm)
£8,200-9,000 *S(S)*

German School (16thC)
Saint Barbara; and Saint Catherine
A pair, both oil on gold ground panel
20¼ x 6½in (51 x 16cm)
£23,000-30,000 *S*

*Both these saints suffered unpleasant fates.
Barbara was imprisoned by her father in a
tower (hence her attribute), but nevertheless
managed to smuggle a priest in to baptise her.
Her unsympathetic parent handed her over to
the Romans for torture and then killed her
with his own sword, being deservedly struck
dead by a bolt of lightning at the moment of
her execution. Among female saints,
Catherine was second only to Mary
Magdalene in popularity. For her faith she
was bound to a spiked wheel (her attribute)
but when that was destroyed, yet again by a
convenient thunderbolt from heaven, the
Emperor Maxentius had her beheaded.
Barbara and Catherine are often presented as
companions.*

**Imitator of Hugo
van der Goes**
(c1570)
Flemish
A Praying Saint
Oil on panel
7½ x 6in (19 x 15.6cm)
£5,000-6,000 *P*

Attributed to Andrea Mantegna
(1421-1506)
Italian
The Flagellation: With the Pavement
Engraving, late 1460s
16 x 12½in (40.4 x 31.5cm)
£135,000-150,000 *C*

*The Flagellation: With the Pavement
is one of the foremost engravings
of the Italian Renaissance.*

After Leonardo da Vinci (1452-1519)
Italian
The Last Supper
Oil on panel
27½ x 55½in (69.8 x 141cm)
£1,300-1,800 *CSK*

*After the Tempera in the Refectory, Santa
Maria delle Grazie, Milan.*

Israhel van Meckenem (15th/16thC)
German
Judith with the Head of Holofernes
Engraving
8½ x 12¼in (21.5 x 31.4cm)
£34,000-38,000 *S*

Hans Memling (active 1465-94)
Flemish
The Virgin and Child enthroned with two
angels
Oil on panel
27 x 20½in (68.5 x 52cm)
£190,000-220,000 *C*

Andrea Mantegna (1421-1506)
Italian
The Virgin and Child
Engraving
9¼ x 10¼in (23.5 x 26cm)
£15,500-16,500 *S*

The Master of Santa Lucia sul Prato
(active c1485-c1500)
The Adoration of the Shepherds with Saint
Jerome, the Annunciation to the Shepherds
and the Journey of the Magi beyond
Signed or inscribed with initials P B, oil on
panel   63¾ x 66½in (162 x 169cm)
£57,000-70,000 *C*

*The surface of the panel shows several small
burns caused by the flames of candles on the
altar above which it was originally placed.*

Jan Muller (1571-1628)
Dutch
The Creation of the World
A set of seven engravings
10½in (27cm) diam.
£11,000-12,000 *S*

Attributed to Bernart van Orley
(1494-1542)
Flemish
The Coronation of the Virgin
Inscribed, oil on panel
19½ x 28¼in (49.5 x 71.8cm)
£38,000-45,000 *S(NY)*

Jacob Cornelisz. van Oostsanen
(c1470-1533)
Dutch
The Crucifixion: The Central Panel of a
Triptych
Dated on the central horse's bridle ANNO
DN M+CCCCC.ET.VII, oil on panel
39 x 31in (99 x 76.7cm)
£420,000-460,000 *S(NY)*

*In addition to producing paintings, Jacob
also illustrated books, painted choir vaults,
and made designs for stained glass,
embroidery and prints. Amsterdam, where
van Oostsanen lived most of his life, was,
until his arrival, devoid of an art tradition.
In fact, Jacob van Oostsanen was probably
the earliest and most important artist
working in Amsterdam and it is from his
work that the great artistic tradition of that
city derives.*

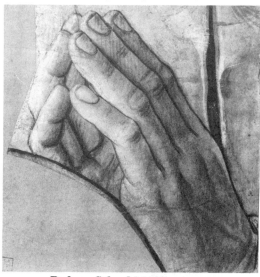

Paduan School (c1480)
Study of Praying Hands
Drawing with brush in black ink over black
chalk with red and brown wash and white
heightening, irregular shape, laid down
7¼ x 6¾in (18 x 17.8cm)
£10,000-11,000 *S(NY)*

Follower of Pedro Orrente (1570-1644)
Spanish
The Story of Noah: God appearing to Noah;
The Building of the Ark; The Embarkation;
The Deluge; and Noah's Sacrifice
A set of 5, oil on panel
38½ x 67½in (97.5 x 171cm)
£13,000-14,000 *C*

Giovanni di Paolo (1403-83)
Italian
Head of Christ: A Fragment of a Painted
Cross
Gold ground, tempera on panel
14 x 16¾in (35.6 x 42.5cm)
£60,000-70,000 *S(NY)*

After Sebastiano del Piombo
(1485-1547)
Italian
The Flagellation
Oil on copper
25 x 21in (63.6 x 53.4cm)
£950-1,200 *CSK*

After the fresco in San Pietro Montorio, Rome.

Giovanni di Pietro, called lo Spagna
(c1450-1528)
Italian
The Madonna and Child
Tempera, oil and gilt on panel
12¾ x 8½in (32.4 x 21.6cm)
£30,000-40,000 *S(NY)*

Circle of Johann Rottenhammer
(1564-1625)   German
The Assumption of the Virgin
Pen and black ink, grey wash
15 x 10in (38.3 x 25cm)
£850-1,200 *C*

Jan Saenredam (1565-1607)
Dutch
The Wise and the Foolish Virgins
A set of 5 engravings
£1,800-2,300 *S*

Circle of Giulio Pippi, Giulio Romano
(c1499-1546)
Italian
The Holy Family with a Virgin Martyr
Red chalk heightened with white (partly oxidised), incised
11½ x 9¾in (29 x 24.2cm)
£3,400-4,000 *C*

Andrea Previtali, called Cordeliaghi
(1470-1528)
Italian
The Nativity
Oil on panel
15 x 8in (38 x 20.5cm)
£60,000-70,000 *S*

**Studio of Girolamo Siciolante da
Sermoneta** (1521-80)
Italian
Saint Catherine
34½ x 27½in (87.6 x 70cm)
£9,000-10,000 *C*

**Circle of Francesco Ubertini, called
Bachiacca** (1494/95-1557)
Italian
The Adoration of the Shepherds
Oil on panel
13 x 10¼in (33 x 26cm)
£9,000-10,000 *P*

Locate the Source

*The source of each
illustration in Miller's can
be found by checking the
code letters below each
caption with the list of
contributors.*

**Michele Tosini, called Michele di Ridolfo
del Ghirlandaio** (1503-77)
Italian
The Madonna and Child with the Infant
Saint John the Baptist
Oil on panel
37¾ x 29¼in (95.5 x 74.5cm)
£55,000-65,000 *C*

Giovanni Battista Trotti, il Malosso
(1555-1619)
Italian
An Angel
Inscribed, pen and brown ink, grey wash,
squared in black chalk
8 x 5in (20 x 13cm)
£850-950 *C*

17th Century

Theodor Boeyermans (1620-78)
Flemish
The Finding of Moses
Oil on canvas
54¼ x 81¼in (137.8 x 206.5cm)
£13,500-14,500 *S*

**Giovanni Francesco Barbieri, il
Guercino** (1591-1666)
Italian
The Executioner holding the Head of Saint
John the Baptist
Pen and brown ink, brown wash, on light
brown paper
11¾ x 8½in (29.7 x 21.6cm)
£56,000-70,000 *CNY*

Jacques Callot (1592-1635)
French
La Tentation de Saint Antoine
Etching, 1635
14 x 18in (35.7 x 46cm)
£8,500-9,500 *C*

Circle of Carlo Cignani (1628-1719)
Italian
Saint Sebastian
Oil on canvas
52½ x 39in (128 x 98.7cm)
£6,700-7,700 *C*

Circle of Giulio Carpione (1611-74)
Italian
Abraham, Isaac and the Angel
Oil on canvas
27¼ x 30¼in (69 x 77cm)
£4,700-5,700 *S*

Ridolfi di Domenico, called Ghirlandaio
(1583-1661)
Italian
The Visitation, accompanied by St Francis
and St Elizabeth of Hungary
Oil on panel
74½ x 68in (189 x 173cm)
£15,000-20,000 *P*

Circle of Marcantonio Franceschini
(1648-1729)
Italian
Christ healing the blind man
38¾ x 53in (98 x 134.7cm)
£5,200-6,000 *C*

Follower of Frans Francken (16th/17thC)
Flemish
The Madonna and Child
Oil on copper
6 x 4¾in (15.3 x 12.2cm)
300-400 *CSK*

Frans Francken the Younger (1581-1642)
Flemish
The Building of the Tower of Babel
Oil on copper
27¼ x 34in (69.2 x 86.4cm)
£24,000-28,000 *S(NY)*

Giovanni Battista Gaulli, il Baciccio
(1639-1709)
Italian
The Martyrdom of a Royal Saint at the door
of a church (Saint Edmund?)
Black chalk, pen and brown ink, brown wash
heightened with white, on light brown paper
10½ x 8in (26.2 x 20cm)
£21,000-26,000 *CNY*

Louis Laguerre (1663-1721)
French
The Departure of the Prodigal Son; and The
Return of the Prodigal Son
A pair, oil on canvas
19 x 46½in (48 x 118cm)
£58,000-70,000 *S*

Attributed to Sebastian de Llanos Valdes (c1605-77)
Spanish
Saint Andrew
Inscribed, oil on canvas
65¾ x 42in (167 x 107cm)
£11,000-12,000 *S*

Follower of Paolo di Matteis (1662-1728)
Italian
The Holy Family and the infant Saint John
Oil on canvas
24¾ x 36½in (63 x 93cm)
£4,000-4,500 *CSK*

After Bartolomé Esteban Murillo
(1617-82)
Spanish
The sleeping Christ Child
Oil on canvas
24¾ x 27½in (62.6 x 69.8cm)
£2,000-3,000 *C*

Giacomo del Po (1652-1726)
Italian
The Magdalen washing Christ's feet
Oil on canvas
53½ x 39½in (136 x 100cm)
£8,000-9,000 *P*

Rembrandt Harmensz. van Rijn
(1606-69)
Dutch
Saint Peter and Saint John healing the
cripple at the Gate of the Temple
Etching with drypoint and engraving, 1659
6¾ x 8¾in (18 x 22cm)
£6,000-7,000 *C*

*According to Rembrandt's contemporaries, the
artist carefully manipulated the market for
his prints. 'Thanks to his engravings he
achieved great riches and this bred a
proportionate pride and self conceit,'
commented F. Balducini (1681)
disapprovingly, who goes on to relate how
when it seemed to Rembrandt that his prints
were not making as much money as they
deserved, he bought them up himself from all
over Europe at great expense, so as to control
their market value and stimulate demand.
Another clever trick, as A. Houbraken writing
in 1718 notes, was the device of making slight
changes and unimportant additions to prints
so that they could be sold again as fresh
works. 'Nay, the demand was at that time so
great that people were considered true
amateurs who did not possess the Juno with
and without the crown, the Joseph with the
light and the dark head and so on.'
Fortunately for Rembrandt, the concept of the
limited edition print did not yet exist.*

Sir Peter Paul Rubens (1577-1640)
Flemish
Constantine worshipping the True Cross
Oil on panel
14 x 13¼in (35.4 x 33.7cm)
£265,000-300,000 *C*

Follower of Sir Peter Paul Rubens
(1577-1640)
Flemish
The Continence of Scipio
Oil on panel
29 x 41½in (74 x 105.2cm)
£7,000-8,000 *S*

**Manner of Giovanni Battista Salvi,
called Sassoferrato** (1609-85)
Italian
The Madonna at Prayer
Oil on canvas
29 x 23½in (73.3 59.7cm)
£600-700 *CSK*

Giovanni Battista Salvi, il Sassoferrato
(1609-85)
Italian
Hands joined in Prayer
Black and white chalk, on blue paper
5¼ x 7¾in (13.5 x 19.4cm)
£2,500-3,000 *CNY*

Alonso del Arco, il Sordillo (1625-1700)
Spanish
The Visitation with Saint Joseph and Joachin
Inscribed, black chalk, pen and brown ink,
brown wash
9 x 14in (22.6 x 36cm)
£800-1,000 *C*

*Alonso del Arco was nicknamed El Sordillo
de Perada on account of his deafness and his
apprenticeship with Antonio de Perada. His
entire career was spent in Madrid, where he
and his workshop produced a succession of
pictures for the churches and monasteries of
the city.*

Attributed to Luis Tristan (c1585-1649)
Spanish
Saint Anthony Abbot
With signature and date F Herrera 16..
64 x 43in (162.7 x 109.2cm)
£7,800-8,800 *C*

Venetian School (17thC)
The Adoration of the Magi
Oil on panel
25¼ x 31½in (64.5 x 79.5cm)
£3,800-4,800 *S(S)*

Eustache le Sueur (1617-55)
French
David dancing before the Ark of the
Covenant
Inscribed, black chalk, grey wash, squared in
black chalk
10 x 14¼in (25.5 x 36.2cm)
£11,500-12,500 *CNY*

*Le Sueur was known as 'Le Raphael Français'
and was considered a prodigious talent. Le
Brun was extremely jealous of his
contemporary's success, and on hearing of his
untimely death commented with relief: 'I feel
now as if I had a thorn just taken out of my
foot.'*

Follower of Simon Vouet (1590-1649)
French
Judith with the head of Holofernes
Oil on canvas
46½ x 38½in (117.8 c 97.5cm)
£15,500-17,000 *S(NY)*

18th Century

Carington Bowles (Publisher) (18thC)
British
The Prodigal Son
A set of 6 coloured mezzotints, 1775,
varnished and laid on canvas
9¾ x 13¾in (25 x 35cm)
£1,000-1,400 *S*

Follower of Corrado Giaquinto (1690-1765)
Italian
The Martyrdom of Saints Ippolito, Taurino
and Ercolano
Oil on canvas
24 x 29in (61 x 74cm)
£2,200-3,000 *S*

Johann Josef Anton Huber (1737-1815)
German
Samson and Delilah; and The Death of Samson
Oil on canvas
39 x 56¾in (99 x 143.8cm)
£8,000-9,000 *C*

Francesco Salvator Fontebasso
(1709-68/9)
Italian
The Magdalene washing Christ's feet
Black and red chalk, pen and brown ink,
brown, grey and reddish wash heightened
with white, with ink borderline
19½ x 13¾in (49 x 35cm)
£42,000-50,000 *C*

Nicolas Bernard Lepicie (1735-84)
French
The Conversion of St Paul
Signed and dated 1767, oil on canvas
39½ x 31in (100 x 79cm)
£165,000-175,000 *JMI*

Neapolitan School (18thC)
The Virgin and Child with Saint John
Oil on paper (?) laid on panel, in an ornate
carved and gilt wood frame
6½ x 8¾in (16.5 x 22.3cm)
£2,700-3,500 *S*

Thomas Rowlandson (1756-1827)
British
Susannah and the Elders
9 x 10in (22.8 x 25.7cm)
£600-700 *Bon*

North Italian School (c1700)
The Magdalene in a landscape
Oil on panel, in a period Dutch ebonised
frame with ripple mouldings
9 x 6¾in (23 x 17cm)
£1,500-2,000 *S*

Giovanni Battista Piazzetta (1682-1754)
Italian
An Allegory of the Reign of Pope Benedict
XIV (Lambertini) with Divine Wisdom and
True Religion banishing Heresy
Black chalk
15¾ x 11½in (40 x 29cm)
£8,300-9,300 *CNY*

Jean-François de Troy (1679-1752)
French
Joseph and Potiphar's Wife
Black chalk, pen and brown ink, brown wash
heightened with white
12 x 9½in (30 x 23.5cm)
£30,000-35,000 *C*

19th and 20th Centuries

Jean Jules Antoine Lecomte du Noüy
(1842-1923)
French
Démosthène s'exerce à la Parole
Signed and dated 1870, oil on panel
19 x 14¾in (47.3 x 37.5cm)
£9,500-10,500 *S(NY)*

Hugues Merle (1823-81)
French
Abraham banishing Hagar and Ishmael
Signed and dated 1872, oil on canvas
36 x 21in (92 x 53.5cm)
£5,000-6,000 *S*

After William Holman Hunt (1827-1910)
British
The Triumph of the Innocents
Inscribed, photogravure, 1887
24 x 36in (61 x 91.4cm)
£550-650 *C(S)*

Simeon Solomon (1840-1905)
British
A Vision of wounded Love
Signed and dated 1893, pencil
15 x 18¾in (38.5 x 47.5cm)
£2,800-3,500 *C*

Marsden Hartley (1878-1943)
American
Abelard Ascending (A Fantasy)
Oil on board, painted c1942
28 x 22in (71 x 56cm)
£42,000-50,000 *S(NY)*

Russell Reeve (1895-1970)
British
Nuns in Tramcar
Aquatint
12 x 14in (30.5 x 36cm)
£800-850 *PN*

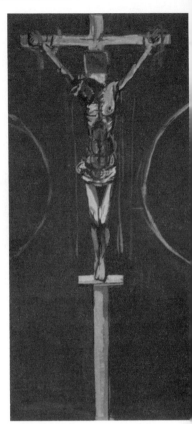

Doris Zingeisen
(b1898)
British
The Virgin and the
Unicorn
Signed, oil on canvas
23½ x 19¼in
(59.5 x 49cm)
£600-700 *S(S)*

Graham Sutherland (1903-80)
Study for the Crucifixion
Red background, gouache on beige paper
14 x 6¾in (35.5 x 17.2cm)
£5,000-6,000 *C*

David Hosie (20thC)
British
Exodus
Oil on canvas
90 x 72in (228.5 x 182.5cm)
£7,500-9,000 *JGG*

Linda Sutton (b1947)
British
Dance of Salome
Oil on canvas
94 x 84in (238 x 213cm)
£7,000-8,000 *BRG*

Dutch School (18thC)
Ducks on a Pond
Oil on canvas
24 x 28¾in (61 x 73cm)
£4,000-5,000 *S(NY)*

Herman Henstenburg (1667-1726)
Dutch
Swans, a Spoonbill, a Mallard, a Wigeon and other
Ducks on a River below a Ruin
Signed and dated 1694, bodycolour on vellum, black
ink framing lines
11½ x 9¾in (29 x 24.5cm)
£5,600-6,600 *C*

Charles Collins (c1680-1744)
British
A Guinea Hen
Signed, inscribed and dated August 1743,
watercolour heightened with bodycolour
15 x 21in (39 x 54cm)
£2,700-3,500 *S*

Jakob Bogdani (c1660-1724)
Hungarian
Two Peacocks on a Stone Plinth,
Poultry and Hollyhocks in the
Garden of a Villa
Signed
91 x 59in (231 x 150cm)
£95,000-120,000 *C*

Tobias Stranover (1684-1731)
Czechoslovakian
A Pheasant, a Shellduck, a
Kingfisher, two green Parrots, a Ruff
and a Partridge in a landscape
Oil on canvas, in a carved wood frame
39 x 53in (99 x 134.5cm)
£30,000-40,000 *S*

Max von Schmaedel (b1856)
German
The Grapes of Wrath
Signed, oil on canvas
33½ x 63¾in (85 x 161cm)
£7,200-8,200 *C*

John Cyril Harrison (1898-1985)
British
Pheasant Breaking Cover
Signed, pencil and watercolour
29¼ x 22¼in (74.3 x 56.6cm)
£4,700-6,000 *C*

Sir Peter Scott (1909-89)
British
Wigeon in the Afternoon, Chew Valley Lake
Signed and dated 1975, bears title on label on
stretcher, oil on canvas
28 x 36in (71 x 91.5cm)
£8,500-10,000 *S*

Richard Robjent (b1937)
British
Woodcock, Winter Sunset
Signed and inscribed, watercolour with bodycolour
heightened with white
18¾ x 24¼in (47.5 x 61.5cm)
£1,800-2,200 *S*

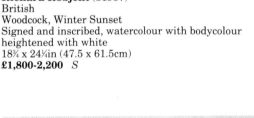

Rodger McPhail (b1953)
British
Woodcock Amid Bracken In Winter
Signed, pencil and watercolour heightened
with white
17 x 21in (43.5 x 53.4cm)
£4,000-5,000 *C*

George Edward Lodge (1860-1954)
British
Red-legged Partridge - Juvenile (moulting), Adult
Male, and Adult Female
Signed, watercolour and bodycolour
9½ x 14¼in (23.8 x 36.2cm)
£3,200-4,200 *C*

Archibald Thorburn (1860-1935) British
Mallard, Gadwall, Ruddy Shelduck, Common Shelduck
Signed, inscribed and dated 1914, pencil, watercolour
and bodycolour on grey paper
18 x 14½in (45.7 x 37cm)
£16,500-18,500 *C*

Archibald Thorburn (1860-1935)
British
Woodcock on the Nest
Signed and dated 1923, watercolour and
bodycolour
14½ x 19¼in (37 x 49cm)
£35,000-45,000 *S*

Archibald Thorburn (1860-1935) British
The First Touch of Winter
Signed and dated 1910, watercolour and bodycolour
10½ x 14½in (27 x 37cm)
£26,000-32,000 *S*

Archibald Thorburn (1860-1935)
British
An Eagle Owl
Signed and dated 1914, watercolour
and bodycolour
18 x 13¾in (45.5 x 35cm)
£15,000-20,000 *S*

Archibald Thorburn (1860-1935)
British
Peacock and Peacock Butterfly
Signed and dated 1917, watercolour and
bodycolour
34½ x 44in (87.5 x 111.5cm)
£40,000-50,000 *S*

Archibald Thorburn (1860-1935)
British
Blackcocks At The Lek
Signed and dated 1901, watercolour and
bodycolour
14½ x 21in (37 x 53.5cm)
£25,000-35,000 *S*

Veni Gligorova-Smith (20thC)
Flock 1
Watercolour
15½ x 19½in (39.5 x 49.5cm)
£400-450 *AMC*

David Hurrell (b1953)   British
A Christmas Tune
Signed, executed 1989, watercolour
and bodycolour
14in (35.5cm) diam.
£1,000-2,000 *BRG*

Michael Coulter (b1937)
British
Swan Watching, Abbotsbury
Watercolour
15 x 20in (39 x 51cm)
£850-900 *PHG*

Valerie Greeley (b1953)
British
Blue is the Sky in Fading Light
Sees the Moon Now Say
Goodnight!, watercolour with
bodycolour, 6¼ x 4¾in (16 x 12cm)
£750-850 *CBL*

Harrison William Weir (1824-1906)
British
A Robin among Blossom, a Song Thrush, a Wren;
and a Lesser Redpoll
All signed and dated 1863, watercolour and
bodycolour
11in (28cm) diam.
£2,100-2,600 *C*

Charles Frederick Tunnicliffe, R.A. (1901-79)
British
Blue and White Fantails
Inscribed, watermark, pencil and watercolour
heightened with white on grey paper
9 x 9¾in (23 x 24.8cm)
£3,000-3,500 *C*

Liz Underhill (b1948) British
'Oh deary, deary me!' wailed Miss
McTaffety. 'However did you all get
here? Whatever shall I do?'
Watercolour with bodycolour
7½ x 8in (19 x 20cm)
£1,350-1,450 *CBL*

l. **Isabelle Brent**
(b1961)
British
Cat on a Flying Carpet
Gilded watercolour
8 x 6½in (20 x 16cm)
£775-875 *PHG*

Eugène Bidau (19th/20thC)
French
Preparations for the Ball
Signed, oil on canvas
34½ x 45¼in (88 x 115cm)
£18,000-20,000 *S*

r. **Ruskin Spear**
(1911-90) British
The Marmalade Cat
Signed, oil on canvas
18 x 11in (45 x 29cm)
£3,300-3,500 *ULG*

Rosemary Strachey (20thC)
British
Three White Cats on Chair
Signed and dated 1974, oil on canvas
22 x 18in (56 x 46cm)
£400-450 *Cae*

Gerard Hoffnung (1925-59) British
My Cat Timothy Laughing Heartily at his
Own Reflection in a Mirror
Signed and inscribed with title, pen, ink,
watercolour and bodycolour
5½ x 5¾in (13.5 x 14cm)
£1,150-1,250 *CBL*

Donna Crawshaw (20thC)
British
A Shared Meal!
Acrylic on canvas
12 x 16in (31 x 41cm)
£650-750 *OM*

Alfred Duke (d c1905)
A Hard Act to Follow
Signed, oil on canvas
18 x 24in (45.8 x 61cm)
£3,000-3,800 *C*

Maud Tindal Atkinson (active 1906-37)
British
Red Setter in a Meadow
Monogrammed watercolour
4¼ x 6¼in (11 x 16cm)
£1,200-1,400 *PH*

Arthur Wardle
(1864-1949)
British
Chips Off The Old Block
Signed, oil on canvas
22 x 14in (56 x 35.5cm)
£7,000-8,000 *S*

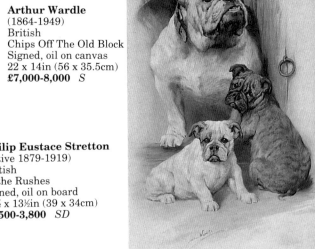

Philip Eustace Stretton
(active 1879-1919)
British
In the Rushes
Signed, oil on board
15½ x 13½in (39 x 34cm)
£3,500-3,800 *SD*

Tel: 081-446 7896

The Totteridge Gallery

Fax: 081-446 7541

FINE 18TH-MID 20TH CENTURY BRITISH & CONTINENTAL OIL PAINTINGS, WATERCOLOUR DRAWINGS & LIMITED EDITION SIR WILLIAM RUSSELL FLINT PRINTS

61/63 TOTTERIDGE LANE, (OPP. TOTTERIDGE TUBE STATION), TOTTERIDGE, LONDON N20 0HD

"Cooling Streams"
Pastel 6¾ x 10¾ inches

Arthur Wardle
Signed, insc'd verso

The Puppy Show, Newmarket 1898
Oils on canvas, 42 x 56 inches

Godfrey Douglas Giles (1857-1941)
Signed & insc'd & dated 1898 verso

A continuously changing stock of fine oil paintings, watercolours & limited edition
Sir William Russell Flint Prints at reasonable prices.
Restoration of oils & works on paper, valuations and free advice.

open Monday-Saturday 10.30-7

Joseph Kirkpatrick (active 1898-1928)
British
Trespassers
Signed, watercolour
25½ x 37½in (65 x 95cm)
£4,000-5,000 *S*

John Frederick Herring, Snr. (1795-1865)
British
Goats in a Farmyard
Signed and dated 1849, oil on canvas
13½ (34.5cm) square
£18,500-20,000 *S*

Louis Bosworth Hurt (1856-1929)
British
A Highland Drove at Strathfillan, Perthshire
Signed and dated 1891, oil on canvas
24 x 36in (61 x 91.5cm)
£11,500-13,500 *S*

William Nicholson (19thC) British
Old English Breed (from a group of 4)
Coloured lithograph after a painting by William
Shields, drawn on stone and printed in London,
1842, 16½ x 12⅝in (42 x 32cm)
£4,000-4,250 *OG*

Whessel (early 19thC)
British
The Craven Heifer
Colour printed stipple engraving by Whessell after a
painting by Fryer, dedicated to the Duke of Devonshire,
published in 1812.
£2,300-2,500 *OG*

Charles Emile Jacque (1813-94)
French
A Shepherdess with her Flock in a Wood
Signed, oil on panel
14½ x 18in (37 x 46cm)
£8,700-10,000 *S*

Ben Blathwayt (b1951)
British
Bramble in the Snowy Field
Watercolour with pen and ink
9¼ x 8in (23 x 20cm)
£400-450 *CBL*

Edgar Hunt (1876-1953)
British
Farmyard Companions
Signed and dated 1922, oil on canvas
20 x 30in (51 x 76cm)
£23,000-25,000 *FAO*

William Weekes
(active 1864-1904)
British
Outnumbered
Signed
19½ x 29¾in (49.5 x 75.5cm)
£3,200-4,000 *S(S)*

Richard Whitford (19thC)
British
A Shorthorn Bull and Two Ducks in a Stable
Signed with monogram and dated 1870
16½ x 20½in (42 x 52cm)
£2,200-2,800 *S(S)*

Eugène-Joseph Verboeckhoven
(1798-1881)
Belgian
Sheep in a Barn
Signed and dated 1875, oil on panel
12½ x 9¾in (31.8 x 24.8cm)
£11,200-12,200 *C*

George Stubbs, A.R.A. (1724-1806)
British
The Godolphin Arabian
Colour print, dated 1794
£9,500-10,000 *BRG*

George Stubbs, **A.R.A.** (1724-1806) British
A Bay Hunter, a Springer Spaniel, and a Sussex
Spaniel in a wooded river Landscape
Signed and dated 1782, 22¾ x 29in (57.8 x 73.7cm)
£125,000-150,000 *C*

John Wootton (1686-1765)
British
The Godolphin Arabian
Signed and dated 1734
39 x 47in (99 x 119.4cm)
£20,000-25,000 *C*

Daniel Quigley (active c1764-73) Irish
Breasy Tom with Jockey up, followed by His
Groom on a Racecourse
Inscribed, oil on canvas, 38 x 48½in (96.5 x 123cm)
£9,500-11,000 *S*

John Vanderbank (1694-1739)
British
A Gentleman on a Grey Charger being
schooled in an Arena
Oil on canvas
30 x 25in (76.2 x 63.5cm)
£6,000-7,000 *C*

Louis Hubner (active 1740-69)
German
Dismal, a Grey Racehorse with Jockey Up
Signed, inscribed and dated 1746, oil on canvas
40 x 50½in (101.5 x 128cm)
£9,000-10,000 *S*

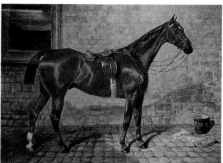

Benjamin Cam Norton (active late 19thC)
British
A Saddled Chestnut Hunter in a Yard
Signed and dated 1874, oil on canvas
19½ x 26¼in (49.5 x 67cm)
£2,000-2,500 *S(S)*

John Frederick Herring, Snr. (1795-1865)
British
In the Stable at Meopham
Signed and dated 1855, oil on canvas
35 x 45in (89.5 x 114cm)
£140,000-150,000 *FAO*

Arthur Winter-Shaw (1869-1948)
British
The Toilers' Return
Signed, oil on canvas
12½ x 18½in (32 x 47cm)
£4,000-4,500 *BSG*

Thomas Barratt of Stockbridge
(active 1852-93) British
Virago with John Wells up and with his Trainer,
Mr John Day, and the stable lad, W. S. Cooper
Oil on canvas
33¼ x 43¼in (84.5 x 110cm)
£9,500-10,500 *S*

John Emms (1843-1912)
British
Daisy
Signed and dated
11½ x 10in (29 x 25.5cm)
£700-750 *SH*

James Ward, R.A. (1769-1859)
British
The Jenkinson Barb, a bay Arab horse, in an extensive landscape
with Pitchford Hall beyond
Signed and dated 1822
31½ x 42¾in (80 x 108.6cm)
£55,000-75,000 *C*

Sean McMamon (20thC)
British
Triptych
Acrylic
20 x 24in (51 x 61cm)
£1,400-1,600 *EAG*

Paul Guiramand (b1926)
French
Original zinc plate lithograph
13¾ x 21in (35 x 54cm)
£280-310 *TES*

Charles Church (20thC)
British
Rowley Mile
Signed, oil
19 x 27in (48 x 69cm)
£350-375 *EAG*

Margaret Barrett (20thC)
British
Snow Work
Oil
14 x 18in (36 x 46cm)
£550-600 *EAG*

Alexander Charles-Jones (b1959)
British
July Meeting, Newmarket
Signed, oil on canvas
24 x 30in (61 x 76cm)
£2,000-3,000 *BSG*

David Howell (20thC)
British
Neck and Neck
Pastel
16 x 20½in (40 x 52cm)
£350-390 *EAG*

James Ramsay (1786-1854)
British
Portrait of a Gentleman with two
Hounds Coursing
Signed and dated 1808, oil on canvas
27½ x 34in (69.8 x 86.2cm)
£7,000-8,000 *L*

John Nost Sartorius (1759-1828)
British
A Sportsman on his Horse with a Keeper and two Hounds
Signed and dated 1798
15 x 19in (38 x 48cm)
£14,500-16,500 *C*

Dirck Maas (1659-1717)
Dutch
William III of England and his Hunting Party
Oil on canvas
31 x 35¼in (78.7 x 89.5cm)
£13,000-14,000 *S(NY)*

Nathan Drake (1728-78)
British
Gentlemen Out Hunting with their Harriers
in a hilly Landscape
Oil on canvas
37¾ x 47¾in (96 x 121.5cm)
£8,000-9,000 *S*

John E. Ferneley, Snr.
(1781-1860)
British
Thomas Goosey with the Belvoir
Hounds leaving Kennels,
Belvoir Castle beyond
Signed and inscribed, oil on
canvas
40¼ x 50½in (102.2 x 128.3cm)
£115,000-135,000 *C*

Aster R. C. Courbould (active 1841-1905)
Partridge Shooting; Pheasant Shooting
A pair, both signed and dated 1860, oil on canvas
16 x 30¼in (40.5 x 77cm)
£8,000-10,000 *S*

Basil Bradley, R.W.S. (1842-1904)
British
The Keeper's Boy
Signed and dated 1904 on reverse, oil on canvas
16¾ x 24¼in (42.5 x 61.5cm)
£3,000-4,000 *S*

John Frederick Herring, Snr. (1795-1865) British
The London-to-Edinburgh Royal Mail Coach racing
downhill
Signed and dated 1833, in a carved giltwood frame
26¼ x 35¾in (66.7 x 90.8cm)
£30,000-40,000 *C*

George Wright (1860-1942)
British
On the Scent
Signed, oil on canvas
12 x 18in (30.5 x 45.8cm)
£4,700-6,000 *C*

Sir Francis Grant, P.R.A.
(1803-78) British
Portrait of Colonel John
Anstruther Thomson,
mounted on his bay hunter
with the Pytchley Hounds
Oil on canvas
15½ x 16in (39.5 x 40.5cm)
£12,000-13,000 *S*

Heywood Hardy, A.R.W.S.
(1843-1933)
British
The Arrival at the Inn
Oil on canvas
30 x 50in (76 x 127cm)
£45,000-50,000 *FAO*

William Walls (1860-1942)
British
Jaguars at Play
Signed and inscribed twice, oil on canvas
36 x 48in (92 x 122cm)
£9,500-11,000 *S*

Edward Lear (1812-88)
British
Study for the Head of a Leopard
Inscribed, watercolour over traces of
pencil, 6 x 8¼in (15 x 21cm)
£5,200-6,000 *S*

William Huggins (1820-84)
British
A Tiger confronting a Snake beside a
Stream in a wooded Landscape; and a
Lion wounded by an Arrow in a
Clearing of a tropical mountainous
Forest
A pair, both signed and dated, 1840
and 1841
each 24 x 28½in (61 x 72cm)
£18,500-20,500 *C*

David Shepherd (b1931)
British
Tiger
Signed and dated 90, oil on canvas
8 x 11in (20 x 28cm).
£3,200-4,000 *S*

Wilhelm Kuhnert (1865-1926)
German
A Kaffir Buffalo in Prairie Grass
Signed and inscribed, oil on canvas
15¼ x 25½in (39 x 65cm)
£25,000-30,000 *C*

l. **Antoine-Louis Barye** (1795-1875)
French
Tigre chassant
Signed, watercolour heightened with gum
arabic on paper laid down on paper
10 x 13¼in (25 x 34cm)
£60,000-80,000 *C*

George Edwards (1694-1773)
British
The Ring-Tailed Macauco; and another study of the animal
Inscribed, watercolour over pencil
12 x 19in (30.5 x 48cm)
£1,500-2,000 *S*

Simon Drew
(b1952)
British
Mollusc of the Glen
Signed and inscribed,
pen, ink and coloured
pencil
6in (15cm) square
£400-450 *CBL*

Tracey Boyd (b1957)
British
'As the King and Queen arrived, they
were greeted by the entire crew lined up
like a school photograph, all ready and
ship-shape'
Watercolour with pen and ink
12½ x 9in (32 x 22.5cm)
£1,000-1,250 *CBL*

Valerie Greeley (b1953)
British
'Where is the sun? Ripening the corn'
Watercolour
6¼ x 4¾in (16 x 12cm)
£800-850 *CBL*

Clarence Lawson Wood (1878-1959)
British
'I heard that one at the Club'
Signed and inscribed, watercolour with
body colour
14½ x 11¼in (37 x 29cm)
£2,650-2,750 *CBL*

MYTHOLOGICAL
16th & 17th Centuries

Attributed to Francesco Brizio
(1574-1623)   Italian
Omphale
Oil on canvas
31½ x 24¾in (80.4 x 63cm)
£11,500-12,500   C

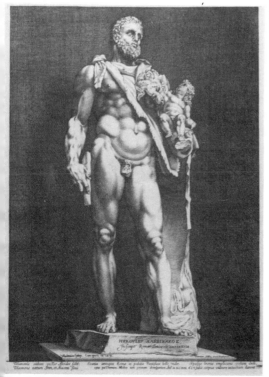

Hendrik Goltzius
(1558-1616)
Dutch
The Emperor Commodus
as Hercules
Engraving
Pen and wash
16¼ x 11¾in (41.5 x 30cm)
£2,800-3,500   S

Cornelis Cort (1533-78)
Dutch
The Immortality of Virtue
Engraving, 1564
12½ x 16in (32 x 41cm)
£1,500-2,000   C

Lucas van Leyden (1494-1538)
Dutch
Mars, Venus and Cupid
Engraving, 1513
7½ x 9½in (18.6 x 24cm)
£1,200-1,600   C

Jean Mignon (active c1544)
Bataille sous Troie
Etching, c1545
12¾ x 17½in (32.5 x 44.7cm)
£13,200-14,200   C

**Attributed to
Hendrik Goltzius**
(1558-1616)
Dutch
Old Master drawing
Pen and wash
6¾ x 10¾in (17 x 27cm)
£750-800   JD

Jan Brueghel II (1601-78)
Flemish
An Allegory of Love
Oil on panel
22 x 30in (55.8 x 76cm)
£65,000-80,000 *C*

Jacopo Negretti, Palma il Giovane
(1548-1628)
Italian
Venus and Adonis
Black chalk, pen and brown ink, brown and
grey wash, watermark anchor
10 x 13in (25 x 32.8cm)
£6,700-7,500 *CNY*

Circle of Jan Soens (1574-1611)
Dutch
Narcissus Gazing at his reflection
Oil on canvas
30 x 50in (75.3 x 127cm)
£1,800-2,500 *P*

Locate the Source

*The source of each
illustration in Miller's can
be found by checking the
code letters below each
caption with the list of
contributors.*

Manner of Titian (1477-1576)
Italian
The Toilet of Venus
Oil on canvas
32¼ x 47¼in (82 x 120cm)
£2,400-3,000 *S(S)*

François Boitard (1670-1715)
French
The Marriage of Peleus and Thetis
Pen and black ink and grey wash, on vellum
7¾ x 11⅜in (19.5 x 29.5cm)
£3,000-4,000 *S(NY)*

*Benezit (see Biblio) describes Boitard with a
certain sense of disapproval as a nervous and
debauched man, who changed address many
times and was the creator of a series of
obscene works.*

Circle of Noël Coypel (1628-1707)
French
A Vestal Virgin
A feigned, framed polychrome relief
21½ x 33in (54.3 x 83.8cm)
£4,800-5,800 *C*

Luca Giordano, called Luca Fapresto
(1632-1705)
Italian
The Battle of the Lapiths and Centaurs
Bears inscription, oil on copper
31 x 36¼in (79 x 92cm)
€50,000-60,000 *S*

*All that glitters is not gold in the Old Master
market, and the dilapidated and the
extremely dirty state of the present work did
not prevent it from exceeding by far its
£6,000-8,000 estimate at Sotheby's in April
1993.*

Mattia Preti, il Cavaliere Calabrese
(1613-99)
Italian
Daedalus attaching Icarus's Wings
62¼ x 49in (158 x 125.5cm)
£90,000-100,000 *C*

*The story of Daedalus and Icarus was
particularly popular with artists of early
17thC.*

Filippo Lauri (1623-94)
Italian
Glaucus and Scylla
Oil on copper
8 x 9½in (20.3 x 24.5cm)
£1,600-2,100 *P*

Cornelis van Poelenburgh (c1586-1667)
Dutch
Apollo and Coronis
Signed, oil on copper
11½ x 15¼in (29 x 38.7cm)
40,000-45,000 *C*

Manner of Jacob Van Loo (active 1614-17)
Dutch
Diana the Huntress
Oil on canvas
39 x 28¼in (99 x 71.7cm)
£1,500-2,000 *CSK*

Manner of Guido Reni (1575-1642)
Italian
A Sleeping Amor
Oil on canvas
30 x 40¾in (76 x 103.5cm)
£3,000-4,000 *S(S)*

After Guido Reni (1575-1642)
Italian
Nessus and Deianeira
Oil on canvas
45½ x 35in (116 x 89cm)
£8,000-10,000 *S(S)*

Jusepe de Ribera
(1590-1652)
Spanish
The Drunken Silenus
Etching
10½ x 13¾in (27.3 x 35.2cm)
£7,500-8,500 *S*

Floris van Schooten (active 1605-55)
Dutch
Venus and Adonis
Oil on panel
10½ x 15¾in (26.7 x 40cm)
£1,600-2,500 *P*

*Ribera's life was one of dramatic contrasts.
Born to a wealthy Spanish family who
wanted him to follow a conventional career,
he fled to Rome to become an artist, living in
the greatest poverty and surviving from
charity. According to legend, a wealthy
cardinal passing by in his carriage saw the
youth dressed in rags drawing buildings with
the most profound concentration. He was so
impresssed with his talents that he took
Ribera into his service but unable to bear the
shackles of livery, the artist fled from the
comfort of the cardinal's home and back to the
streets and starvation. Moving to Naples,
Ribera's fortunes changed again. He met a
wealthy picture dealer, who, on the balcony of
his house, exhibited Ribera's Martyrdom of
St. Bartholomew. Such a huge crowd came to
see the work, that the authorities thought
there was a riot going on. The Viceroy of
Naples arrived fully armed, but when he saw
the cause of the excitement, he invited the
artist to his palace and appointed him court
painter. After this, Ribera's career was made.
He received commissions from all over Europe
and became one of the richest and most
successful artists of his generation. He
defended his position fiercely - according to
reports, he had in his pay two painter/
swordsmen, whose job was to uphold their
master's superiority with the point of their
swords and to chase from Naples any rivals to
his fame. Many artists came to the city only
to leave again very quickly, threatened by
Ribera's thugs. One, however, who recklessly
returned, died suddenly, believed to be
poisoned and the finger of suspicion was
directed, albeit in a rather tremulous manner
at Ribera.*

Simon de Vos (1603-76)
Flemish
An Allegory of the Five Senses: A Merry
Company in a Palatial Interior
Signed, oil on panel
19 x 24¾in (48 x 62.8cm)
£28,000-35,000 *C*

18th Century

Louis Lagrenée l'aîné (1725-1805)
French
An Episode during the War between Marius
and Sulla
Indistinctly signed, on paper laid down on
board
20 x 23¾in (50.8 x 60.6cm)
£2,800-3,500 *C*

*The subject is an episode from the wars of
Marius and Sulla. According to the account
in Livy (Periocha to Book 79), during a battle
between Pompeius and Cinna, a soldier
recognised that he had slain his own brother
when the latter was stripped of his armour.
In the context of the French Revolution, the
political significance of a subject which set
brother against brother would have been self-
evident.*

Andrea Casali (1705-84)
Italian
Lucretia
Oil on panel
81½ x 64in (207 x 162.5cm)
£35,000-40,000 *C*

Pierre François Ledoulx (1730-1807)
Flemish
Putti building a House of Cards in a Park
Signed and dated 1779, oil on canvas
22 x 35¼in (55.8 x 88.6cm)
£2,300-3,000 *CSK*

Attributed to Francesco Fontebasso
(1709-69)
The Sacrifice of Iphigenia
Oil on canvas
42 x 32in (107 x 81cm)
£8,000-9,000 *S*

Nicolas-André Monsiau (1755-1837)
French
Zeuxis choosing his Model from the most
beautiful girls of Croton
Pen and brown ink and grey and brown wash
heightened with white over black chalk
15½ x 21in (39.5 x 53cm)
£16,500-18,500 *S(NY)*

Charles-Joseph Natoire (1700-77)
French
A Putto
Black, white and touches of red chalk, on
light brown paper
15⅓in (40cm) square
£3,500-4,500 *CNY*

Pierre-Paul Prud'hon (1758-1823)
French
The Mocking of Ceres
Oil on canvas
19¾ x 24⅛in (50.5 x 61.4cm)
£7,800-9,000 *S*

*While looking for her daughter Proserpine,
who had been carried off to the underworld,
Ceres rested and took refreshment at the
cottage of an old woman. The cottager's
young son teased her with being greedy, and
Ceres turned him into a lizard. This legend
suggests that even goddesses resent any
mockery of their weight or appetite.*

George Romney (1734-1802)
British
Antiope and Jupiter
Pen and brown ink and grey washes on laid
paper
11 x 17in (28 x 43cm)
£2,300-3,000 *S*

Heinrich Wilhelm Schweickardt
(1746-97)
German
Two Putti warming themselves beside a fire
contained within a cauldron
Signed and dated 1776, oil on canvas
19¼in (49cm) diam.
£2,000-2,500 *P*

Attributed to Victor Maxmilian Potain
(b1760)
Apollo and Daphne
Oil on canvas
30 x 25in (76.5 x 63.5cm)
£2,500-3,000 *P*

Follower of Jacob de Wit (1695-1754)
Dutch
The Education of Achilles
Oil on canvas, en grisaille
35 x 60in (88.8 x 152.4cm)
£2,300-3,000 *CSK*

Jacob de Wit (1695-1754)
Dutch
Three Putti with a Lyre and a Trumpet
Signed and dated 1748, oil on canvas
45¾ x 58¾in (116.6 x 149.5cm)
£9,000-10,000 *S*

**C. de Mechel
after
Charles Vanloo**
(1705-65)
French
L'Amour Menacant
Engraving
16¼ x 11½in (41.5 x 28cm)
£200-250 *CSK*

19th Century

Angelo de Courten (b1848)
Italian
Diana and the Lion
Signed, oil on canvas
25½ x 32½in (64.8 x 82.6cm)
£4,800-5,800 *S(NY)*

Paul Cézanne (1839-1906)
French
L'Education D'Achille
Pencil, executed c1864-65
11½ x 7½in (29 x 20cm)
£30,000-35,000 *S*

Circle of Jean-Léon Gérôme (1824-1904)
French
Rachel
Bears signature, oil on panel
13 x 8½in (33 x 21.6cm)
£2,300-3,000 *S(NY)*

Walter Crane (1845-1915)
British
The Earth and Spring
Signed, inscribed and dated '75, oil on canvas
12¼ x 29in (31 x 73.6cm)
£9,000-10,000 *C*

Crane was fascinated by the theme of Spring,
returning to the subject repeatedly.

Benjamin Robert Haydon (1786-1846)
British
The Banishment of Aristides
Oil on canvas
26 x 35in (66 x 89cm)
£2,500-3,000 *S*

William Hilton, R.A. (1786-1839)
British
Comus with the Lady in the Enchanted Chair
Oil on canvas
62 x 92½in (157.5 x 235cm)
£24,000-30,000 *S*

Henri Pierre Picou (1824-95)
French
Clipping Cupid's Wings
Signed, oil on canvas
24 x 32in (61 x 81.3cm)
£7,500-9,000 *S(NY)*

Attributed to Michelangelo Maestri
(19thC) Italian
The Infant Hercules and the Snakes;
Reading a Declaration
A pair, both watercolour and gouache
17¾ x 13¾in (45 x 35cm)
£1,500-2,000 *S*

20th Century

K. H. Hödicke (b1938)
German
Prometheus
Signed and inscribed and dated
84, acrylic on linen
114½ x 79in (290 x 200.5cm)
£12,200-13,200 *C*

Henri Matisse (1869-1945)
French
La Chute d'Icare
Signed and dated 1943, original
stencil print using Matisse's cut-outs,
on watermarked Marais paper
13¾ x 10½in (35 x 26.3cm)
£900-950 *WO*

Eric Holt (b1944)
British
Exion and Nephele
Signed and dated 1985, egg
tempera
21 x 13in (53 x 33cm)
£8,250-8,750 *BRG*

D. Mistry (b1957)
Indian
From the North VI
Etching
14½ x 12½in (37 x 32cm)
£235-265 *GPS*

> *Condition is a
> major factor in a
> picture's price*

George Sheringham (1884-1937)
British
Nymphs of the Stream
Signed
Watercolour and bodycolour with gold on
tinted paper
9¾in (24cm) square
£600-650 *CBL*

Pablo Picasso (1881-1974)
Spanish
Minotaure aveugle guidé par une Fillette
dans la Nuit
Signed, aquatint, on Montval, watermark
Vollard
9¾ x 13½in (24.5 x 34.5cm)
£31,000-40,000 *C*

STILL LIFE

One of the happiest stories relating to an individual picture in this year's Price Guide is that concerning Luis Meléndez's still life of sea bream, dating from the 1770s and illustrated on page 408.

The picture had been bought for a few shillings from a street market in England some 30 years ago and when its owner took it to Bonham's in 1992, he thought it was a photographic print. He was in for a big and gratifying surprise. The work turned out to be a rare picture by the 18thC Spanish master Luis Meléndez. As the *Antiques Trade Gazette* noted, still life was a genre that Melendez had been forced to turn to after he fell out with the Royal Academy of San Fernando. Unable as a result to devote himself to the more lucrative avenues of portrait and history painting with the support of major patrons, the artist died a pauper. Ironically, today such Old Master

still lifes command enormous prices at auction and, because of their rarity, are extremely sought after. The present work was described by Bonham's as being in 'wonderful' condition, uncleaned since the 19thC, and coming complete with the surface layer of dirt that is so attractive to the modern buyer. It excited a huge amount of interest from museums, dealers and private collectors across the world, eventually selling to an anonymous European bidder for a hammer price of £850,000, more than doubling the previous auction record for a work by Melendez and making it the highest single price ever achieved by the auction house. Everybody's dream is that somewhere at home they have tucked away a hidden masterpiece, and for the previous owner of this beautiful still life, that dream came true.

16th and 17th Centuries

Attributed to Harmen van Steenwyck
(1612-after 1656)
Dutch
A Larder Still Life
Oil on panel
19½ x 37in (49.6 x 94cm)
£7,000-8,000 *CSK*

Ambrosius Bosschaert the Younger
(1609-45)
Flemish
Still Life of tulips, a rose and other flowers in a glass vase on a ledge
Signed, oil on panel
19¼ x 14½in (48.6 x 37cm)
£105,000-120,000 *S*

Circle of Evaristo Baschenis (1617-77)
Italian
Still Life with Musical Instruments
Oil on canvas
21¾ x 42¼in (55.2 x 107.3cm)
£12,500-13,500 *S(NY)*

Still life painters often specialised in one particular subject: flowers, breakfast scenes, fish or, as in the case of Baschenis, musical instruments. Such still lifes can provide a fascinating pictorial record of the instruments of the period.

Paulus van den Bosch (1615-after 1655)
Dutch
Still Life with roemer, silver beaker, meat pie and bread roll
Indistinctly monogrammed and dated, oil on panel
22¼ x 34½in (56.5 x 87.6cm)
£21,000-30,000 *S(NY)*

Attributed to Vincenzo Campi
(1530/5-91)
Italian
A Fruit and Vegetable Stall in an Orchard
Oil on canvas
57¼ x 84½in (145.5. x 215.6cm)
£52,000-55,000 *C*

Philips Brueghel (b1635)
Flemish
Pike, barbel and other fish in a bowl
Signed, oil on canvas
34¾ x 45½in (88.3 x 115.3cm)
£26,000-35,000 *C*

Meiffren Conte (d1705)
Still Life of silver objects
Oil on canvas
31½ x 39¾in (80 x 101cm)
£16,500-18,000 *S*

*Two of the silver objects represented occur in
several other paintings by Conte. The
candlestick, one of a series of twelve
representing the Labours of Hercules believed
to have been commissioned by Charles Lebrun
for Louis XIV, is frequently represented,
together with the central silver ewer.*

Jan Brueghel the Younger (1601-78)
Flemish
Still Life of flowers in an elaborate gold pokal
on a stone ledge
Oil on panel
18½ x 13¾in (47 x 35cm)
£85,000-95,000 *S(NY)*

French School (17thC)
A Vanitas Still Life
Oil on canvas
17¾ x 22¼in (45 x 56.5cm)
£4,000-5,000 *P*

Johann Michael Hambach
German
(active 1673-after 1686)
A Still Life
Signed, oil on canvas
23¼ x 30¾in (59 x 78.2cm)
£9,500-10,500 *C*

Attributed to Pieter De Ring (1615-60)
Dutch
Still Life of flowers and fruit all suspended
from a ring by a ribbon
Oil on canvas
25¼ x 17½in (64 x 44.5cm)
£14,000-15,000 *S(NY)*

Circle of Giovanni Battista Rueppolo
(1620-85)
Italian
Still Life of Fruit
Oil on canvas laid down on board
25 x 36in (63.5 x 91.4cm)
£7,000-8,000 *CSK*

Johannes Leemans (1633-88)
Dutch
A trompe l'oeil Still Life with a caged bird
and hunting implements
Signed and dated 1677, oil on canvas
23¼ x 30in (59 x 76cm)
£10,500-11,500 *C*

Pieter Gerritsz.-van Roestraeten
(1630-1700)
Dutch
Still Life
Oil on canvas
39¾ x 48½in (101 x 123.2cm)
£11,500-13,000 *Bon*

Tobias Stranover (1684-1735)
Czechoslovakian
Still Life
Oil on canvas
22¾ x 25¾in (58 x 65cm)
£15,000-16,000 *P*

Floris Gerritsz van Schooten (1605-55)
Dutch
Still Life
Initialled, oil on panel
15¾ x 22in (39.7 x 56cm)
£23,000-28,000 *S(NY)*

18th Century

Madeleine-Françoise Basseport (1701-80)
French
Still Life
Gouache on vellum
11 x 8½in (28.5 x 21cm)
£6,500-7,500 *S(NY)*

Wybrand Hendricks (1744-1831)
Dutch
Still Life of flowers in an urn
Oil on canvas
30 x 24½in (76 x 62cm)
£5,200-6,000 *S*

Pieter Casteels II
Flemish
A Still Life of flowers
Oil on canvas
28½ x 23¼in (72.5 x 59cm)
£6,000-7,000 *P*

Follower of Jan van Huysum (1682-1749)
Dutch
Still Life of Summer Flowers
Oil on canvas
30 x 25in (76.4 x 63.8cm)
£25,000-35,000 *S*

Huysum, one of the most successful still life painters of his day, was unusual in that he always tried to work from life, which necessitated a considerable degree of patience both from himself and his clients. In a letter to one patron, he stated that he was unable to finish a picture because he could not obtain a yellow rose, otherwise he would have completed it the previous year. Many of his works are inscribed with two dates, possibly for a similar reason.

Attributed to Francesco Lavagna (18thC)
Italian
Mixed Flowers in an urn on a pedestal
Oil on canvas
19 x 14¾in (48.3 x 37.5cm)
£5,800-6,800 *C*

Gasparo Lopez, called Gaspare dei Fiori
(18thC)
Italian
A Still Life of flowers in a garden setting
Oil on canvas
79 x 59in (200 x 150cm)
£25,500-30,000 *S*

Johann Christiaan Roedig (1751-1802)
Dutch
Still Lifes
A pair, both signed and dated 1705
24½ x 20¾in (62.5 x 52.7cm)
£24,500-25,500 *C*

Johannes (Jacobus) Lindthorst (18thC)
Dutch
Still Life with Butterflies and Bees
Oil on panel
19 x 16in (48 x 41cm)
£26,000-27,500 *HFA*

Mary Moser (1744-1819)
British
Still Lifes with summer flowers
A pair, one signed, the other dated 1762,
gouache over traces of pencil with touches of
gum arabic on laid paper
22 x 16in (57 x 41cm)
£15,000-18,000 *S*

*Mary Moser was the daughter of George
Moser, R.A., Drawing Master to George III.
Both father and daughter were founder
members of the Royal Academy in 1768.
Mary Moser exhibited at the Society of Artists
from 1760-1768 and she was appointed
Flower Painter to Queen Charlotte and
drawing mistress to the Queen's daughters.*

19th Century

Charles Archer (19thC)
British
Plums and Apples on a Mossy Bank
Oil on canvas, signed
10 x 12in (25 x 31cm)
£1,750-1,850 *Dr*

Oliver Clare (c1853-1927)
British
Still Life
A pair, oil on mill board
5 x 8in (12.5 x 20cm)
£3,550-3,750 *BUP*

Thomas Charles Bale (active 1868-75)
British
Still Life of fruit and a flagon
Signed, oil on canvas
20 x 30in (50.5 x 76cm)
£2,600-3,200 *S*

Vincent Clare (1855-1925)
British
Primroses, blossom and a bird's nest
Signed, oil on canvas
5¾ x 9½in (14 x 24cm)
£500-600 *AH*

John F. Francis (1808-86)
American
Still Life with Currants
Signed and dated 1866, oil on canvas
8½ x 13¼in (26.7 x 33.7cm)
£18,000-20,000 *S(NY)*

Oliver Clare (c1853-1927)
British
Still Life with Flowers and a Bird's Nest
Signed, oil on canvas
12 x 10in (30.5 x 22.5cm)
£2,600-2,800 *HFA*

*Jeremy Maas (see Biblio.) notes that 'in the
19thC the interest in still life painting grew in
response to the increasing materialism of the
wealthy middle classes and, of course, to the
pleas of Ruskin to pursue the earnest study of
nature.' William Henry Hunt developed a
delicate and pretty style of still life, based
round fruit, blossom and birds' nests,
arranged on a mossy bank rather than in an
interior, and displaying a winning
combination of the artful and the natural.
Hunt inspired a host of immitators, the so-
called 'bird's nest' school, including Hough,
Sherrin and the Clare family - father George
and brothers Oliver and Vincent.*

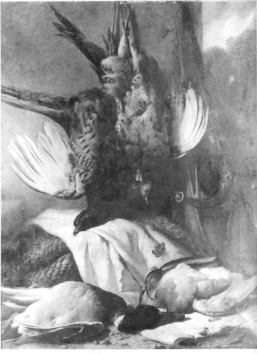

William Duffield (1816-63)
British
Still Life of dead game
Signed and dated 1863, oil on canvas
35 x 26¾in (89 x 68.5cm)
£1,300-1,800 *ALL*

Paul Gagneux (d1892)
French
Peonies and a pitcher on a ledge
Signed, oil on canvas
31 x 38in (79 x 96cm)
£5,000-6,000 *S*

Gennaro Gugliemi (19thC)
Italian
Dead Game
A pair, signed, oil on canvas
14in (36cm) oval
£3,000-4,000 *TCHG*

Maria Harrison (active 1845-93)
British
Still Life
Oil on canvas
11⅛ x 16in (29 x 41cm)
£800-1,000 *P(S)*

William Hughes (1842-1901)
British
Still Life
Signed and dated 1864, oil on board
14 x 18in (35.5 x 46cm)
£2,100-2,600 *S*

Ludwig Adam Kunz (1857-1929)
Austrian
Still Life
Signed, oil on canvas
48 x 38½in (122 x 97.5cm)
£9,500-10,500 *S*

Edward Ladell (1821-86)
British
Still Life
Signed with monogram, oil on canvas
14 x 12in (36 x 31cm)
£18,000-20,000 *FAO*

William Henry Hunt (1790-1864)
British
Still Life
Signed, watercolour over traces of pencil with
scratching out
9 x 12½in (23 x 32cm)
£1,700-2,200 *S*

Albert Durer Lucas (1828-1918)
British
Flowers in a Vase with Jewellery; and
Flowers in a Vase with Coins
A pair, signed, oil on canvas
18 x 12in (46 x 30.5cm)
£3,500-4,500 *TCHG*

E. M. Lister (active 1882-1911)
British
Green Bottle and Blue Bowl
Signed and dated 1910, watercolour
13½ x 9½in (34 x 24cm)
£100-120 *LH*

George Lance (1802-64)
British
Still Life
Signed and dated 1827, oil on panel
23¼ x 18¼in (59.4 x 46.7cm)
£7,000-8,000 *C*

Adolphe Monticelli (1824-86)
French
Nature Morte aux Fleurs des Champs et de
Jardin
Signed, oil on cradled panel, c1875-80
27 x 19in (68.5 x 48cm)
£100,000-120,000 *S*

Johann Wilhelm Preyer (1803-89)
German
Still Life of Fruit and Nuts
Signed and dated 1879, oil on canvas
10½ x 14in (26.5 x 36cm)
£20,500-25,000 *S*

Joseph Henry Sharp (1859-1953)
American
Floral Still Life
Signed, oil on canvas
25 x 30in (63.5 x 72.6cm)
£9,000-10,000   *S(NY)*

Still lifes and flower painting are among the few fields in which one will find a number of women artists before the 20thC. Flowers were seen as a suitable subject for the female brush and still lifes had the advantage of being still, so that a woman could paint them at home. In many cases it was not considered proper for the lady to sketch outside or on the streets and it was not until the turn of the 19thC that women were allowed to draw from nude models, the cornerstone of Western art training. Many 19thC female artists appear either to have been born into a family of painters, or to have married an artist, thus providing themselves with an escort necessary for painting expeditions and support in a male-dominated art world.

Eloise Harriet Stannard (active 1852-93)
British
Fruit, painted from Nature
Signed, inscribed and dated 1860, oil on canvas
24¼ x 20in (61.6 x 50.8cm)
£15,000-18,000   *Bon*

John Sherrin (1819-96)
British
Still Life with Strawberries and Peas
Signed, watercolour and bodycolour
7¼ x 8¾in (18.5 x 22.5cm)
£1,200-1,600   *S*

20th Century

Diana Armfield (b1920)
British
Spring Flowers
Oil on board/panel
14 x 12in (36 x 30.5cm)
£1,800-2,200 *BRG*

Niel Bally (20thC)
British
Carnations,
Signed, oil on canvas
30 x 35in (76.5 x 89cm)
£1,800-2,100 *BSG*

Vladimir Bernadin (b1921)
Russian
Still Life with Violin
Oil on canvas
43 x 32in (17 x 81cm)
£3,500-4,000 *RMG*

Leonard Beard (b1942)
British
White Blossoms
Oil on Panel
15¾ x 11¾in (40 x 30cm)
£300-350 *MT*

Mildred Bendall (active 1920-30s)
British
The Patterned Cloth
Signed, oil on canvas
23in (59cm) square
£1,700-1,800 *NZ*

Warren Brandt (b1918)
American
Blue Studio
Signed, oil on canvas
50 x 56in (127 x 142.2cm)
£3,000-3,500 *CNY*

Bernard Buffet (b1928)
French
Nature Morte au Fond Vert
Signed and dated 64, oil on canvas
35 x 45¾in (89 x 116cm)
£25,000-30,000 *S*

Raymond Campbell (20thC)
British
Chateau Latour
Signed, oil
16 x 18in (14 x 46cm)
£1,100-1,200 *Bne*

Bouvier de Cachard (b1929)
French
La Fenêtre Ouvert sur la Nuit
Signed and dated 1975, oil on canvas
22 x 28in (56 x 71cm)
£3,000-3,250 *CE*

James Cockburn (20thC)
British
Still Life with rain and a fountain
Acrylic on cards
24 x 36in (62 x 92cm)
£1,100-1,250 *HG*

Harold Clayton (1898-1979)
British
Summer Glory
Signed, oil on canvas
24 x 30in (62 x 77cm)
£35,000-40,000 *FAO*

Victoria Crowe (b1945)
British
Silent Assembly - Monk's Cottage
Watercolour and bodycolour
14½ x 36½in (37 x 93cm)
£2,500-2,700 *BSG*

Ivor Davies (b1963)
British
Costreli
Tempera on hand made paper
£1,000-1,100 *MT*

José Escofsy (b1930)
Spanish
Bowl of Peaches
Oil on canvas
18 x 20in (46 x 51cm)
£4,000-4,500 *JAF*

Mary Fedden (b1915)
British
Clematis
Signed, pencil with some watercolour
17 x 27in (43 x 69cm)
£1,600-1,800 *NZ*

Shirley Felts (20thC)
British
Apples on a Table
Watercolour
8 x 7½in (20 x 19cm)
£325-365 *AMC*

Edith Hughes (active 1913-36)
British
White Poppies and Forsythia
Signed, oil
24 x 20in (61 x 51cm)
£1,000-1,200 *Dr*

Harry Houchin (20thC) Irish
Still Life with Camellias
Oil
20 x 24in (50 x 61cm)
£650-750 *JD*

Franz Heckendorf (1888-1962)
German
Still Life with flowers and fruit
Signed and dated 28, oil on canvas
47¼ x 39½in (120 x 100cm)
£13,500-15,000 *P*

John Koch (1909-78)
American
Still Life at Dusk
Signed, oil on canvas
40 x 50in (101.6 x 127cm)
£215,000-240,000 *S(NY)*

Gabriel Fernandez Ledesma (20thC)
Mexican
Los Guantes Negros
Signed and dated 1940, oil on canvas
19¾ x 24⅞in (50.2 x 63.2cm)
£17,000-19,000 *S(NY)*

Vasily Lysov (b1926)
Russian
Still Life with Samarkand Saddlebags
Signed and dated 1959, oil on canvas
25 x 41in (64 x 104cm)
£11,000-12,000 *CE*

Annette Johnson (20thC)
British
Spring Window
Etching, 4 colours
14 x 10¾in (36 x 27.5cm)
£85-95 *CCA*

David Jones (1895-1974)
British
Still Life - Chrysanthemums and a Fruit
Bowl
Signed, watercolour over pencil heightened
with gouache
19 x 15in (48 x 38cm)
£3,000-3,500 *S*

Marevna (Maria Vorobieff) (1892-1984)
Russian
Bouquet de Fleurs
Signed, watercolour on canvas
21¼ x 15¼in (54 x 39cm)
£3,500-4,000 *S*

James McDonald (20thC)
British
Chewed by Mice
Signed, oil
18in (46cm) square
£1,200-1,400 *Bne*

Pippa Mills (b1962) British
Michaelmas Daisies
Gouache
16 x 12in (41 x 30.5cm)
£345-385 *Wyk*

Alberto Morrocco (b1917)
British
Sunflowers
Oil
24½ x 26½in (62 x 67cm)
£6,000-6,500 *A*

Elizabeth Moore (20thC) British
Still Life
Signed, oil on canvas
10 x 12in (25 x 30.5cm)
£400-450 *JD*

Gordon K. Mitchell
(20thC)
British
Collection of a Personal
Nature
Signed, oil on canvas
42 x 54in (106.5 x 137cm)
£2,750-3,000 *RB*

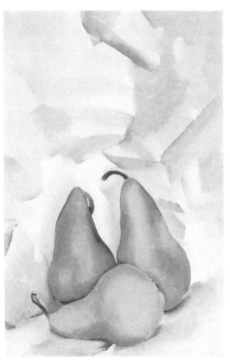

Georgia O'Keeffe (1887-1986)
American
Three Pears
Signed, oil on canvas, painted 1924
18 x 12in (45.7 x 30.5cm)
£120,000-140,000 *S(NY)*

A major exhibition at the Hayward Gallery in London, a television profile and plenty of press attention all helped to stimulate a renewed interest in O'Keeffe's work, both in academic terms and in the saleroom. O'Keeffe is one of the most important of all contemporary American artists, best known for her heavily symbolic and enlarged portrayals of flowers.

Julien Orde (1888-1949)
English
Still Life
Oil on board
11 x 13in (28 x 33cm)
£600-660 *CE*

J. A. Park (20thC)
British
Still Life with Anemones
Oil on canvas
19 x 17½in (48 x 44cm)
£900-1,200 *MBA*

Anne Redpath R.S.A., R.W.A. (1895-1965)
British
Cornflowers in a Glasgow Jug
Signed, oil on panel
21 x 17in (53.3 x 43.2cm)
£6,000-7,000 *C(S)*

Virginia Ridley (20thC)
British
Sweet Peas
Oil
11 x 13in (28 x 33cm)
£300-345 *Wyk*

William Selby, RWS (20thC)
British
Still Life
Oil on panel, 1992
13 x 11½in (33 x 29cm)
£500-800 *AdG*

Frank Taylor (20thC)
British
Gate Coat
Acrylic
14 x 16in (36 x 41cm)
£300-325 *PHG*

Sue Wales
(b1942)
British
Red Pears and
Dahlias
Gouache
21 x 29in
(51 x 74cm)
£700-800
AMC

David Tindle (b1932)
British
African Violets and Rose Petals
Signed and inscribed, oil and
egg tempera on canvas, 1991
16 x 12in (41 x 30.5cm)
£2,650-2,850 *BRG*

Winifred Walker (20thC)
British
Autumn Flowers
Signed, watercolour
12 x 16in (32 x 40.5cm)
£200-250 *SH*

NATURE STUDIES

George Vicat Cole (1833-93)
British
In Richmond Park
Signed with monogram, watercolour
17 x 25½in (43 x 65cm)
£900-1,000 *FWA*

Johannes Bronkhorst (1648-1726/7)
Dutch
Insects
Point of the brush and black ink, watercolour
and gouache
5¾ x 7in (14 x 17.6cm)
£4,500-5,500 *S(NY)*

Jan Jansz van der Vinne (1734-1805)
Dutch
A Passion Flower
Inscribed, pencil, watercolour
17 x 11in (42.6 x 27.7cm)
£1,900-2,400 *C(Am)*

José María Velasco (19thC)
Spanish
Platanilla
Signed and dated 1883, oil on board
18 x 14in (45.7 x 35.2cm)
£88,000-100,000 *S(NY)*

Pancrace Bessa (1772-1835)
French
Three Peaches on a Branch
Signed, pencil, watercolour and bodycolour
on vellum
19½ x 14¾in (49 x 37.5cm)
£9,500-10,500 *C*

*Bessa was a pupil of Redouté. He exhibited
watercolours of flowers at the Paris Salon
from 1806-14. The noted critic Landon
singled him out for praise: 'so far as flower
and fruit pieces are concerned there seems to
be a strong competition between Redouté and
Bessa, being both equally talented, hard-
working and successful.' In 1816 Bessa was
appointed flower painter to the Duchesse de
Berry, and in 1820 he became her drawing
master. His works were in great demand
with Royalty and wealthy foreign visitors,
and King Charles X acquired Bessa's original
drawings for Mordant de Launay's Herbier de
l'Amateur. In 1823 Bessa succeeded van
Spaendonck as the painter on vellum to the
Musée d'Histoire Naturelle. He retired to
Ecouen between 1831 and 1835.*

Elizabeth Blackadder (b1931)
British
Orchidaceae Odontaglossum Grande
Etching
24¼ x 20in (62 x 51cm)
£350-400 *GPS*

BIRDS

The biggest story in the field of bird pictures this year was the sale of works by Archibald Thorburn (1860-1935) from the Thorburn Museum in Cornwall, which took place at Sotheby's on the evening of March 31st 1993. As the *Daily Telegraph* reported, the saleroom was packed to capacity with 'country gentry and Sloane blondes in navy jumpers', an audience taking time off from shooting birds in order to buy pictures of them, and clearly willing to spend vast sums. Most pictures doubled or trebled their estimates. The previous auction high for a work by Thorburn had been £58,000, a record broken four times in the sale and eventually replaced by a new record of £111,500 (including buyer's premium) for a picture entitled 'Swerving from the guns - Red Grouse'. The *Daily Telegraph*, though commenting favourably on various other works, was not impressed by this offering. Thorburn, claimed their reporter, was 'at his weakest in depicting birds in flight...they look as if they hang from invisible strings and are going nowhere. Many are blobs.' Such criticisms were as nothing to the eager bidders who flocked to the bird sale which eventually totalled £2.6 million. (See page 530 for examples of Thorburn's works).

16th - 18th Centuries

Pieter Casteels (1684-1749)
Flemish
Ducks by a Pond
Oil on canvas
24 x 28¾in (61 x 73cm)
£11,500-12,500 *S(NY)*

    The Rev. Christopher Atkinson (1754-95)
    British
    Falcon Gentle (Falco Gentilis)
    Inscribed, pencil and watercolour heightened
    with gum arabic
    12¾ x 10½in (32.5 x 26.7cm)
    £1,200-1,800 *C*

    Christopher Atkinson was the son of the vicar
    of Thorp-Arch, Yorkshire. He was based at
    Cambridge from 1773 to 1785, first at Trinity
    as Pensioner and Fellow, and then as vicar of
    St. Edward's and Fellow of Trinity Hall.
    From 1785 until his death he was vicar of
    Wethersfields, Essex, where he is buried. He
    married Catherine Leicester, sister of Sir
    John Fleming Leicester, Bt., of Tabley in June
    1785.

Giulio Pippi, called Giulio Romano
(1499-1546)
Italian
The Head of an Eagle
Pen and brown ink and wash
4¾ x 8½in (12 x 21.3cm)
£18,000-20,000 *S*

This drawing came complete with a glittering provenance, its owners including artists Jonathan Richardson, Joshua Reynolds and Sir Thomas Lawrence before it made its way into the collection of the Earl of Ellesmere. Probably a study for the gilded stucco eagles in the Sala delle Aquile in the Palazzo del Te, it more than doubled its auction estimate.

Christoph Ludwig Agricola (1667-1719)
German
Finches
A set of 3, bodycolour on vellum
16¼ x 8¼in (28.6 x 21cm)
£3,300-4,000 *C*

Barbara Regina Dietzsch (1706-83)
German
A Still Life of a robin standing on a branch
Gouache
10½ x 7½in (26.7 x 19cm)
£800-1,000 *Bon*

Jakob Bogdani (1660-1724)
Hungarian
Partridges, Muscovy ducks, a juvenile
Herring Gull and other birds in a landscape
Oil on canvas
35¾ x 42in (91 x 107cm)
£19,000-22,000 *S*

George Edwards (18thC)
British
The Horned Indian Pheasant
Copperplate engraving in original colour
7½ x 10in (19 x 25cm)
£400-450 *OG*

Willem van Royen (active 1714-38/42)
Dutch
Two Silver Pheasants and a black crowned
Night Heron in a landscape
Signed, dated 1735 and inscribed,
watercolour and bodycolour, pencil framing
lines
11¾ x17½in (30.3 x 43.7cm)
£2,600-3,000 *C(Am)*

Aert Schouman (1710-92)
Dutch
Trumpet Birds and a Capuchin Monkey in a
tropical landscape
Signed, inscribed and dated 1765, pencil
watercolour and bodycolour heightened with
gold, brown ink framing lines
10½ x 14½in (26.3 x 36.4cm)
£8,000-9,000 *C(Am)*

*The inscription verso states that Schouman
saw these animals in the zoological garden of
Prince Willem V van Orange on the Kleine
Loo by Huis ten Bosch, The Hague.*

Circle of Aert Schouman (1710-92)
Dutch
Pelicans
Pencil and watercolour
10¼ x 15in (26 x 38cm)
£500-600 *C*

19th & 20th Centuries

Winifred Marie Louise Austen
(1876-1964)
British
Beauty Unadorned
Signed and inscribed, pencil and watercolour
12 x 15¼in (30.5 x 38.8cm)
£2,800-3,500 *C*

Isabelle Brent (b1961)
British
Puffin
Signed, gilded watercolour
6 x 5in (15 x 13cm)
£250-300 *PHG*

J. C. Bell (19thC)
British
English Partridge
Signed and dated 1861, oil on canvas
22½ x 30½in (57 x 77.5cm)
£2,800-3,300 *S*

Roland Green (1892-1972)
British
Shelduck over the Sea
Signed and inscribed, pencil, watercolour and
bodycolour
15 x 22in (37.5 x 56cm)
£1,000-1,200 *C*

Basil Ede (b1931)
British
Green Finches
Signed, pencil and watercolour with touches
of white heightening
12½ x 9¾in (31.8 x 24.4cm)
£800-1,000 *C*

John Cyril Harrison (1898-1985)
British
Blackgame by a Lake
Signed, pencil and watercolour with touches
of white heightening
23 x 30¾in (58.4 x 78.2cm)
£7,500-8,500 *C*

Edgar Hunt (1876-1953)
British
Cockerel and Chickens
Signed, oil on board
11 x 15in (28 x 38cm)
£8,500-9,000 *HFA*

*Hunt was in constant demand during his own
period, notes Haynes Fine Art. His patronage
wanted uncomplicated images to which they
could relate immediately and without
troublesome intellectual effort. Hunt also
incorporated an element of sentimentality to
elicit maximum emotional response. His
works are now avidly collected, especially in
the Midlands where he lived.*

James Hill (19thC)
British
A Peacock
Signed and dated 1845, inscribed watercolour
10½ x 8½in (26 x 21cm)
£400-500 *Bea*

*This painting is inscribed: 'Sir Edwin
Landseer said of this that it was the most
extraordinary painting in the world of
miniaturism.'*

Alexander Koester (1864-1932)
German
Ducks at the Lake's Edge
Signed, oil on canvas
47½ x 38½in (120.6 x 98cm)
£122,000-150,000 *C*

Rodger McPhail (b1935)
British
A Red Grouse
Signed, oil on board
12 x 9¼in (31 x 23.2cm)
£2,800-3,500 *C*

George Edward Lodge (1860-1934)
British
A Peregrine Falcon on a Mountainside
Signed, bodycolour
17½ x 11in (44 x 28cm)
£3,700-4,500 *C*

Philip Rickman (1891-1982)
British
Flushed on the Hill
Signed, pencil and watercolour heightened
with bodycolour
10¼ x 14½in (26 x 37cm)
£1,400-1,800 *C*

Sir Peter Scott (1909-89)
British
Pink-footed Geese
Signed and dated 1954, oil on canvas
19¼ x 23¼in (49 x 59cm)
£6,400-7,400 *C*

Richard Robjent (b1937)
British
A Pair of Woodcock in the Snow
Signed, watercolour and bodycolour
12 x 15in (31 x 38cm)
£2,200-2,800 *C*

John Selby (1788-1867)
British
The King Eider
Hand coloured copper plate engraving
23½ x 18½in (60 x 47.6cm)
£800-850 *OG*

*This plate is taken from Selby's extensive
work 'Illustrations of British Ornithology',
published in London 1819-34.*

Alan William Seaby (1867-1953)
British
An Osprey with its Prey
Signed, watercolour and bodycolour on linen
20½ x 29in (52.3 x 73.7cm)
£4,000-5,000 *C*

Frank Southgate (1872-1916)
British
Pheasant drawing onto the Marsh
Signed and inscribed on reverse, pencil and
watercolour and bodycolour
15 x 23in (38 x 59cm)
£1,600-2,000 *C*

Archibald Thorburn (1860-1935)
British
Hoopoes
Signed and dated 1924, pencil and
watercolour heightened with bodycolour on
grey paper
10¼ x 7¼in (26 x 18cm)
£9,200-10,000 *C*

George Fiddes Watt (1873-1960)
British
The Miller's Ducks
Signed and dated 99, oil on canvas
40 x 30in (101.5 x 76cm)
£9,500-10,500 *C(S)*

Janet Whittaker (b1942)
British
Tawny Owl
Signed watercolour and gouache
12 x 9in (31 x 23cm)
£400-450 *Dr*

A regular past illustrator for the RSPB

CATS AND DOGS

Sara Davenport - Fine Paintings, specialises in the lucrative and ever-popular area of dog pictures and we spoke to the gallery at the Fine Art & Antiques Fair at Olympia, London, in June 1993. According to their representative, the majority of their canine portraits come from the 19thC, when the fashion for having your pets painted was set by Queen Victoria and her circle. The dogs that are most in demand are pugs and King Charles spaniels, ('especially pugs, they're a minor miracle') while the breeds more rarely found in pictures include dalmations, labradors and pit bull terriers. Though one might expect, given our national dog-loving heritage, that the British would be the major collectors in this field, Americans and Italians are perhaps stronger contenders and there is an international clientele of canine collectors around the world. The gallery claims that most dog pictures will go to specialist collectors in the field, some of whom will have literally dozens of doggy pictures. One of the primary reasons for buying an animal picture is the warm glow the subject inspires in a buyer's heart. This sentimental impulse seems to be particularly resilient to external pressures and, according to the gallery, the market for pictures of 'man's best friend' has survived the recession well.

'Cats, dogs and animal pictures always sell well so long as they are not too portraity,' explains dealer Tony Haynes of Haynes Fine Art. 'They should have what I call 'Queen Victoria appeal,' she wanted her animals to convey and inspire human feelings. Anything that makes you say 'Aaah' is likely to make a lot of money, and the best Victorian works in this genre will combine 'Aaah' appeal with academic quality.'

Cats

Attributed to Ferdinand van Kessel
(1648-c1696)
Flemish
A Concert of Cats
Oil on copper
5½ x 7½in (14 x 19cm)
£5,000-6,000 *C*

Tsuguharu Foujita (1886-1968)
Japanese
Le Chat
Signed in Japanese and dated 1939, pen and ink and watercolour on card
9½ x 10½in (24 x 26cm)
£15,000-16,000 *S*

This work belonged to the American writer Paul Gallico (1897-1976), best known for his novel The Snow Goose, but who also wrote a number of stories about cats.

Wilson Hepple (1854-1937)
British
Three Kittens and a mother-of-pearl Jewellery Box
Signed and dated 1921, watercolour
14 x 21in (36 x 53cm)
£2,500-3,000 *AG*

John Nixon (c1750-1818)
Canadian
Corporal Trim-Sparrow, Mouser General
Inscribed pen, grey ink and watercolour over pencil
5 x 6¼in (13 x 16cm)
£1,200-1,600 *S*

Bessie Bamber (active late 19th/early 20thC)
British
All in a Row
Signed with initials and dated '09, oil on panel
12 x 40⅛in (31 x 103cm)
£1,400-1,800 *Bon*

Arthur Heyer (1872-1931)
German
Cats
Signed, oil on canvas
18½ x 26in (47 x 66.5cm)
£2,000-2,500 *LT*

Carl Kahler (b1855)
Austrian
A Contemplative White Cat
Signed and indistinctly dated 77, oil on canvas
27 x 22in (69 x 56cm)
£7,500-8,500 *S*

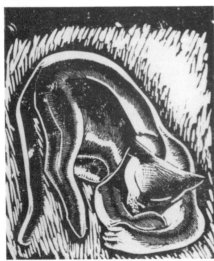

Leon Underwood (b1890)
British
Sleeping Cat
Signed, dated and numbered 2/12, print
5½ x 4½in (14 x 12cm)
£175-200 *BLD*

Ruskin Spear, R.A. (1911-90)
British
Cat and Daffodils
Signed, oil on board
27½ x 21½in (70 x 55cm)
£6,000-7,000 *S*

Jules Leroy (1833-65)
French
A Box of Treasure
Signed, oil on canvas
24¼ x 32in (62 x 81.5cm)
£2,800-3,500 *P*

Louis Wain (1860-1939)
British
Cat at a Piano
Signed, gouache
9 x 7in (23 x 18cm)
£2,500-3,000 *DN*

'Wain first drew cats, of which he was a devotee, in 1883, and these became a few years later the principal subject of his art,' notes the Dictionary of National Biography. 'A rapid worker, he could produce as many as 600 paintings in a single year and the list of his cat books occupies several columns of the British Museum Catalogue. His original treatment of cats, which he usually depicted as human beings in comical situations, quickly took the public fancy, and by the nineties his name had become a household word.

This success did not last, however, and the latter part of Wain's life was sadly at variance with his humorous drawings. During the 1914-18 war, his works fell from popularity and the artist sank into poverty. Lacking business acumen, he had sold all the rights to his drawings along with the works themselves and he lost his fortune in an ill-advised commercial venture.

Isabelle L. Perkin (active late 19thC)
British
Kittens Playing with a Tortoise
Signed and dated 1894, oil on canvas
17 x 21½in (43 x 55cm)
£2,000-2,400 *S*

Dogs

Abraham Danielsz. Hondius (1625-95)
Dutch
Hounds Attacking a Bear
Signed and dated 1681, oil on canvas
71 x 81in (180 x 206cm)
£6,200-7,500 *P*

Tobias Stranover (1684-c1731)
Czechoslovakian
A Hound with Two Spaniels, a Cat and a Parrot in a Landscape
Oil on canvas, in a carved wood frame
33 x 42in (84 x 107cm)
£63,000-75,000 *S*

Richard Ansdell, R.A. (1815-85)
British
Old Friends
Signed and dated 1861, oil on canvas
28 x 36in (71 x 92cm)
£37,000-45,000 *C*

E. Aistrop (19thC)
English School
Sailor prince
Inscribed, oil on board
3½ x 5in (9 x 12.5cm)
£1,000-1,200 *SD*

George Armfield (c1808-93)
British
Portrait of a Terrier
Signed with monogram, oil on panel
10½ x 8½in (26 x 21cm)
£5,000-5,800 *SD*

Cecil Charles Windsor Aldin (1870-1935)
British
Alsation and Two Terriers on Couch
Signed, crayon and pastel on ivorine
10 x 16½in (25 x 42cm)
£4,500-4,750 *CG*

Circle of George Townley Stubbs
(1756-1815)
British
A Spanish Pointer in a Landscape, and A
Spaniel in a Landscape
A pair, oil on canvas
5½ x 6in (14 x 15cm)
£5,800-6,800 *C*

Alfred Duke (late 19thC)
British
After the Shoot
Signed, oil on canvas
15 x 20in (38 x 51cm)
£1,750-2,000 *FdeL*

John Berry (b1920)
British
Family of Cockers
Signed, oil on canvas
28 x 36in (71 x 92cm)
£4,300-4,800 *Dr*

William Bottomley
(1816-1900)
British
Amongst the Pets
Oil on canvas
£12,000-12,500 *THo*

Wright Barker (d1941)
British
A Terrier on a Settee
Signed, oil on canvas
18 x 24in (46 x 61.5cm)
£4,000-5,000 *Bon*

Alfred Duke (late 19thC)
British
The Dog's Dinner
Signed, oil on canvas
18 x 24in (46 x 62cm)
£5,800-6,500 *C*

Maud Earl (1864-1963)
British
Three Fox Hounds
Signed and dated 1884, oil on canvas
35 x 27in (89.5 x 69cm)
£28,000-30,000 *HFA*

*Maud Earl exhibited regularly in England
and Europe. She was a prolific and much
sought after artist who painted many of the
important dogs of her day (including those
belonging to famous dog fanciers such as
Edward VII and the Duchess of Newcastle)*

Marion Harvey (b1886)
British
Portrait of a Boxer
Signed, pastel on paper
16 x 20in (41 x 51cm)
£900-950 *SD*

Donna Crawshaw (20thC)
British
On the Scent
Acrylic on canvas
16 x 12in (41 x 31cm)
£700-750 *OM*

William Weir Harrison
(1824-1906)
British
Pointers and Grouse
in Heather
A pair, signed,
watercolours
13 x 19in (33 x 48cm)
£4,500-5,500 *TCHG*

Frederick Lewis (19th/20thC)
British
Portrait of a Spaniel
Signed and dated 1912, oil on board
12½ x 19½in (32 x 49cm)
£2,300-2,600 *SD*

Lucy Ann Leavers (19thC)
British
Three Against One
Signed, oil on canvas
34¼ x 48½in (87 x 123cm)
£6,000-7,000 *CNY*

F. Mabel Hollams (active 1896-1912)
British
Portrait of James
Signed, oil on panel
13 x 17in (33 x 43cm)
£2,000-2,250 *SD*

E. Magill (20thC)
British
Head Study of a Terrier
Signed, oil on board
12 x 9in (31 x 23cm)
£1,800-2,000 *SD*

Francis Wilfred Lawson R.A. (1842-1935)
British
The Grocer's Shop
Signed, watercolour
7 x 6in (18 x 15cm)
£850-950 *BW*

George Paice (1854-1925)
British
Jim, Cocker Spaniel
Signed and dated '97, oil on canvas
10 x 14in (25 x 36cm)
£500-550 *Dr*

Colin Graeme Roe (19thC)
British
Two gundogs with dead game in a Moorland
Landscape
Signed and dated 1889
24 x 30in (61 x 76cm)
£1,500-1,800 *HSS*

Herbert Sidney (early 20thC)
British
Rosette Blanche, A Japowitz Poodle
Signed, inscribed and dated Jan 1904, oil o
canvas
30 x 20in (76 x 51cm)
£1,400-1,800 *S*

George Paice (1854-1925)
British
Duchess
Signed, oil on board
8½ x 11in (21 x 28cm)
£575-625 *BCG*

Arthur Wardle (1864-1949)
British
Two Spaniels
Signed, oil on canvas
22 x 19in (56 x 48cm)
£16,000-17,000 *HFA*

Wardle was one of the most successful animal painters of his generation. He worked in oil, watercolour and pastel, painting domestic and wild animals as well as sporting subjects. Wardle was a favourite painter with dog breeders at the turn of the century, greatly admired for his ability to capture the characteristic expressions of the breeds he portrayed. The artist clearly had the popular touch and a series of pictures that he produced in this format were reproduced as cigarette cards.

E.A. Simkins (19thC)
British
Portrait of Mike
Signed, oil on canvas
12 x 16in (31 x 41cm)
£1,200-1,400 *SD*

FARMYARD ANIMALS

In 19thC Europe, every country had its specialist master in painting cows, sheep and farmyard animals. Many of these artists commanded vast prices and some were so popular that they inspired not only imitators but fakers. There seemed to be an endless demand for these conservative and restful portrayals of farmyard animals and country life, portraying a world of spotless sheep, sweatless ploughmen, and a countryside that always smells sweet.

Circle of Stephen Elmer (1714-96)
British
A pair of rabbits in a landscape
Oil on canvas
12 x 16in (31 x 41cm)
£2,000-2,500 *C*

Thomas Baker (1809-69)
British
In Stoneleigh Park
Signed, oil
13 x 19in (33 x 48cm)
£3,550-3,750 *Dr*

'Thomas Baker's paintings are quite unique in style and treatment and once familiar, his work can always be recognised,' writes David Gilbert of the Driffold Gallery. Richly toned greens and ochres applied with a creamy extravagance, fine feathery foliage on his trees, charming doll-like figures, a dominant, part-clouded sky and a strong pronunciation of light and shade. These were the hallmarks of Thomas Baker's paintings. His signature was painted lightly 'T. BAKER' in capitals blending in neatly with the foreground and most pictures were dated. His subjects often featured cows in meadowland or on river banks and sometimes rural lanes and buildings with figures.

Henri de Beul (1845-1900)
Dutch
Cattle and a Chicken
Signed and dated 1897, inscribed Bruxelles, oil on panel
9½ x 7½in (24 x 19cm)
£500-600 *DN*

Pietro Barucci (1845-1917)
Italian
Shepherdess with sheep in a landscape
Signed and inscribed Roma, oil on canvas
31½ x 19¼in (80 x 49cm).
£5,000-6,000 *P*

After John Boultbee (1753-1812)
British
A portrait of a two year old ram of the New
Leicestershire kind; and a portrait of a two
year old ewe of the New Leicestershire Kind
Aquatints by F. Jukes, published by the
artist, 1802
17 x 22½in (43 x 57cm) each
£900-1,200   *S(S)*

Rosa Bonheur (1822-99)
French
Studies of Cows, Hens, Roosters, a Goose and
a Sheep
Signed with initials, oil on canvas
21¼ x 25½in (54 x 65cm)
£7,000-8,000   *CNY*

After J. Bradley (19thC)
British
The Airedale Heifer
Aquatint engraving by Richard Gilson Reeve,
hand coloured, published by R. Aked
18½ x 24¾in (47 x 63cm)
£1,100-1,500   *P(L)*

Charles Collins (active 1867-1903)
British
A Surrey Homestead
Signed and dated 1889, oil on canvas
36 x 28in (92 x 71cm)
£4,200-5,000   *S*

> *Condition is a
> major factor in a
> picture's price*

Thomas Sidney Cooper, R.A. (1803-1902)
and **Frederick Richard Lee, R.A.**
(1798-1879)
British
The Watering Place
Signed and dated 1850, oil on canvas
50¼ x 72in (128 x 183cm)
£25,500-35,000   *C*

*Cooper and Lee worked together on many
works and to great acclaim, Queen Victoria
was among those who admired their joint
efforts, calling them 'the Beaumont and
Fletcher of Art'.*

*The division of labour was decided by Lee,
who would leave areas of his landscapes
unpainted where he wished Cooper to
introduce the animals. However, even after
their collaboration ceased, the demand for
'joint' works induced owners of Lee's
paintings to commission Cooper to add cattle
into finished works, the practise continuing
long after Lee's death in 1879.*

Henry Hadfield Cubley (active 1882-1930)
British
Spring near Wall Grange, Lichfield
Signed, oil on canvas
19 x 29in (48 x 74cm)
£575-675 *BCG*

Thomas Sidney Cooper, R.A. (1803-1902)
British
Sheep in Canterbury Meadows
Signed, watercolour
12 x 9in (31 x 23cm)
£2,750-2,850 *WG*

Henry Earp Snr. (1831-1914)
British
Cows by a Pond
Watercolour with bodycolour
13¼ x 19½in (34 x 49cm)
£1,000-1,200 *PCA*

Edgar Hunt (1876-1953)
British
White Pony and Domestic Fowl outside a
Stable
9 x 14in (23 x 36cm)
£8,600-9,600 *GAK*

Charles Emile Jacque (1813-94)
French
Sheep grazing on the banks of a river with a
shepherdess and her dog
Signed, oil on canvas
28½ x 47½in (72 x 121cm)
£5,800-6,800 *C(S)*

*The animal painters who were most admired
in the 19thC were those who managed to
imbue their animals with a sense of human
feeling. 'Ah! would that no one ever again
declare that animals don't think,' declared
one enthusiastic critic at the time of Jacque's
death. 'We would refer such prosaic objectors
to the sheepfolds and farms of Charles
Jacque, who saw nature as clearly as he knew
how to observe her creations.'*

Louis Bosworth Hurt (1856-1929)
British
The Highland Pass
Signed, oil on canvas
24 x 40in (61 x 101.5cm)
£13,000-14,000 *HFA*

Robert Jobling (1841-1923)
British
A Young Girl milking a Cow
Signed and dated, watercolour
9½ x 12¾in (24 x 32cm)
£900-1,200 *AG*

Charles Jones (1836-92)
British
Landscape with castle ruins in background
and sheep to the fore
Signed with monogram and inscribed on
reverse, oil on canvas
14 x 22in (36 x 56cm)
£1,800-2,300 *BWe*

Edgar Longstaffe (1849-1912)
British
Highland Cattle - Loch Beauly
Monogrammed, oil on canvas
10 x 14in (25 x 36cm)
£800-850 *Dr*

Jochaim van Leemputten (19thC)
Belgian
Cattle in a Meadow
Signed, oil on canvas
26 x 40in (66 x 101.5cm)
£750-850 *CSK*

William Luker Snr. (1828-1905)
British
In the Heat of the Day
Signed, oil on canvas
14 x 22in (36 x 56cm)
£1,150-1,350 *Dr*

Adolf Heinrich Mackeprang (1833-1911)
Danish
Cattle at a Woodland Pond
Signed and dated 1877, oil on canvas
45 x 37½in (114 x 95cm)
£3,400-4,000 *C*

George Shalders (c1826-78)
British
The young shepherdess
Signed, oil on canvas
17¾ x 25½in (45 x 65cm)
£1,000-1,275 *BCG*

John MacWhirter, R.A. (1839-1911)
British
Highland Flock, Kyle of Lochalsh
Watercolour
13½ x 20¼in (35 x 51cm)
£1,000-1,150 *CG*

G. T. Maxwell (late 19th/early 20thC)
British
Highland Cattle
A pair, both signed and dated 1908, oil on canvas
26 x 30in (66 x 76cm) each
£4,200-5,200 *S*

Gourlay Steell (1819-94)
British
A Highland Bull
Signed, oil on board
11 x 16in (28 x 41cm)
£450-550 *S(S)*

Louis Pierre Verwee (1807-77)
Belgian
Sheep in a Barn
Signed, oil on panel
18¾ x 25¾in (48 x 68cm)
£4,000-4,250 *HAR*

William Watson (19th/20thC)
British
Morning in Highland
Signed and dated 1909, oil on canvas
24 x 36¼in (61 x 92cm)
£3,800-4,300 *CNY*

Robert Watson (active early 20thC)
British
Cattle going south, Argyllshire
Signed and dated 1909, oil on canvas
41½ x 69½in (105 x 176cm)
£7,000-7,600 *FWA*

Herbert William Weekes
(active 1864-1904) British
Our Member of the Commons
Signed, oil on board
10½ x 14½in (26 x 37cm)
£5,500-5,750 *BuP*

Herbert William Weeke
(active 1864-1904)
British
An Urban Council
Signed, oil on panel
11 x 7½in (28 x 19cm)
£5,000-6,000 *Bon*

BULLS & BULLFIGHTING

'The painters of Spain, dipped their brushes in pain,' rhymed the American poet Stevie Smith. The bloody and glorious theme of the bullfight has fascinated many artists, most notably perhaps the Spanish painters Goya and Picasso. Goya's bullfighting scene (see below) is one of the few works by the artist to come on the open market in recent years and which set a new auction record for his works in December 1992, when it sold at Sotheby's to the J. Paul Getty Museum, California.

Follower of Samuel Alken (18thC)
British
Bull Baiting
Inscribed, oil on canvas
25¼ x 30½in (64 x 77cm)
£800-900 *CSK*

José Benlliure y Gil (1855-1937)
Spanish
The Bullfighter's Salute
Signed and dated 1870, oil on panel
8½ x 5½in (21 x 14cm)
£2,000-2,500 *P*

Frank Myers (1899-1956)
American
The Bullfight
Signed, oil on canvas
20 x 24in (51 x 61cm)
£900-1,200 *S(NY)*

Pablo Picasso (1881-1974)
Spanish
Corrida en Arles
Aquatint and scraper, printed in colours, 1952
16½ x 21½in (42 x 54.5cm)
£13,800-15,000 *S*

Francisco de Goya (1746-1828)
Spanish
Bullfight: Suerte de Varas
Inscribed, oil on canvas
19¾ x 23½in (50 x 60cm)
£5,000,000-5,500,000 *S*

FISH

Ernest Henry Griset (1844-1907)
British
Mr Lovejoy's Holiday Trip to the Highlands
A set of nine, all signed, pen and black ink
and watercolour
7 x 5¾in (17.4 x 14.3cm)
£3,500-4,500 *C(S)*

Kiyoshi Hasegawa (b1891)
Japanese
Petit Aquarium
Signed in pencil, drypoint, dated 1929
10½ x 11in (26.5 x 28cm)
£1,600-2,000 *S*

William Geddes (19thC)
British
Prize Takers from the Isla
Signed and dated 1879, oil on canvas
20 x 30in (51 x 76.5cm)
£7,200-8,000 *S*

Peter Alexander Hay, R.S.W. (19thC)
British
Trout
Signed and dated 98, watercolour
19 x 23in (48.5 x 58.5cm)
£1,600-2,000 *S*

John Russell (19thC)
British
Trout and a Salmon
Signed, oil on canvas
17½ x 36in (44.5 x 91cm)
£1,700-2,000 *S*

A. Roland Knight (19thC)
British
A Salmon Taking a Fly
Signed, oil on canvas
14 x 21in (36 x 53cm)
£2,000-2,500 *S*

HORSES

A number of works in the following sections are prints. As Ian Mackenzie notes (see Biblio.), the great age of the British sporting print stretches from the late 18th century through to the mid-19th century. The principal medium used was the aquatint, a specialised etching technique introduced to Britain from the Continent in the 1770s.

In brief, the process is as follows: a metal plate is sprinkled with acid resistant resin. Parts intended to appear white are stopped out with varnish, the plate is immersed in acid, which bites between the resin particles to produce an evenly pitted surface. The plate, etched in intaglio, is then inked and used for printing. Aquatints were hand coloured with watercolour and from the 1820s were often partly printed in colour, to reduce the amount of additional painting needed.

Popular sporting aquatints of the early 1800s were often reprinted many times. Generally speaking, early impressions are the most desirable since the more it is used the more worn a plate becomes and the more details the resulting print will lose. The condition of a print will also affect its value - fading, staining, torn edges, cut margins, etc., can all damage the price. Rarity is another important factor. As Mackenzie notes:

'Firstly, the older the print the fewer impressions are likely to have survived; and secondly, even if a print is common because many impressions were printed at the time or later, the more difficult it will be to find a print in good condition.'

While portraits of individual racehorses were issued separately, hunting prints were often issued in sets. Each plate will have its own value but a full set will always command a better price than an incomplete one. Works can be desirable both for their artist and their subject: a famous horse, a fashionable hunt or an important sporting event. The fact that sporting prints were so popular and hung in pride of place in the home means that many of them have suffered badly from the effects of light and domestic wear and tear. Early unfaded works are increasingly difficult to find, warns Mackenzie, and the embryonic collector should beware of reprints, which might look very similar to first impressions but which may only be worth a fraction of the price.

16th - 18th Centuries

Albrecht Dürer (1471-1528)
German
The Large Horse
Engraving, dated 1505
6½ x 4¾in (16.8 x 12cm)
10,000-11,000 *S*

Circle of Pieter van Bloemen, called Standard (1657-1720)
Flemish
A Riding School
Oil on canvas
20¼ x 28in (51.4 x 71.4cm)
£5,800-6,800 *C*

Sawrey Gilpin, R.A. (1733-1807)
British
A Horse Frightened by a Snake
Signed, dated 1782, pen and brown ink and watercolour over pencil
8½ x 11⅜in (21.5 x 29cm)
£700-1,000 *S*

William Shaw (active 1758-72)
British
Matchem
Signed, dated and inscribed Matchem/W.
Shaw 1757
40 x 50in (101.5 x 127cm)
£13,000-15,000 *C*

*Matchem by Cade was one of the most
successful horses of his day. He lived to the
remarkable age of 33, the greatest recorded
age for any important stallion and was
described by a contemporary as having a
'general want of symmetrical proportion'. He
was one of the 3 stallions foaled in the mid-
18thC, with Herod and Eclipse, from whom
every racehorse traces its descent in the male
line.*

James Seymour (c1702-52)
British
The Duke of Devonshire's Plaistow beating
the Duke of Bolton's Doctor at Newmarket on
October 1st 1735
Oil on canvas
34½ x 49in (87 x 124.5cm)
£7,200-8,200 *S*

Francis Sartorius (1734-1804)
British
Daniel
Signed, oil on canvas
17½ x 26½in (44 x 67cm)
£13,300-15,000 *C*

Circle of George Stubbs (1724-1806)
A saddled grey hunter held by a groom with
his two dogs beneath a tree, in an extensive
river landscape
Signed and dated 1778, oil on canvas
40 x 50in (101.5 x 127cm)
£7,500-8,500 *C*

James Ross (active early 18thC)
British
Meeting at Clifton & Rawcliffe Ings, York,
September 1709
Signed, oil on canvas
17 x 23½in (43 x 60cm)
£23,500-28,000 *S*

*Whilst the history of racing at York can be
traced back to the time of the Romans, who
competed on the Campus Martius, properly
organised annual races did not begin until
1709 and this important picture
commemorates their first year.*

Francis Stringer (active c1760-72)
British
A saddled bay hunter held by a groom in a
landscape
Signed and dated 1769, oil on canvas
26 x 34in (66 x 86cm)
£11,000-12,000 *C*

19th Century

Nathaniel Hughes Baird (b1865)
(active 1883-1935)
British
Mooring a Coastal Barge
Signed with monogram, watercolour
19 x 20in (48 x 51cm)
£5,250-5,750 *CSG*

Charles James Adams (1859-1931)
British
Ready for Work; and Done for the Day
A pair, signed, watercolours
15 x 21½in (38 x 54cm) each
£10,000-10,500 *CSG*

After Harry Hall (active 1838-86)
British
Gladiateur
Hand coloured aquatint by J. Harris,
published August 20 1865 by A.H. Bailey &
Co, London and Goupil & Co, Paris
18 x 26in (46 x 66cm)
£700-785 *CG*

John Ferneley Snr. (1781-1860)
British
Priam, with Sam Day up
Signed, inscribed and dated 1830, oil on
canvas
33½ x 42in (85 x 106.5cm)
£72,000-80,000 *C*

*Ferneley's clients were predominantly the
sporting gentlemen of Melton Mowbray, where
he settled from 1814 onwards. According to
the Quarterly Review 1825, there were
certainly enough clients and equine subjects
to keep him going, since the writer noted that
the average sportsman kept a stable of ten
horses in the town, which made an estimated
income of some £50,000 a year from its
hunting residents. Ferneley charged ten
guineas for a horse portrait, a price that
remained constant throughout his career, and
that in this instance at least, certainly
represents a good investment.*

R. Beavis (1824-96)
British
A Horse and Donkey grazing in a pastoral
landscape
Signed and dated 1878, watercolour
17 x 27in (43 x 69cm)
£600-800 *L&E*

Walter Harrowing (19thC)
British
Midday's Rest
Signed, oil on canvas
17 x 14½in (43 x 37cm)
£1,000-1,250 *SH*

J.R. Mackrell after John Frederick Herring (1815-1907)
British
Pyrrhus the First
Aquatint printed in colours, published by Bailey Brothers 1846,in original maple frame
15 x 20in (38.3 x 50.5cm)
£1,000-1,150 *CG*

After John Frederick Herring (1815-1907)
British
Bay Middleton
Coloured aquatint, published by S & J Fuller
16 x 20in (41 x 51cm)
£450-550 *CSK*

George W. Horlor (19thC)
British
Moorland Ponies in the Highlands
Signed, oil on canvas
18 x 24in (46 x 61cm)
£2,550-2,750 *Dr*

Attributed to Friedrich Wilhelm Keyl
(1823-71)
German
A Well Earned Rest
Oil on canvas
26 x 35in (66 x 89cm)
£5,500-6,000 *McE*

Ben Marshall (1767-1835) **and Henry Bernard Chalon** (1770-1849)
British
A Chestnut Hunter saddled up and tethered to a gate, with a terrier, in an open landscape
Signed and dated 1802, oil on canvas
28 x 36in (71 x 92cm)
£9,000-10,000 *C*

Painted in 1802 for Frederick Reeves of East Sheen, Surrey, the three-legged dog belonging to his wife was added in 1813 by Henry Bernard Chalon.

Basil Nightingale (1864-1940)
British
Grasshopper
Signed and dated 1896, oil on canvas
24 x 29in (61 x 74cm)
£7,000-7,800   *CGa*

I. Clark after Henry Alken (19thC)
British
National Sports of Great Britain
Racing, a set of three
Aquatint published by T. McLean, January 1
1820
£1,000-1,250   *CG*

Benjamin Cam Norton (1835-1900)
British
Chestnut Hunter
Signed and dated 1874, oil on canvas
19½ x 26¼in (49 x 67cm)
£2,750-3,000   *SH*

Harold Swanwick (1866-1929)
British
Ah-Whoa-Whup
Signed and dated 1892, oil on canvas
36 x 24in (92 x 61cm)
£13,000-14,000   *CSG*

Martin Theodore Ward (1799-1874)
British
Pony and sheep in upland landscape
Oil on canvas
10 x 12in (25 x 31cm)
£2,000-2,200   *Dr*

F. Whaley (19thC)
British
Hunter in a Stable
Signed and dated 1898, oil on canvas
18 x 23in (46 x 59cm)
£1,200-1,400   *SAV*

20thC

Renate Blan (20thC)
Drawing
11 x 15in (28 x 38cm)
£100-125 *EAG*

Alice Des Clayes (b1890)
Canadian
Queenie and Peter in a Landscape
Signed and inscribed, pastel
16 x 19in (41 x 48cm)
£1,100-1,300 *Dr*

Amanda Gooseman (20thC)
British
Early Morning, Newmarket
Pastel
15 x 18½in (38 x 47cm)
£200-225 *EAG*

Neil Cawthorne
(20thC)
British
At the Start
Oil on canvas
26 x 36in (66 x 92cm)
£200-500 *EAG*

Stephen Cook (20thC)
British
July Bums
Oil on canvas
9 x 11in (23 x 28cm)
£250-325 *EAG*

Gilbert Holiday (1879-1937)
British
A Finish at Goodwood
Inscribed and dated 1929, coloured pastel
11¾ x 18¾in (30 x 48cm)
£1,800-2,400 *C*

E. Meade King (20thC)
British
Mare and Foal
Oil on canvas
11½ x 16in (29 x 41cm)
£400-450 *EAG*

Stanley Lloyd
(English School, c1920)
The Race
Signed, oil on canvas
16 x 20in (41 x 51cm)
£1,200-1,400   *HI*

Lydia Minahan (20thC)
British
Early Morning
Oil on canvas
8 x 12in (20 x 31cm)
£350-400   *EAG*

Sir Alfred James Munnings (1878-1959)
British
Donkeys on Crestwick Common
Signed and dated 1904, oil on canvas
29¼ x 37½in (74 x 95cm)
£23,000-28,000   *C(S)*

Munnings specialised in rural scenes and equestrian portraits. Hugely successful in his own day, knighted in 1944 and President of the Royal Academy for five years, this ultimate establishment figure has not always found favour with subsequent critics. 'His first job was designing chocolate boxes - a talent he clearly never lost,' commented Waldemar Januszczak dryly in The Guardian. Munnings himself became famous for his own outspoken criticism of abstraction and the 'damn nonsense' of this 'so-called modern art.'

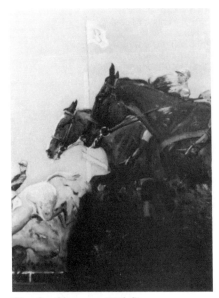

Charles Simpson (20thC)
British
Beechers Brook
Initialled, oil on canvas
24 x 20in (61 x 51cm)
£3,000-3,250 *Dr*

Bert Greer Phillips (1868-1956)
American
Taos Indian with his Horse
Signed, oil on canvasboard
9¼ x 12in (23.5 x 31cm)
£11,000-12,000 *S(NY)*

Norman Thelwell (b1923)
British
Wake Up!
Signed with initial, pen and ink
2¼ x 4¾in (6 x 12cm)
£600-650 *CBL*

Martin Williams (20thC)
British
Michael Roberts
Watercolour
15 x 11½in (38 x 29cm)
£400-500 *EAG*

HUNTING & SPORTING

Hunting, 'the Sport of Kings', or as Oscar
Wilde put it 'the unspeakable in full pursuit
of the uneatable.' Opinions about hunting
are increasingly divided, with the rights and
wrongs of the debate being endlessly
disputed in Parliament and, with more
obvious violence, in the hunting field itself.
Leaving aside exceptional or highly
decorative paintings, average hunting
pictures tend to appeal to a hunting clientele,
a loyal but limited audience.

Arent Arentsz, called Cabel
(1585/6-before October 1635)
Dutch
A hunter shooting duck by a beacon by a
frozen waterway
Monogram, oil on panel
9 x 12¼in (23 x 31cm)
£125,000-150,000 *C*

Lucas Cranach (1472-1553)
German
The Saxon Prince on a Boar Hunt
Woodcut, c1507
7 x 5in (18 x 12cm)
£4,700-5,500 *S*

Philips Wouwermans (1619-68)
Dutch
A hawking party in a hilly landscape
Signed with monogram, oil on panel
16 x 22¼in (41 x 56.5cm)
£255,000-285,000 *S*

Highly decorative, the present work more than trebled its top estimate of £70,000 at Sotheby's in December 1992.

T. Davey after Henry Calvert
(active 1813-61)
British
Wynnstay Hunt
Hand coloured engraving published by
Thomas Agnew August 1 1855, in original
maple frame
19½ x 32in (49 x 81.5cm)
£800-845 *CG*

Bernard Lens III (1682-1740)
British
Gentlemen out Shooting
Watercolour over pencil
9¼ x 13in (23.5 x 33cm)
£6,000-7,000 *S*

This rare early watercolour dates from the late 1720s or early 1730s.

Lionel Dalhousie Robertson Edwards
(1878-1966)
British
In Full Cry
Signed, watercolour and bodycolour
10½ x 17¾in (26 x 45cm)
£5,000-5,500 *BSG*

Jean Richard Goubie (1842-99)
French
Choosing the Best Hunter
Signed and dated 1878, oil on canvas
24 x 35¾in (61 x 91cm)
£20,000-25,000 *CNY*

Samuel Egbert Jones (active 1820-45)
British
Pheasant shooting with guns and spaniels
A pair, signed, oil on canvas
19½ x 23½in (49 x 60cm)
£5,000-6,000 *DA*

After George Henry Laporte (1799-1873)
British
Coursing
A pair of hand coloured aquatint engravings
by Henry A. Papprill, published London 1854
12 x 22½in (31 x 57cm)
£300-400 *P(L)*

After W. Webb (active 1819-50)
British
John Mytton Esq of Halston, Salop
Hand coloured by W. Giller, mixed method
engraving, published May 1 1841, by J.
Davies, Shrewsbury and R. Ackerman,
London
18½ x 24½in (47 x 61.5cm)
£800-850 *CG*

Raffaelo Sorbi (1844-1931)
Italian
The Departure of the Hunting Party
Signed and dated 1926, oil on canvas
23¾ x 39½in (61 x 100cm)
£74,000-80,000 *S(NY)*

William Webb (active 1819-50)
British
Portrait of William Cooper on a dark bay
hunter with his hounds
Oil on canvas
33 x 41in (84 x 104cm)
£9,500-10,500 *DN*

Gilbert Scott Wright (1880-1958)
British
Full Cry
Signed, oil on canvas
20 x 28in (51 x 71cm)
£3,500-4,000 *C*

Julius Zimmermann (1824-1906)
German
Frederick II with His Hunting Party
Indistinctly signed and dated 184..., oil on
canvas
40 x 60¾in (101.5 x 154cm)
£8,000-9,000 *CNY*

COACHING

The first half of the 19thC saw the golden age of the stage coach and the coaching picture, a form of transport and a pictorial subject that were both extinguished by the advent of the railway.

Joseph Crawhall (1861-1913)
British
A Winter Journey
Signed, pencil, black crayon and watercolour
9½ x 14in (24 x 36cm)
£1,600-2,000 *C*

Rubens Arthur Moore (active 1881-1920)
British
The Cock Tavern, Bishopsgate Street, London; and Interior, La Belle Sauvage, Ludgate Hill, London
A pair, both signed and inscribed, oils on board
7½ x 9in (19 x 23cm) each
£2,000-2,500 *S*

Henry Alken Jnr. (1810-94)
British
The Chester to London Coach on the Open Road
Oil on canvas
12½ x 20½in (32 x 52cm)
£2,000-2,400 *S*

English School (19thC)
A Stage Coach from Ninan & Co. Westminster, on the Open Road
Oil on canvas
51¾ x 85in (131 x 216cm)
£2,700-3,200 *S*

John White (1851-1933)   British
Going by the Coach, The Ship Inn, Porlock
Signed and dated 1906, watercolour
13 x 20in (33 x 51cm)
£2,600-2,800
HO

Charles Cooper Henderson (1803-77)
British
The London to Brighton Royal Mail Coach
Signed with initials, oil on panel
16 x 25in (41 x 64cm)
£1,200-1,600 *DN*

WILDLIFE

Jacobus Perkois (1756-1804)
Dutch
A Redhanded Tamarin (Saguinus midas)
Signed, dated and inscribed July 1776,
pencil, watercolour and gum arabic, pencil
framing lines, watermark fleur-de-lys above
shield
16½ x 10½in (42 x 27cm)
£3,400-4,000 *C(Am)*

Richard Ansdell, R.A. (1815-85)
British
Fallow Deer
Signed and dated 1857, oil on canvas
20 x 60in (51 x 152cm)
£7,000-8,000 *S*

Wenzel Hollar (1607-77)
Czechoslovakian
The Dead Mole
Etching, 1646
2¾ x 5½in (7 x 14cm)
£1,400-1,800 *S*

Christopher Huet (d1759)
French
A Mastiff, a Spaniel and three costumed
monkeys, 5 studies on a monochrome ground
17½ x 28¼in (44 x 72cm)
£3,000-3,500 *C*

*Monkeys have figured in European art since
the Middle Ages, but it was not until the late
17thC that the vogue for singeries took off,
reaching its height of popularity in the 18thC.
This decoration featuring monkeys dressed in
human clothes and aping human behaviour
appeared in murals and marquetry designs,
on ceramics and printed textiles. The French
rococo painter Huet was the leading exponent
of the genre, his fanciful and light-hearted
singeries decorating the walls of palaces and
capering throughout the decorative arts.
Falling from grace c1800, singeries later
reappeared in a host of 19thC pictures, cruder
than their 18thC ancestors, verging on the
grotesque, and owing more to caricature than
to rococo elegance.*

> ## Locate the Source
> *The source of each
> illustration in Miller's can
> be found by checking the
> code letters below each
> caption with the list of
> contributors.*

Johann Melchoir Roos (1659-1731)
German
Bears Playing in a Pine Forest
Oil on canvas
31¾ x 40½in (81 x 103cm)
£21,000-26,000 *P*

Ferdinand-Victor-Eugène Delacroix
(1798-1863)
French
Tigre couché
Stamped with artist's initials, pencil, pen and
black ink and brown wash on paper laid
down on paper
8¼ x 12½in (21 x 32cm)
£32,000-37,000 *C*

*The tiger was said to have been given to King
Louis Philippe by the Sultan of Morocco (see
Delacroix's letter to Pierret from Morocco, 2
April, 1832.*

Wilhelm Kuhnert (1865-1926)
German
The Captured Gorilla
Signed and indistinctly inscribed,
watercolour and bodycolour
16 x 10½in (41 x 26cm)
£1,000-1,500 *P*

Zacharias Noterman (1813-74)
Belgian
Reading the News
Signed and dated 81, oil on panel
12 x 15in (31 x 38cm)
£1,500-1,800 *CSK*

Archibald Thorburn (1860-1935)
British
A Stoat in summer coat, and an
Irish Stoat   Signed and dated
1919, pencil and watercolour
heightened with white on grey
paper
14¼ x 18¼in (37 x 47cm)
£14,000-15,000 *DA*

John Berry (b1920)
British
Hannibal on the Beach
Signed, gouache
9 x 14in (23 x 36cm)
500-550 *Dr*

*This is the original illustration for Ladybird
Books Hannibal Series.*

Willem S. de Beer (20thC)
South African
Leopards
Oil on canvas
20 x 30in (51 x 76cm)
£2,450-2,650 *BRG*

John Bratby, R.A. (1928-92)
British
Apes
Signed and dated '62, oil on board
47¾ x 48in (121 x 122cm)
£1,200-1,500 *Bea*

Isabelle Brent (20thC)
British
Cheetah in Moonlight
Gilded watercolour
8 x 5½in (20 x 14cm)
£400-450 *PHG*

Ruskin Spear, R.A. (1911-90)
British
The Monkey, c1985
Signed, oil on board
15¼ x 21¼in (39 x 54cm)
£1,500-2,000 *Bon*

Norbertine Von Bresslern-Roth (b1891)
American
A Tiger Cub
Woodcut
6½ x 9in (16 x 23cm)
£100-110 *HHG*

David Shepherd (b1931)
British
Indian Jumbos
Signed and inscribed, pencil
7 x 11in (18 x 28cm)
£300-350 *CSK*

Arthur Wardle (1864-1949)
British
The Tiger Pool
Signed, oil on canvas
29 x 37in (74 x 94cm)
£59,000-69,000 *S(NY)*

Jean Michel Basquiat (1960-88)
American
Untitled, painted 1981
Acrylic and oilstick on canvas
51½ x 74in (130.8 x 188cm)
£50,000-60,000 *S(NY)*

Rudolf Bauer (1889-1954)
Polish/American
Titel Unbekannt
Signed, oil on canvas, painted c1920
27½ x 23½in (70 x 59.4cm)
£15,000-16,000 *S(NY)*

Josef Albers (1888-1976)
American
Homage to the Square: Slate Against Sky
Signed with monogram and dated 62, oil on
masonite
40in (101.6cm) square
£45,000-55,000 *C*

Valerio Adami (b1935)
Italian
Vetrina
Signed, inscribed and dated 68, acrylic on canvas
28½ x 36in (72.5 x 91.3cm)
£15,000-16,000 *C*

Horst Antes (b1936)
German
Portrait Landschaft
Gartner
Signed, titled and dated
1968, acrylic on canvas
27½ x 23½ in
(70 x 59.7cm)
£22,000-27,000 *S(NY)*

Karel Appel (b1923)
Dutch
Woman with Bird
Signed and dated 73, oil on
canvas
55¾ x 39¾in (141.5 x 101cm)
£24,000-28,000 *C*

Sandra Blow (b1925)
British
Green and Blue
Construction
Collage and acrylic
14⅝in (37cm) square
£800-850 *OLG*

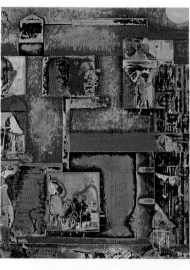

Romare Bearden
(b1914)
American
The Tenement World
Signed and dated 1969,
collage on board
19 x 14¾in (48.3 x 37.5cm)
£11,000-12,000 *S(NY)*

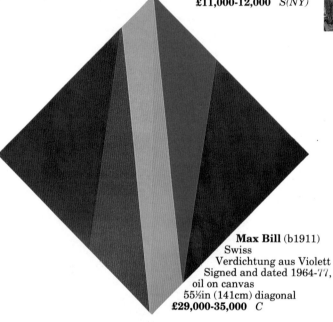

Bram Bogart (b1921)
Jaunegeel
Signed and dated 73, pigment
and composition on board
27⅛ x 28½ x 13in (70 x 72.5 x
13cm)
£4,200-5,000 *C*

Max Bill (b1911)
Swiss
Verdichtung aus Violett
Signed and dated 1964-77,
oil on canvas
55⅛in (141cm) diagonal
£29,000-35,000 *C*

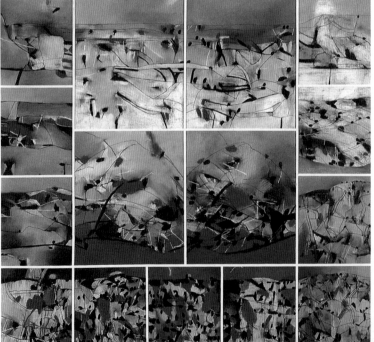

Anthony Benjamin
(20thC)
British
Borderlands II
Silkscreen, 17 colours
30 x 22¼in
(76 x 56.5cm)
£150-175 *CCA*

David Blackburn (b1939)
British
A Landscape Vision No 10,
1991-92
Pastel
63 x 69in (160 x 175cm)
£15,000-20,000 *HaG*

Mary Clare Foa (b1956)
British
Finding a Boat to Sail In
Oil on board
48in (122cm) square
£700-800 *KG*

Christo (b1935)
Bulgarian/American
The Umbrellas
Signed and dated 1990,
collage with pastel,
charcoal, photograph,
diagram, oil, glue and
fabric on card mounted
on 2 boards
8 x 131in
(147.4 x 332.8cm)
64,000-74,000 *C*

Phillippa Clayden (b1955)
British
Inland
Collage and mixed media on
board
42 x 78in (107 x 198cm)
£7,500-8,000 *BOU*

Alexander Calder
(1898-1976)
American
Untitled lithograph,
1966
10 x 7½in
(25.5 x 19cm)
£115-125 *WO*

**Pierre-Marie
Brisson** (b1955)
French
Original carborundum
engraving
43½ x 28½in
(111 x 73cm)
£380-430 *TES*

Robert Combas (b1957)
French
Deux Langues
Acrylic on canvas, painted
in 1980
63¾ x 51in (162 x 130cm)
£8,800-9,500 *C*

Friedel Dzubas (b1915)
American
Cross River
Signed and dated 1986
Acrylic on canvas
72in (183cm) square
£14,500-15,500 *S(NY)*

Ithell Colquhoun
(1906-88)
British
Autumnal Equinox 1949
96 x 40in
(243.5 x 101.5cm)
£9,000-9,500 *JBA*

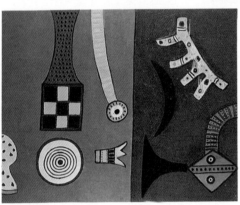

Alan Davie (b1920)
British
Shaman No 7
Oil on canvas, painted 1969
48 x 60in (124 x 150cm)
£13,000-14,000 *C*

Jim Dine (b1935)
American
Four Big Hearts
Signed and dated 1970, spraypaint on waxed
paper mounted on paper on board
29½ x 27¾in (75 x 70.2cm)
£25,000-30,000 *C*

Kenneth Draper (b1944)
British
Red Earth 1990
Signed and dated 1990, pastel on paper
22 x 26in (56 x 66cm)
£1,800-2,000 *HaG*

Jane Deakin (20thC)
British
Arise, Fair Sun 1991
Oil on canvas
48in (122cm) square
£1,300-1,500 *LG*

Terry Frost (b1915)
British
Two Suns
Gouache and acrylic on paper
24 x 36in (61 x 92cm)
£1,000-1,175 *OLG*

Peter Evans (b1943)
British
Posters near Blaye
Acrylic
36in (92cm) square
£5,000-5,500 *CSG*

Gilbert and George (b1943 and 1942)
British
Finding God
Signed and dated 1982, 84 hand dyed photographs mounted in metal frames
166 x 237in (422 x 602cm)
£42,000-50,000 *C*

Sam Francis (b1923)
American
Son of Fire
Acrylic on paper, painted
in 1989
72 x 36in (183 x 91.4cm)
£38,000-45,000 *S(NY)*

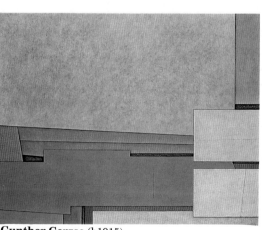

Gunther Gerzso (b1915)
Mexican
Naranja-Azul-Verde
Signed and dated V-79, acrylic and sand on masonite
28 x 35½in (70.8 x 90cm)
£23,000-27,000 *S(NY)*

Shoichi Hasegawa (b1929)
Japanese
Butterfly Flight
Original engraving
11½ x 17½in (29.5 x 45cm)
£240-280 *TES*

Adolph Gottlieb (b1903)
American
Gray Bars
Signed and dated 1973, oil on canvas
48 x 36in (122 x 91.4cm)
£38,000-45,000 *S(NY)*

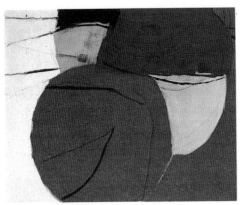

Roger Hilton (1911-75)
British
June 60 (Red)
Signed and dated June 60, oil on canvas
25 x 30in (63.5 x 76cm)
£15,500-16,500 *C*

Hans Hartung (1904-89)
French
T 1956-23
Signed and dated 56, oil on canvas
71 x 45in (180 x 115cm)
£100,000-120,000 *C*

Marsden Hartley (1878-1943) American
Abstraction
Oil on canvas, painted in 1913
47 x 39½in (119.4 x 100.3cm)
£800,000-900,000 *S(NY)*

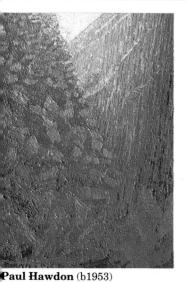

Paul Hawdon (b1953)
British
The Ladder
Signed and dated 1991, oil on canvas
45 x 60in (114 x 153cm)
£1,800-2,000 *Mer*

Wassily Kandinsky (1866-1944)
Russian
Arrow Toward the Circle
Signed with monogram and dated 30,
oil on canvas
31½ x 43¼in (80 x 110cm)
£510,000-600,000 *S*

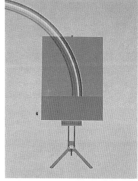

Yves Klein (1928-62)
French
Signed, pigment and
synthetic resin on
fabric laid down on
board
29¾ x 21¾in
(77.5 x 55cm)
£95,000-115,000 *S*

Patrick Hughes (b1939)
British
Life is a Pale Imitation of
Art
Oil/acrylic on panel
40 x 30in (101.5 x 76cm)
£2,000-3,000 *BRG*

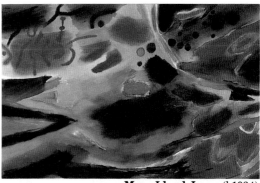

Mary Lloyd Jones (b1934)
British
Song Lines
Watercolour
24½ x 39in (63 x 100cm)
£800-850 *MT*

Michael Kenny (b1941)
British
Lost Beliefs
Mixed media
30 x 40in (76 x 101.5cm)
£1,000-1,275 *OLG*

Dirk Larsen (b1951)
British
Good Parents
Oil on board
24 x 43in (61 x 108cm)
£2,250-2,500 *EW*

John Mackay (20thC)
Landscape 21st Century
Signed and dated MCMLXXXIII
40 x 45½in (101.5 x 115.5cm)
£3,100-3,700 *CSK*

George Large (b1936)
British
Arthur Hill's Windmills
Watercolour
20 x 26in (51 x 66cm)
£1,000-1,125 *GL*

Fernand Léger (1881-1955)
French
Le Moteur (1er Etat)
Signed and dated 1918, oil on canvas
16 x 13in (40.8 x 32.8cm)
£510,000-550,000 *S*

Roy Lichtenstein (b1923)
American
Cubist Still Life
Signed and dated 74, oil and magna on canvas
20 x 24in (50.8 x 61cm)
£115,000-130,000 *S(NY)*

Rodolfo Morales (b1925)
Mexican
Untitled
Signed, oil on canvas, painted 1986
23¾ x 27½in (60.3 x 70cm)
£8,400-9,400 *S(NY)*

Carlos Mérida (b1893)   Mexican
Adriana y el Laberinto
Signed and dated 1975, oil on amate paper laid down on masonite
20¾ x 24in (52.7 x 61cm)
£21,000-26,000 *S(NY)*

Joan Miró
(b1893-1983)
Spanish
Tête de Femme dans
la Nuit
Oil on canvas
16 x 9¾in
(40.5 x 24.5cm)
£83,000-100,000 *S*

John Miller (20thC)   British
Garden II
Découpage, c1992-3
12 x 20in (31 x 51cm)
£650-750 *DM*

Matta (b1911)
Chilean
Sign of the Times
Oil on canvas, painted c1967
34½ x 42¾in (87.8 x 108.3cm)
£21,000-26,000 *C*

René Magritte (1898-1967)
French
L'Homme et La Nuit
Signed, gouache
16 x 11½in (41 x 29cm)
£320,000-350,000 *S*

Kenneth Noland (b1924)
American
Inner Dark Outer Light
Signed and dated 1964, acrylic on canvas
45in (114.5cm) square
£40,000-50,000 *C*

Serge Poliakoff (1906-69)
Russian
H.S.T. Composition
Signed, oil on canvas, painted in 1967
28½ x 23½in (72.4 x 59.7cm)
£50,000-60,000 *S(NY)*

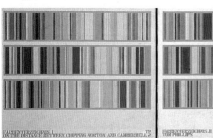

Tom Phillips R.A. (b1937)
British
Farbenverzeichnis 1969 I + II
Signed and dated 1969, oil on canvas (diptych)
20 x 48¼in (51 x 122.5cm) overall
£7,500-8,500 *C*

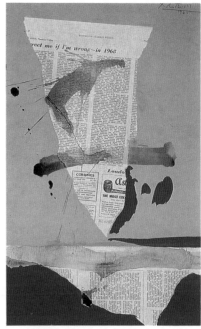

Robert Motherwell (b1915)
American
Guardian 3
Signed and dated 1966, collage with
newspaper and acrylic on board
22 x 14in (56 x 35.6cm)
£28,000-35,000 *C*

Matt Mullican (b1951)
Signs
Gouache on 16 cardboard panels, 1980
23¾ x 24in (60 x 61cm) each panel
£3,700-4,700 *C*

Milton Resnick (b1917)
American
Untitled
Signed and dated 1969, oil
on canvas
63 x 37in (160 x 94cm)
£8,000-8,500 *S(NY)*

Gerhard Richter (b1932)
German
Untitled 682-3
Signed and dated 1988, oil on canvas
28¼ x 24½in (72 x 62cm)
£33,000-40,000 *C*

John Rattenbury
(20thC)
British
Migration
Oil, wax on paper, 1992
44 x 30in (112 x 76cm)
£900-950 *MT*

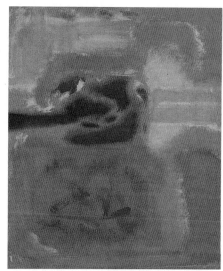

Mark Rothko (1903-70)
American
No. 9
Oil on canvas
17½ x 15in (44.5 x 38cm)
£68,000-78,000 *S(NY)*

Robert Rauschenberg (b1925)
American
Press
Signed, titled and dated 1964
Oil and silkscreen ink on canvas
84 x 60in (213.4 x 152.4cm)
£760,000-800,000 *S(NY)*

Dillwyn Smith (b1958)
British
An Act of Contrition 1990/92
Acrylic on cotton
84 x 68in (213 x 173cm)
£4,000-4,500 *MAA*

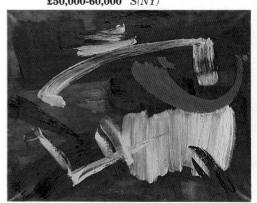

Donald Sultan (b1951) American
Quinces
Signed with initials, titled and dated 1989,
latex and tar on vinyl composite tile over
masonite
96in (243cm) square
£50,000-60,000 *S(NY)*

Frank Stella (b1936)
American
Kagu
Signed and dated 80, ground glass, oil, crayon
and collage on tycore board
61 x 88in (155 x 223.5cm)
£42,000-50,000 *S(NY)*

Gérard Schneider (1896-1986)
Swiss
Opus 42C
Signed and dated III/57, oil on canvas
35 x 45½in (89 x 115.5cm)
£17,500-18,500 *S*

Julian Schnabel (b1951)
American
Oil on velvet, painted 1983
108 x 84in
(274.3 x 213.4cm)
£130,000-140,000 *S(NY)*

Kenny Scharf (b1958)
American   New Frontier
Signed and dated 84, acrylic
and spray paint on canvas
85¼ x 87in (217 x 221cm)
£8,800-9,800 *C*

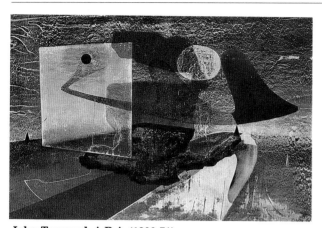

John Tunnard, A.R.A. (1900-71)
British
Untitled (Eve of D-Day)
Signed and dated 1944, oil and tempera on board
14½ x 21in (37 x 53.5cm)
£3,800-4,800 *S*

Sophie Täuber-Arp (1889-1943)
Swiss
Composition
Signed and numbered 27, watercolour,
gouache and collage laid down on the
artist's mount, executed c1920
8 x 5½in (20.5 x 14cm)
£24,000-30,000 *S*

Joe Tilson R.A. (b1928)
British
Ziggurat 1967
Oil and acrylic on wood relief
42 x 42 x 4in (107 x 107 x
10cm)
£25,000-30,000 *C*

Graham Wills (b1963)
British
Fusion
Relief monotype, hand
coloured, monoprint
19¾ x 16½in (50 x 42cm)
£200-225 *CCA*

Michael Tingle (20thC)
British
Reclining Hill Man
Oil on panel
6 x 11in (15 x 28cm)
£600-800 *BRG*

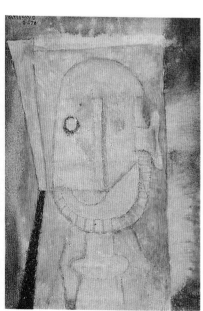

Rufino Tamayo (b1900)
Mexican
Cabeza en Blanco
Signed and dated 0-70,
oil, sand and charcoal on
canvas
19¾ x 14in
(50.2 x 35.6cm)
£59,000-70,000 *S(NY)*

Vladimir Sulyagin (20thC)
Russian
All Saints Day
Dated 1988, oil on canvas
55 x 72½in (140 x 184cm)
£3,000-3,250 *EW*

Janet Ahlberg (b1944)
British
Oddbodds
Pen, ink and watercolour
9 x 6½ in (23 x 16.5cm)
£600-650 *CBL*

Peter Cross (b1951)   British
The Umpires collected the scores and rushed them over to the gym
where they were added up. After several recounts, the result was
announced: 'I, the Returning Officer for the world, northern
hemisphere, hereby declare the winners to be Biggin Hill!'
Signed with initials and inscribed with title
7½ x 12½in (19 x 32cm)
£800-850   *CBL*

Michael Foreman (b1938)
British
A Fitting for the Glass Slipper
Watercolour, pen and ink with pencil
and bodycolour
11⅛ x 9½in (29 x 24cm)
£1,550-1,650   *CBL*

Ralph Idris Steadman (b1936)
Maxwell Splat
Signed and dated 92, pen ink and watercolour
27¾ x 19in (71 x 48cm)
£2,000-2,250   *CBL*

Harry Rountree
(1878-1950)
British
We must burn the
house down
Pen, ink and
watercolour
12¾ x 8in
(32 x 20cm)
£4,250-4,500   *CBL*

George Moutard Woodward
(1760-1809)   British
Old Maids consulting an Eminent
Naturalist
Signed, watercolour and pen and
black ink over pencil
6¼ x 7in (15.5 x 18cm)
£1,500-1,800   *S*

Jon Davis (b1928)
British
As the two pals are leaving, Big Ben
starts to chime - at exactly the right
moment - as usual!
Pen, ink and watercolour
6½ x 6¼in (17 x 16cm)
£325-375 *CBL*

Walt Disney Productions (1970s)
Winnie The Pooh
Production celluloid on watercolour background
16 x 12in (41 x 31cm)
£1,200-1,500 *CAT*

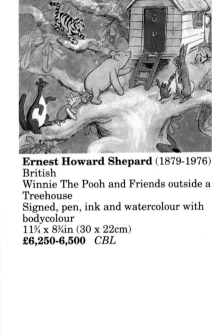

Studio John Coates TVC
The Snowman (1982)
Production celluloid on a production
background
12 x 10in (31 x 25cm)
£1,000-2,000 *CAT*

Ernest Howard Shepard (1879-1976)
British
Winnie The Pooh and Friends outside a
Treehouse
Signed, pen, ink and watercolour with
bodycolour
11¾ x 8¾in (30 x 22cm)
£6,250-6,500 *CBL*

20th Century Fox
The Simpsons
Created by animator Matt Groening
Production celluloid
16 x 12in (41 x21cm)
£500-550 *CAT*

Ralph Goings (b1928)
American
Yellow Ford Camper
Signed and dated Dec 69, oil on canvas
45 x 51½in (114.3 x 130.8cm)
£46,000-56,000 *S(NY)*

Osler (19thC)
The Centrepiece of the
Great Exhibition
Chromolithograph, c1851
17½ x 10in (44.5 x 25cm)
£100-135 *MJW*

Erté (1892-1990) French
Costume design for the Turkish Sultana -
La femme et le diable
Signed, gouache and silver paint
10¼ x 12¼in (26.2 x 31cm)
£4,400-5,400 *S*

Caroline Thomson (b1959)
British
Sweet Dreams
Signed and dated 1991, oil on panel
12 x 16in (31 x 41cm)
£800-850 *BRG*

Jack Miller (20thC)
Rosy Bar
Silkscreen, 15 colours
20 x 27in (51 x 68.5cm)
£125-150 *CCA*

**G. Ottaviani, after Savarelli and
Camparesi** (18thC)
Italian
Loggia di Rafaelo d'el Vaticano
Copperplate engraving with heavy
gouache colour of Raphael's work in
the Vatican in Rome, published
1769-77
£800-850 *OG*

TRANSPORT

Filippo Passarini (1638-98)
Italian
Design for a carriage, decorated with putti,
harpies and an eagle
Black chalk, pen and brown ink, brown wash
13½ x 8in (34.6 x 20.4cm)
£1,300-1,600 *C*

Thomas Uwins (1782-1857)
British
The 'Royal' balloon on exhibition at the
Bowling Green of the Bedford Arms, Camden
Town
Pencil, inscribed in a contemporary hand
4¼ x 6¾in (10.8 x 17.3cm)
£4,500-5,500 *Bon*

Don Eddy (20thC)
American
Private Parking IV
Signed, titled and dated 71, acrylic on canvas
48 x 66in (122 x 167.6cm)
£10,000-11,000 *S(NY)*

Will Barnet (b1911)
American
Girl on a Bicycle
Signed and dated 1971, mixed media on
board
26¾ x 27½in (68 x 70cm)
£3,000-3,500 *S(NY)*

Daniel Ralph Celentano (b1902)
The Auto Accident
Signed, oil on canvas, charcoal on
paper, and another,
25½ x 23½in (64.8 x 59.7cm)
£8,400-9,400 *S(NY)*

Ronald Embleton
British
George Stephenson's Cottage
Signed
18½ x 26¼in (47 x 66.5cm)
£350-450 *AG*

Marie Laurencin (1885-1956)
French
La Première Voiture Renault 1898
Signed in pencil, 1936, lithograph hand
coloured in blue, yellow and pink
19 x 14⅜in (48 x 37.6cm)
£1,400-1,800 *S*

E. Oscar Thalinger (b1885)
American
The 10.14
Signed, oil on masonite
22 x 24in (56 x 61.3cm)
£1,500-2,000 *S(NY)*

Lyonel Feininger (b1871)
American
Steam Train
Coloured crayon on paper, executed c1908
5½ x 9in (14 x 22.5cm)
£2,700-3,200 *S(NY)*

Kaj Stenvall (20thC)
Finnish
No Winner
Oil on canvas
22 x 28in (56 x 71cm)
£1,550-1,750 *JBA*

Julian Trevelyan, R.A. (1910-88)
British
Railway Station
Signed and dated 55, pen, black ink and
watercolour heightened with white
10 x 15in (25 x 38cm)
£800-1,000 *C*

Friedensreich Hundertwasser (b1928)
Austrian
The Endless Way To You
Signed and dated in pencil 1967, lithograph
printed in colours
20¼ x 24in (51.5 x 61cm)
£2,300-2,800 *S*

Peter Roberson (1907-91)
British
Ugh! Seaweed
Pen, ink and watercolour
10¼ x 7in (26 x 18cm)
£125-145 *CBL*

Maurice de Vlaminck (1876-1958)
French
Le Tracteur Rouge
Signed, oil on canvas, painted in 1956
15 x 21¾in (38 x 55cm)
£17,000-18,000 *S*

THEATRE & COSTUME DESIGNS

Roman School (c1600)
A Street: Design for the Stage, recto; Studies
of a Church Interior and Nudes in Combat,
verso
Black and red chalk, pen and brown ink
13¼ x 8½in (34 x 22cm)
£2,000-2,500 *C*

Erté (1892-1990)
Russian
Design for a Harper's Bazaar Cover
Signed, gouache on board
15¾ x 11½in (40 x 29cm)
£24,000-30,000 *S(NY)*

Louis Jean Desprez (1743-1804)
French
Design for a Stage Set: Aeneas in the
Underworld
Pen and black ink and watercolour,
heightened with white, red, yellow and blue
bodycolour over black chalk
20½ x 32½in (52.5 x 82.5cm)
£26,000-35,000 *S(NY)*

Georges Barbier (1882-1932)
French
La Danse
Signed and dated 1915, gouache and pen and
ink
12 x 19in (31 x 48cm)
£2,500-3,000 *S*

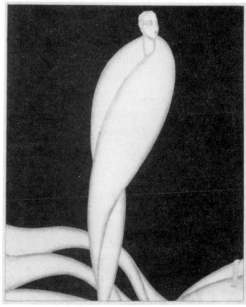

Jaques Darcy (20thC)
French
Fashion Studie
Signed, ink, graphite and charcoal on paper
14¼ x 12¼in (37 x 31cm)
£800-1,000 *S(NY)*

Erté (1892-1990)
Russian
Costume Design for a Dancer
in Yellow Signed, inscribed and
numbered 10.713,
gouache
14½ x 10½in (37 x 26cm)
£1,800-2,400 *S*

Ceri Richards (1903-71)
British
Ruth, Scene III
Signed and dated 1956,
extensively inscribed,
watercolour, pen and black ink
and pencil
12 x 9in (31 x 23cm)
£470-600 *CSK*

Leslie Hurry (1909-78)
British
Costume and Set Designs for Saint
Joan Fifty two leaves, the majority
signed and inscribed, pen and black
and coloured inks and watercolour,
many with fabric samples,
framed as fourteen
£5,800-6,500 *S*

Michael Ayrton (1921-75) **and John
Minton** (1917-57)
British
Costume and Set Designs for Macbeth
Thirty eight leaves, many inscribed, pen and
black ink, watercolour and gouache, framed
as fourteen
Various sizes
£5,800-6,500 *S*

*In early 1941, Ayrton was invited by Sir John
Gielgud, to provide sets and costumes for his
touring production of Macbeth. Ayrton, who
anticipated imminent call-up, asked Minton
to collaborate on the project, and according to
the production credits both artists designed
the sets, while Ayrton alone carried out the
costumes. In the event, Ayrton was called up
for the RAF in October 1941, while Minton
enlisted in the Pioneer Corps in December, so
that the final stages of the project were
completed during the pair's 48-hour leave
periods.*

Did you know?
*MILLER'S Picture Price
Guide builds up year by
year to form the most
comprehensive photo
reference library
available.*

David Hockney (b1937)
British
Costume Design for Ubu; Ubu Roi (Alfred
Jarry), Royal Court Theatre (Iain
Cuthbertson), 1966, and a print of a Set
Design
Inscribed, pencil and coloured crayons
13½ x 10¾in (34 x 27cm)
£2,000-2,500 *C*

DECORATIVE DESIGNS

Venetian School (17thC)
A Study for a Decorative Pendentive Design
Pen and brown ink with grey and blue wash
11 x 8¾in (28 x 22cm)
£280-350 *P*

Attributed to Pieter Jansz. (1602-72)
Dutch
Stained Glass incorporating the Arms of
Amsterdam with Figures at a table beneath a
Portico, inscribed with the date '15/75', black
lead, pen and brown ink, green and grey
wash heightened with white, partly oxidised,
black lead framing lines, watermark crowned
coat-of-arms with letter below
15 x 11in (38.5 x 29cm)
£3,500-4,000 *C(Am)*

Carlo Bianconi (1732-1803)
Italian
Design for a Cartouche with an Eagle
Black chalk, pen and brown ink, brown wash
8 x 5in (20 x 13cm)
£1,200-1,600 *C*

David Vinckboons (1576-1632)
Flemish
A Design for a Title Page
Inscribed, pen and brown ink, grey-brown
wash heightened with white, partly oxidised,
incised for transfer
6 x 4in (15 x 9.5cm)
£8,500-10,000 *C(Am)*

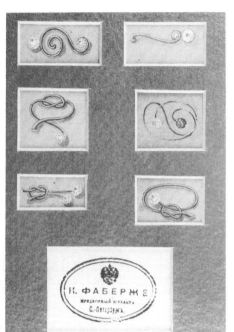

German School (18thC)
Two Vignettes within a drawn Rococo frame:
A Man chasing doves from a Dovecote and a
Lady Resisting the Embrace of an Amorous
Gentlemen
Gouache and watercolour on vellum
4 x 6½in (10.7 x 16.7cm)
£400-500 *S*

The House of Carl Fabergé (1846-1920)
Russian
A group of Designs in watercolours for
brooches, pendants, earrings and other small
items of jewellery
Various sizes
£900-1,200 *Bea*

*Fabergé was perhaps the most famous
jeweller of his generation. His father was a
jeweller in St Petersburg and in 1870,
Fabergé took over the shop which soon became
the leading jewellers in the city, receiving the
Imperial appointment in 1881. Branches
were opened in Moscow, Kiev and London
and Fabergé employed a staff of over 500
craftsmen and assistants. He himself
designed only the most important works,
notably the elaborately wrought and
ingeniously contrived Easter eggs that both
Alexander III and Nicholas II gave annually
to their wives.*

Apsley Pellatt (19thC)
British
A chromolythograph print of a
Group of Glass
from the Exhibition of 1851
16 x 11in (41 x 28cm)
£100-135 *MJW*

Pierre-Maximilien Delafontaine
(1774-1860)
French
Design for a Medal celebrating the Re-
establishment of the Church
Signed and inscribed, black chalk, pen and
brown ink, brown and grey wash
12¾ x 10in (32 x 25cm)
£1,800-2,500 *CNY*

*The medal, cast in 1806, celebrates the
signature of the treaty between Rome and
France on 8 April 1802 (18 Germinal an IX),
which re-established the public worship of the
Catholic Faith.*

CARTOONS & ILLUSTRATIONS

The Chris Beetles Gallery in London has pioneered research into the work and history of British illustrators, raising their profile and establishing their position in the international art market. While it is a cliché to say that Britain has produced very few great artists, we have certainly produced, as Beetles stresses, many of the greatest illustrators. Their art grew up in tandem with that of the writer and, through books, has become internationally recognised. 'English literature is disseminated throughout the world,' explains Beetles. 'English is the second language for so many nations, and students grow up on a diet of British books and their pictures.'

It is often the illustrators of books read in childhood that the collector will return to as an adult - to Rackham and Dulac, perhaps the most important illustrators of fairy stories of all time; to those artists who provided the pictures for great children's classics, and whose images, like the texts themselves, have become part of our national heritage. 'The current generation of disposable income collectors,' says Beetles, 'were raised on magnificent illustrators during the war, such as E.H. Shepherd (visual creator of Winnie the Pooh), and it's the work of these artists that they buy today.'

It is not only illustrations by figures from the past that are collectable, but increasingly those by contemporary illustrators, many of whom are familiar figures from the world of children's books, a field in which Britain remains supreme. Quentin Blake (who collaborated with Roald Dahl on many books) is already an extremely popular artist and other names to watch out for, cited by Chris Beetles, include Alan Lee, Rodney Matthews, Peter Cross, Jonathan Langley and the immensely gifted, if somewhat over-prolific, Michael Foreman - whose book 'Warboy', an illustrated account of his wartime childhood (first published in 1989), stands among the great classics of modern illustrated books.

According to Beetles, illustrations tend to be purchased by specific collectors rather than those buying for investment, and as such the market has sustained itself throughout the recession. Though prices continue to rise, he maintains that the field is extremely undervalued compared to other areas of the market. 'For only a few hundred pounds, you can get the best examples of an illustrator's work. To even begin buying paintings of an equivalent standard and quality, you would need to spend thousands. It really is a wonderful area for the collector.'

George Dance the Younger (1741-1825)
British
An Encaenia Procession, Oxford
Pen and ink and grey washes
5 x 11in (12.5 x 28cm)
£650-750 *S*

'Encaenia' means a festival of dedication or commemoration.

Giovanni Battista Tiepolo (1696-1770)
Italian
Caricature of a Gentleman Smoking a Pipe, and a study of a glass
Black chalk, pen and black ink, grey wash, watermark cross with K
7½ x 5½in (19 x 13.5cm)
£9,800-11,000 *C*

Sir Nathaniel Dance-Holland, Bt., R.A.
(1735-1811)
British
Shock of an Earthquake
Inscribed, pencil and coloured washes, with a pen and ink sketch
4½ x 9½in (11.5 x 24cm)
£1,400-1,800 *S*

James Gillray (1757-1815)
British
National Conveniences
Coloured etching, laid down on card, with 4
other hand coloured etchings
14 x 10in (36 x 25cm)
£2,000-2,500 *CSK*

Thomas Rowlandson (1756-1827)
British
The Winning Stroke
Pen and Wash
9 x 13½in (23 x 34cm)
£3,000-5,000 *AdG*

*The artist and the subject matter of billiards,
a theme much in demand but only rarely
portrayed, would guarantee a ready market
for this drawing.*

**George Louis Palmella Busson Du
Maurier** (1834-96)
British
Disastrous result of Beautymania
Signed and inscribed, pen and ink
9 x 9¾in (23 x 24cm)
£850-950 *CBL*

John Hassall (1868-1948)
British
City Notes, Company Results
Signed, pen ink and watercolour on tinted
paper
10½ x 8in (26 x 20cm)
£650-750 *CBL*

Honoré Daumier (1808-79)
French
En Chemin de Fer... Un Voisin agréable
A lithograph, 1862, on Chine appliqué
7¾ x 9¾in (19.5 x 24.5cm)
£2,300-3,000 *C*

*Daumier's satirical illustration goes to show
that it is not only in our own times that
smoking has been considered an anti-social act.*

Philip William May (1864-1903)
British
Phil May Digs Deep
Signed and dated '93,
pen and ink
8½ x 6½in (21 x 16cm)
£550-650 *CBL*

Sir John Tenniel (1820-1914)
British
King John
Signed with monogram,
charcoal and
coloured chalks
5¾ x 9in (14.5 x 22.5cm)
£1,250-1,450 *CBL*

Edward Ardizzone, R.A. (1900-79)
British
What! Mr. Household Gone!
Signed and inscribed, watercolour, pen and
black ink, 3 illustrations in 2 frames
4½ x 6in (11.5 x 15cm)   **£2,400-3,000** *C*

Sir John Everett Millais, Bt, P.R.A.
(1829-96)
British
An Illustration to Framley Parsonage
Pen and ink
7 x 5in (18 x 12.5cm)
£1,200-1,800 *S*

*This drawing depicts Mrs Gesham and Miss
Dunstable in Anthony Trollope's Framley
Parsonage.
The great 19thC novelist has been much in
the news in the past year with the publication
of a new biography and Prime Minister John
Major's revelation that Trollope is his
favourite author. The combination of popular
artist and popular subject matter ensured
that the current illustration went comfortably
over its £600-800 auction estimate.*

Cicely Mary Barker (1895-1973)
The Bluebell Story Book
Signed with initials, watercolour with pe
and ink
13¼ x 9¼in (33.5 x 23cm)
£3,000-3,250 *CBL*

Sir Max Beerbohm (1872-1956)
Mr. Churchill
Signed, inscribed and dated 1943, pencil and
watercolour
8½ x 8¼in (21.5 x 20.5cm)
£3,250-3,500 *CBL*

Sir Max Beerbom (1872-1956)
British
A Recollection: Conder, Max, Rothenstein
and Wilde at the Cafe Royal
Signed, inscribed and dated 1929, pen, brush,
black ink and grey wash on grey paper
8 x 11½in (20 x 28.5cm)
£7,000-8,000 *C*

*With a cutting attached of some words by
William Rothenstein 'I was often called upon
for sympathy when / Conder was in
difficulties. Sober men are, / alas, poor
comforters and sorry companions / for men
crowned with vine leaves.' 'Will, / don't look so
sensible' said Oscar Wilde one / evening as I
sat with him and Conder and Max / at the
Cafe Royal.'*

Rowland Emett, O.B.E. (1906-90)
British
Smugglers Cove
Signed, pen, ink and monochrome
watercolour
9 x 10¾in (22.7 x 27cm)
£1,550-1,750 *CBL*

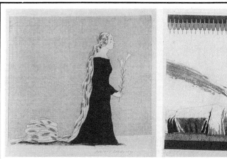

David Hockney (b1937)
British
Illustrations for Six Fairy Tales from The
Brothers Grimm
Four albums, signed, many inscribed verso,
etchings with aquatint, 1969
18¾ x 12¾in (47.5 x 32.2cm)
£7,200-8,200 *C*

Gerard Hoffnung (1925-59)
British
Icing the Cake
Signed, pen, ink, watercolour and bodycolour
6¾ x 8in (17 x 20cm)
£1,650-1,750 *CBL*

*Though he was only 34 when he died,
Hoffnung enjoyed a hugely successful career
as a humourist. His illustrations were
published in books and magazines, he staged
a famous series of comic concerts at the Royal
Festival Hall and was a noted speaker and
broadcaster. Cats (see page 531) were one of
his greatest passions, and according to his
wife, he would mimic them, winding himself
round her legs and rubbing his head against
her with such feline perseverance that she
'had the uncanny feeling he really was a cat.'*

Henry Mayo Bateman (1887-1958)
British
Tact
Signed and dated 1916, watercolour and
black ink
£2,200-3,000 *Bon*

William Heath Robinson (1872-1944)
British
'Stand by Everybody, for Big Ben and
weather report'
Signed and inscribed, pen, ink and
monochrome watercolour
15¾ x 11¼in (40 x 28.5cm)
£2,550-2,750 *CBL*

Eric George Fraser (1902-83)
British
The Travels of Marco Polo
Signed with initials, inscribed, pen and ink
7½ x 6½in (18.5 x 16cm)
£125-150 *CBL*

Joe Lee (20thC)
British
Scenes from London Life
Six etchings c1930, 4 on wove, 2 on Japan
£280-350 *S*

Ernest Howard Shepard (1879-1976)
British
Pooh and Owl Visiting in Owl's parlour
Signed, pen, ink and coloured pencil
4¾ x 5¼in (12 x 13cm)
£12,000-12,500 *CBL*

Schulz (Charles Monroe Schulz) (b1922)
British
This Valentine Candy
Signed and inscribed, pen and ink
5½ x 19in (13 5 x 48cm)
£1,650-1,750 *CBL*

P. J. Lynch (b1962)
British
'...she with the long nose began to wash away
as hard as she could, but the more she
rubbed and scrubbed, the bigger the spots
grew'.
Watercolour
19 x 28in (48 x 71cm)
£2,000-2,250 *CBL*

Donald McGill (1879-1962)
British
'May I share the ocean with you?'
Watercolour, published as a postcard, c1930
8¾ x 6¼in (22.5 x 16cm)
£300-400 *Bon*

*McGill was dubbed the 'King of the Postcards'
by his obituarist in the Telegraph. From 1905
onwards, McGill designed over 3,000 different
postcards, many featuring the figure of a fat
lady with her weedy companion, and
including the example bearing the immortal
one-liner 'I can't find my little Willie'. Given
his sense of humour, it is perhaps not
surprising to discover that McGill was a
rugby player, and was only prevented from
taking up the sport professionally because of
an injury.*

Henry Moore (1898-86)
British
Book Illustration for Herbert Reed, 1945
Double-sided watercolour
11 x 9in (28 x 23cm)
£6,000-7,000 *Bon*

Ronald Searle (b1920)
British
Racin
Signed, watercolour, pen and ink, executed
1969
12½ x 19¼in (31.5 x 49cm)
£1,400-1,800 *Bon*

ANIMATION CELS

An animation cel is a painting on a clear sheet of acetate, usually 10½ x 12½in (26 x 32cm) or larger. These are laid over the backgrounds in sequence to give the illusion of movement. The following cels come from the Catto Gallery in London. They include 'production cels' - a cel which actually appears in the film, and 'limited edition cels' - a cel which has been recreated from the original pencil drawing used in the film. They celebrate some of the most famous cartoon creations of the 20thC.

Warner Bros Studios
Bugs Bunny and Witchazel
Limited edition cel
£350-450 *CAT*

This limited edition cel depicts Witchazel and Bugs Bunny. Bugs is undoubtedly one of the most famous characters of all time. He is known to his admirers as being a street smart rabbit who has confidence and an impenetrable cool. Bugs' popularity is so great that he became the second cartoon character (after Mickey) to receive a star of the Hollywood 'Walk of Fame'.

Chuck Jones
Acme Rocket
Studio: Warner Bros
Limited edition cel
£500-600 *CAT*

Coyote and Roadrunner cartoons were conceived by their creator Chuck Jones as being a parody of all chase cartoons. Roadrunner does nothing to antagonize Coyote beyond merely existing, and it is Coyote's self-defeating hunger that is responsible for all the action that happens within the cartoons. Chuck Jones made five rules for the cartoons:

1. All settings are to be in the desert in the American southwest.
2. Roadrunner never leaves the road.
3. No dialogue.
4. Coyote never injures Roadrunner.
5. The audiences sympathy must always remain with the Coyote.
It was the Coyote and Roadrunner cartoons that gave birth to that famous company ACME - the company that supplies everthing that a coyote could want to help him catch a roadrunner.

Walt Disney Productions
Dumbo 1941
Voice of Timothy Mouse: Ed Brophy
Based on a story by Helen Aberson and Harold Pearl
Production cel on Courvoisier background
£5,500-6,000 *CAT*

Timothy is a fiesty character who helps Dumbo to succeed when nobody else believes in him. He is a streetwise mouse, yet soft hearted.

Walt Disney Studio
Pinocchio, 1940
Jiminy Cricket
Transparency is an animators pencil drawing
£500-550 *CAT*

Jiminy Cricket is appointed Pinnochio's conscience by the Blue Fairy and he leads him through the real life adventures of boyhood.

Fred Quimby, M.G.M. Studio
Just Ducky, 1953
Signed, production cel
£2,000-2,500 *CAT*

This rare piece is a production cel from 1953 applied to a key background from the short 'Just Ducky'. The piece is signed by Fred Quimby who was the producer of the series up until his retirement in 1955. Tom and Jerry debuted in 1940. They were created by William Hanna and Joseph Barbera, who later left MGM to open their own studio called Hanna-Barbera Productions who created such characters as Fred Flintstone, Yogi Bear and Huckleberry Hound. After Hanna and Barbera left the studio Tom and Jerry shorts failed to retain their original humour consequently they dropped in popularity. Tom and Jerry were also among the first animated characters to appear in live action sequences. They appeared in two classic MGM musicals - 'Anchors Aweigh' (1944) with Gene Kelly and 'Dangerous When Wet' (1953).

Walt Disney Productions
Roger Rabbit, 1988
Production cel on a specially prepared studio background, based on book 'Who Censored Roger Rabbit?' by Gary K. Wolf
10 x 16in (25 x 41cm)
£2,700-2,900 *CAT*

Walt Disney Productions
Snow White & The Seven Dwarfs 1937
Production cel on a watercolour
production background
£7,000-7,500 *CAT*

ABSTRACT & MODERN

Over the past season the market for modern and contemporary works has been slowly finding its feet again and the mood has been one of cautious, but quietly returning, confidence. At many auctions bidding has been selective, but still stronger than in the recent past, with an increased number of bidders for individual works, for which previously there might have been only one or two contenders. Buyers remain reluctant to overspend, however. Although there are always successful exceptions, pictures have often tended to fall below or just within their auction estimate. Low estimates have, on several occasions, inspired considerable and competitive enthusiasm, while high predictions have simply served to frighten off potential buyers. Along with sensible prices, in this as in other fields, the serious collector wants quality above all, whether buying at auction or from a dealer.

'Our volume of sales might have gone down, but the prices that people are prepared to pay have gone up,' says Anna-Mei Chadwick who deals in contemporary art from her King's Road gallery in London. 'A lot of smaller collectors have fallen by the wayside but serious collectors are buying serious works, and over the past couple of years we have made what are for us some record sales.' 'I think things are definitely picking up and we have gone through the worst times,' agrees the neighbouring Gagliardi Gallery, which deals in some very 'daring' contemporary works, and which makes a conscious attempt to promote new artists. 'Like all galleries, however, we've had to look very carefully at our pricing. Today's artists have to accept that they are not going to make a fortune overnight and I don't think that we are ever going to get back to what it was like in the 80s, when you put a picture in the window and it would be snapped up straight away.'

The 'yuppie' buyers who bought contemporary art along with red Porsches and cordless telephones might well have disappeared, but for those collectors who remain, today's market can offer some very exciting opportunities. 'It's a very good time to buy at the moment,' claims John Brandler of the Brandler Galleries, 'and I estimate that these low price levels will only last for another 12 to 18 months. In real terms, many things are the cheapest they have ever been, and this is possibly the last chance to buy pictures that would otherwise be outside one's price range. Look at prices for an artist such as Carel Weight. In a few years time I bet you won't be able to buy a major Weight without selling your house.'

While times might still be difficult for many dealers in the modern and contemporary field, as far as collectors are concerned it is certainly a buyer's market.

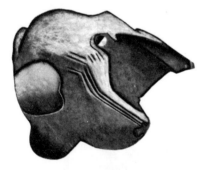

Eileen Agar (1899-1991)
British
Rock Forms, 1930s
Shaped collage and pastel
16 x 20in (41 x 51cm)
£700-750 *JBA*

'Everyone walks with two legs,' declared Agar in her memoirs, 'one of mine is surrealist and one is abstract. Abstract art and surrealism were the two movements that interested me the most and I see nothing incompatible in that.' Agar was one of the seminal figures of the British surrealist movement and the first female artist to join their ranks.

Pierre Alechinsky (b1927)
Belgian
Sans la coquille
Signed, inscribed and dated 1978NY, acrylic on paper mounted on canvas
39¼ x 60½in (100.4 x 153.5cm)
£28,000-35,000 *C*

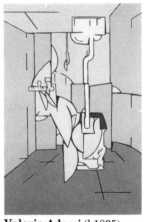

Valerio Adami (b1835)
Italian
Interno
Signed and dated 17/2/67 - 30/3/67
Oil on canvas
76¾ x 51in (195 x 130cm)
£11,500-12,500 *S*

Eileen Agar (1899-1991)
British
Autumn Leaves
Signed and dated 1964, oil on canvas
30 x 22in (76 x 56cm)
£2,000-2,500 *C*

Horst Antes (b1936)
German
Gefleckter kopf mit Stirnband
Signed, oil on canvas, executed 1970
27¼ x 23¼in (69 x 59cm)
£9,500-10,500 *S*

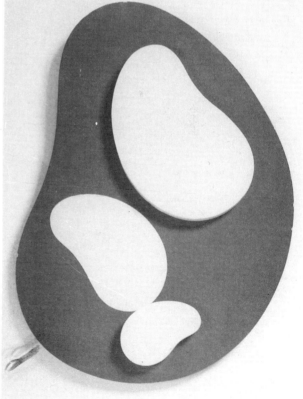

Arman (b1928)
Spanish
Poubelle Organique
Accumulation of garbage, executed 1972
40¼ x 20 x 4¾in (102.3 x 50.7 x 11.6cm)
£13,500-14,500 *S*

Jean (Hans) Arp (1887-1966)
French
Constellation des formes blanches sur fond
bleu clair
Signed, oil on carved wood relief, executed in
1953
18½ x 24¾in (47 x 62.8cm)
£17,000-18,000 *C*

Karel Appel (b1923)
Dutch
Head with Birds
Signed and dated 58, oil on canvas
45¾ x 57in (116 x 145cm)   **£35,000-45,000** *S*

Frank Auerbach (b1931)
British
Head of Gerda Boehm
Oil on board, painted in 1964
24in (61cm) square
£47,000-60,000 *S*

*Auerbach is acknowledged as one of Britain's
leading contemporary painters. He belongs to
the post-war figurative tradition of artists,
that became known as the School of London
and included such figures as Leon Kossof,
Lucien Freud and Francis Bacon. Auerbach's
working method is meticulous. Since 1954 he
has worked in the same Camden Town studio,
according to reports, from 7.00 a.m. till 9.00
p.m., often seven days a week. He might take
many months to finish a single canvas and
will often go over the same piece again and
again. 'One does the persistent thing,' he
remarked, 'and then the really remarkable
happens.' As the artist has explained, he
begins not with an idea but a piece of
'recalcitrant fact', a model in the studio, a
local cityscape - his subject matter is
deliberately restricted and like Freud he
prefers to paint only those people he knows
well. 'What I have in mind is as it were the
lump of the subject, the 3 dimensional entity
which I somehow try to inhabit and become,
in the way an actor would don a character or
a part.' The subject is built up with thick,
impastoed layers of paint, launched on the
canvas with powerful velocity, giving his
works dramatic, almost sculptural quality,
and a strong physical sense of the paint from
which they are made.*

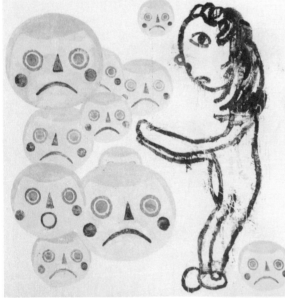

Donald Baechler (b1956)
American
Fears of Abstraction
Signed with initials, inscribed and dated 88,
acrylic and canvas collage on canvas,
executed 1988
75in (190.5cm) square
£17,500-19,000 *C*

Enrico Baj (b1924)
Italian
Piccolo
Signed, collage with paper, oil and gouache
on paper laid down on board, executed in
1962
19¾ x 28in (50.2 x 71cm)
£7,500-8,500 *C*

GAGLIARDI DESIGN & CONTEMPORARY ART

The Gagliardi Gallery is ideally located in the heart of Chelsea, and regularly presents challenging and imaginative collections of 20th century paintings, drawings and sculpture, including well established artists and sought after collectables from emerging international talents. The gallery is happy to advise and research for your collection.

HENRY MOORE: 'HEAD', 13.5 CM HIGH, BRONZE.

Monday to Saturday
10am - 5.30pm

509 KINGS ROAD, CHELSEA, LONDON, SW10 0TX

Tel: 071 352 3663 Fax: 071 351 6283

Georg Baselitz (b1938)
German
Elke (Schwarzer Akt)
Signed, titled and dated 76, oil on canvas
98½ x 78¾in (250 x 190cm)
£170,000-200,000 *S*

Georg Baselitz (b1938)
German
Orangenesser
Signed and dated 81, blue wash on paper
19 x 15in (48 x 38cm)
£3,600-4,200 *S*

Ben (b1935)
Swiss
On ne peut pas toujours parler des mêmes
Signed twice, inscribed with title and dated
on reverse *alors si vous parliez de moi un peu
au lieu de Warhol, 1971,* oil on canvas
23¾ x 28¾in (60.3 x 73cm)
£4,000-5,000 *C*

Roger Bissière (1884-1964)
French
Les Feuilles Mortes
Signed and dated 55, oil on canvas
23¾ x 28¾in (60 x 73cm)
£14,500-15,500 *S*

Romare Bearden (b1914)
American
Conjunction; and Firebirds
A pair, each signed in pencil and dated 1979,
lithographs printed in colours
28 x 21in (71.5 x 53cm)
£3,000-3,500 *S(NY)*

Billy Al Bengston (b1934)
American
August Watercolour
Watercolour on paper,
executed in 1985
42 x 29in (106.7 x 73.7cm)
£1,500-2,000 *S(NY)*

David Blackburn (b1939)
British
Red Landscape
Signed and dated 1992, pastel
25 x 21in (64 x 53.5cm)
£1,300-1,500 *HaG*

Sandra Blow (b1925)
British
Untitled
Collage and acrylic
14½in (37cm) square
£800-850 *OLG*

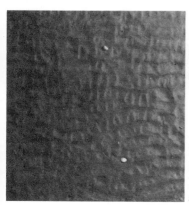

Mark Boyle (b1934)
British
Sand Dune 1969
Mixed media, construction
57in (145cm) square
£4,200-5,000 *C*

Albert Bloch (1882-1961)
American
Eine Gruppe Andaechtiger Gestalten
Signed with initial, dated 1914, oil
on canvas
54 x 40in (137.2 x 101.6cm)
£12,000-13,000 *S(NY)*

Martin Bradley (b1931)
British
Crossings Out 1957
Signed and dated, oil on board
36in (91.5cm) square
£2,000-2,500 *Bon*

Erik Brauer (b1929)
Austrian
For Two Zuzin
Signed recto, watercolour on paper,
executed 1983
20 x 14½in (50.8 x 36.8cm)
£2,700-3,500 *S(NY)*

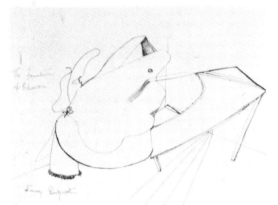

Emmy Bridgwater (b1906)
British
The Foundations of Behaviour
Signed, pen and ink, c1940
7 x 9in (17.5 x 22.5cm)
£600-650 *JBA*

Alexander Calder (1898-1976)
American
Spheres Behind the Sun
Signed and dated 71, gouache on paper
29¼ x 43¼in (74.3 x 110cm)
£5,000-6,000 *S(NY)*

Marcel Broodthaers (1924-76)
Belgian
ABC
Printing ink on towelling,
executed in 1974
41½ x 20in (105 x 51cm)
£20,000-25,000 *S*

Leonora Carrington (b1917)
British
El Baño
Signed and dated 1957, oil on canvas
25¾ x 44¼in (65.4 x 112.4cm)
£120,000-140,000 *S(NY)*

From her childhood, Carrington rebelled against the upper class British society into which she was born. The daughter of a wealthy textile manufacturer, she was expelled from several boarding schools for her unruly behaviour and eventually abandoned the life of an English debutante to become the mistress of Max Ernst in Paris. She exhibited with the surrealists and began to publish stories 'about an imaginery land of ghosts and wonders, where she-goats hatch the alchemical egg, hyenas go to the ball and white rabbits feed on human flesh,' the same kind of fantastic imagery that fuels her pictures. When Ernst was interned during the war, Carrington fled to Spain where she suffered a nervous breakdown and was institutionalised. After her recovery, she moved to New York and then to Mexico, where she married the Hungarian photographer Chiqui Weisz and where she has lived, written and painted ever since.

Leonora Carrington (b1917)
British
Ab Eo Quod
Signed and dated 1956, oil on canvas
28 x 24in (71 x 61cm)
£110,000-130,000 *S(NY)*

Francesco Clemente (b1952)
Italian
Untitled
Oil on four metal parts, executed 1984
Each part 44¾ x 34in (113.5 x 86.5cm)
£28,000-35,000 *C*

Phillippa Clayden (b1955)
British
Jiggery Pokery
Ink and collage
33 x 22¾in (84 x 58cm)
£1,300-1,500 *BOU*

Miller's is a price
GUIDE not a price
LIST

Sandro Chia (b1946)
Italian
Il mestoero del mistero
Indistinctly signed and dated on reverse 80,
knife, spoon and oil on 3 canvas panels,
executed 1980
41½ x 40¼in (105 x 102cm)
£17,000-19,000 *C*

Robert Combas (b1957)
French
Quand elle le regarde il est tout embrousiné
Signed and dated on reverse 10 October 82,
acrylic on synthetic fibre
54½ x 44¾in (138.5 x 113.7cm)
£1,000-1,500 *C*

Guillaume van Beverloo Corneille
(b1922) Dutch
L'herbe comme un tapis rouge
Signed and dated 65, gouache on paper
19¾ x 26½in (50 x 67cm)
£5,500-6,500 *C*

George Condo (b1957)
American
The Intoxication of Freedom
Signed and dated twice 84, oil on canvas,
painted 1984
59in (150cm) square
£11,000-12,000 *C*

*The artist discusses this work in an interview
as follows: 'I made a painting called The
Intoxication of Freedom which showed a pile
of gold coins and each coin had some sort of
drawing on it: some grapes, a house, a dollar
sign, a mystical sign, the eye on the pyramid -
and at the top a rat holding the world in his
hand. And this was just the idea that once
you'd achieved all these steps of
understanding you could hope to hold the
world in your hand and you would be
sheltered under a great gold coin.'*

Le Corbusier (1887-1965)
French
Composition
Signed with initials and date
gouache and pen and Indian
27½ x 19¾in (70 x 50cm)
£12,000-13,000 *S*

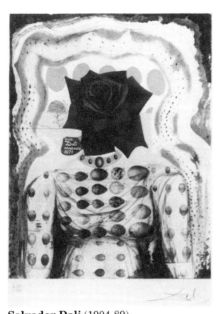

Salvador Dali (1904-89)
Spanish
Memories of Surrealism
Signed, 12 etchings with photo offset printed
in colours
29¾ x 21in (75.2 x 53.5cm) each
£5,500-6,500 *S(NY)*

Salvador Dali (1904-89)
Spanish
Instrument Masochiste
Oil on canvas, painted in 1933-34 and signed
at a later date
24½ x 18½in (62 x 47cm)
£460,000-500,000 *S*

*The title Instrument Masochiste sums up
several of the masochistic/erotic motifs
running throughout Dali's work. The female
torso seen through a window refers back to a
childhood story when Dali deliberately threw
a toy out of his window in order to see the
ample bosom of a fruit picker framed within
it. The cypress tree with the sword cutting
through its branches and the limp violin are
further sexual symbols, the latter illustrating
Dali's fear of impotence.*

John Craxton (b1922)
British
Cretan Gorge
Signed, watercolour and gouache on board
16½ x 6½in (42 x 16.5cm)
£1,000-1,500 *CSK*

Alan Davie (b1920)
British
Mechanism of the Plants
(Florentine Mobile)
Signed and dated 48, oil on canvas
35 x 37½in (89 x 95cm)
£13,000-14,000 *C*

Stuart Davis (1892-1964)
American
Study for Package Deal
Signed, gouache on paper
13¼ x 12in (33.7 x 30.5cm)
£42,000-50,000 *S(NY)*

*'The various Package Deal pictures ... are all
based on a firm and generous structure of
intensely coloured planes, typical of Davis's
work of the late 1950s and early 1960s. They
depend a good deal on the playful shuffling of
familiar advertising slogans ... At first
reading, the works all seem to have come from
the grocery packages: large, new, free, 100%,
bag, juice, cow. But ... among all these
workaday fragments are Davis's personal
watchwords: 'any' and 'pad'. 'Any' is the
familiar allusion to the validity of any
subject. 'Pad' recalls the series of pictures
that includes Pad No. 4 and The Mellow Pad
among others, but it also has a larger
meaning. As the hip word for home, the place
where the groceries have been taken, it
metaphorically locates the floating words.
And the juxtaposition of pad with cat, placed
directly below, removes us from the realm of
pet food, which we might reasonably expect
from the supermarket context, and returns us
to Davis's world of jive-talking jazz fans.'
Karen Wilkin - 1987.*

Kenneth Draper (b1944)
British
Stone, 1990
Pastel on paper
26 x 22in (66 x 56cm)
£2,000-2,500 *HaG*

Arthur G. Dove (1880-1946)
American
Brick Barge with Landscape
Signed, titled and dated Oct. 1930 on
backing, oil on board
30 x 40¼in (76.2 x 102.2cm)
£170,000-190,000 *S(NY)*

Jean Dubuffet (1901-85)
French
Promenade Agreste
Signed with initials, dated 74, vinyl on
canvas
76¾ x 39½in (195 x 100cm)
£145,000-165,000 *S*

Sylvia Edwards (20thC)
American
Still Life in Turquoise
Silkscreen, 31 colours
17 x 23½in (42.8 x 60.5cm)
£200-225 *CCA*

Jean Dubuffet (1901-85)
French
Circulation
Signed with initials, dated 79, acrylic and
collage on paper laid down on canvas
25¼ x 20in (64 x 51cm)
£30,000-35,000 *S*

Max Ernst (1891-1976)
German
Forêt et Soleil
Signed, oil on paper laid
down on board,
painted 1932
9½ x 12¾in (24 x 32cm)
£116,000-130,000 *S*

Helmut Federle (b1944)
Swiss
Desolation Row
Signed, inscribed with title and dated on
reverse 84, acrylic on canvas
80¾ x 132¾in (205 x 337cm)
£20,000-25,000 *C*

Öyvind Fahlström (1928-76)
Swedish
Column No. 1 (Wonderbread)
Signed, titled and dated 72, acrylic and china
ink on paper
23½ x 19in (59 x 48cm)
£21,000-25,000 *S*

Eric Fischl (b1948)
American
Untitled
Signed and dated 85,
oil on paper
21¾ x 34½in (55 x 88cm)
£14,500-16,000 *S*

Lucio Fontana
(1899-1968) Italian
Concetto Spaziale
Signed, titled and inscribed on reverse,
waterpaint on canvas, executed in 1960
35 x 45¾ in (89 x 116cm)
£90,000-120,000 *S*

*Fontana became most famous for his monochromatic
ripped canvases, which transformed 2 dimensional
paintings into 3 dimensional concepts - the slashes
bringing in to the picture the idea of the space that
lies behind the canvas and, according to some critics,
also providing 'a culmination of that conception of
art which regards it as a record of action and
gesture', that is where the subject of the work becomes
the physical and artistic processes that produced it.*

Terry Frost (b1915)
British
Cordoba
Mixed media
30 x 23in (76 x 59cm)
£900-975 *OLG*

Sam Francis (b1923)
American
Untitled No. 54
Gouache on paper, executed in 1972
40½ x 27in (102.5 x 69cm)
£15,500-16,500 *S*

Peter Griffin (b1947)
British
Head, Hand and Concorde
Oil on canvas
54 x 42in (137 x 106.5cm)
£4,000-4,300 *MAA*

Albert Gleizes (1881-1953)
French
Deux Nus
Signed, gouache on paper, executed in 1920
12¾ x 9½in (32.5 x 24cm)
£22,000-27,000 *C*

Maggi Hambling (b1945)
British
Conversation
Signed and inscribed on reverse,
oil on 3 canvases
Each canvas 20 x 16 x 3in (50.5
x 40.5 x 7.5cm)
£2,000-4,000 *BRG*

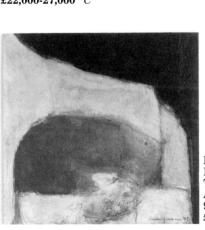

Brian Graham (b1945)
British
The Orange Farm, Purbeck
Acrylic on board
9¾ x 10¼in (24.5 x 25.5cm)
£225-250 *OLG*

Rodney Alan Greenblatt (20thC)
American
Royal Armoire
Acrylic on wood with lights, executed in 1984
84¾ x 47¼ x 29⅛in (215.5 x 120 x 74cm)
£800-1,000 *C*

Richard Hamilton (b1922)
British
Swinging London 67
Silkscreen, pastel, oil and glitter on paper
28 x 34⅜in (71 x 88cm)
£29,000-35,000 *S*

*Executed in 1968-69, this image was realised
by the artist from a press photograph of
Robert Fraser and Mick Jagger. Both were
arrested on 12th February 1967 in the house
of Keith Richards and charged with unlawful
possession of various drugs: this particular
photograph was taken on 28th June 1967 by
the Daily Mail photographer, John Twine, as
both arrived handcuffed in a police van at the
Chichester court building. Six versions on
canvas exist but only one work on paper of
several rough studies made for them was
preserved because it developed interesting
qualities of its own.*

Marsden Hartley (1878-1943)
American
Seashells on a violet cloth
Signed and dated 1929 on reverse, oil on
panel
21 x 13in (53.3 x 33cm)
£23,000-28,000 *S(NY)*

Hans Hartung (1904-89)
French
Composition
Signed and dated 61, coloured crayons on
card
25¼ x 19¼in (64 x 49cm)
£12,000-13,000 *S*

Keith Haring (1958-90)
American
3 Children Playing
Signed with initials, dated 88, acrylic on canvas
71¾in (182cm) square
£28,000-35,000 *S*

Adrian Heath (b1920)
British
Untitled, 1960
Signed and dated 60, oil on canvas
78 x 72in (198 x 183cm)
£7,800-9,000 *S*

Auguste Herbin (1882-1960)
Composition
French
Signed and dated 1919, oil on canvas
28½ x 23½in (72.4 x 59.7cm)
£80,000-100,000 *C*

Auguste Herbin (1882-1960)
French
Composition (Volutes)
Signed, oil on canvas, painted c1939
36 x 29in (92 x 73.5cm)
£25,000-30,000 *C*

Jack Hellewell (20thC)
British
Rocking Stone, Ilkley Moor
Acrylic on paper
18 x 26in (46 x 66cm)
£350-400 *KHG*

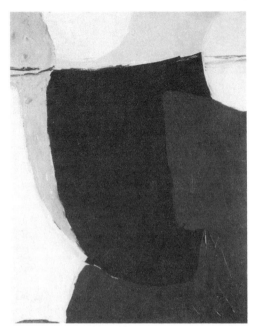

John Hoyland (b1934)
British
Abstract 1969
Signed and dated 69, acrylic and gouache on paper
21½ x 28½in (54.5 x 72.5cm)
£750-1,000 *CSK*

Roger Hilton (1911-75)
British
June 61
Signed, inscribed and dated June 61, oil on canvas
50 x 40in (127 x 101.6cm)
£12,000-13,000 *C*

Paul Hawdon (b1953)
British
Muse
Limited edition etching (50), signed and dated 1989
31½ x 19½in (80 x 50cm)
£150-175 *Mer*

David Hockney (b1937)
British
Simplified Faces State I; and Simplified Faces State II
Two soft-ground etchings printed in colours, 1974, each signed in pencil
13 x 12¾in (33.5 x 32.5cm), and 12¾ x 13in (32.5 x 33cm)
£1,500-2,000 *S*

Michael Hyam (20thC)
British
Collage II
Mixed media
11 x 18in (28 x 46cm)
£600-650 *PHG*

Friedensreich Hundertwasser (b1928)
Austrian
Regen im haus, regen im berg
Signed and dated 1961, mixed media on rice
paper laid down on burlap
31½ x 39¼in (80 x 100cm)
£50,000-60,000 *S*

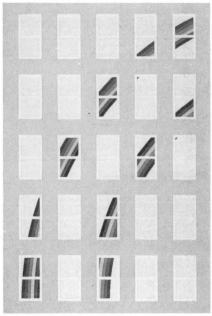

Patrick Hughes (b1939)
British
Double Vision
Silkscreen, 15 colours
23¼ x 15½in (59.5 x 39.5cm)
£85-95 *CCA*

Alexej von Jawlensky (1864-1941)
Russian
Stilleben mit Kanne
Oil on board laid down on panel, painted
c1913
26½ x 19in (67.4 x 48.6cm)
£290,000-340,000 *C*

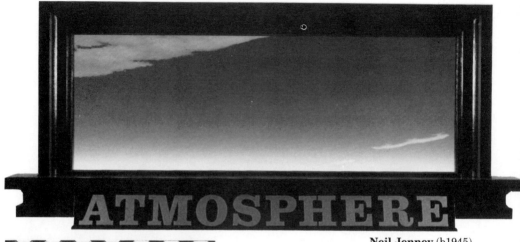

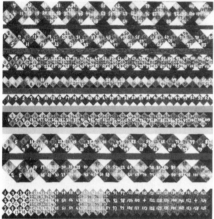

Alfred Jensen (1903-81)
American
Mayan mat patterns' number structure
Oil on canvas, painted in 1974
72in (183cm) square
£50,000-60,000 *S(NY)*

Neil Jenney (b1945)
American
Formation No.2
Oil on wood, painted in 1984-91
33 x 79in (83.8 x 200.7cm)
£95,000-120,000 *S(NY)*

Wassily Kandinsky (1866-1944)
Russian
Knabe
Signed with monogram and dated 16,
watercolour and brush and Indian ink
9 x 11¼in (22.8 x 29cm)
£110,000-130,000 *S*

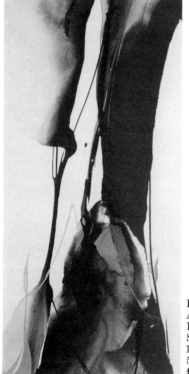

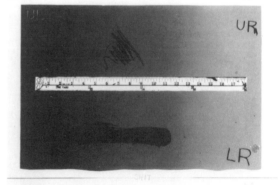

Paul Jenkins (b1923)
American
Phenomenon by a Shield of Red
Signed, inscribed and dated
1966 on canvas overlap
50 x 24in (127 x 61cm)
£2,500-3,000 *CSK*

Jasper Johns (b1930)
American
Untitled (Shit)
Signed in pencil, silkscreen
printed in colours, 1971
18½ x 24¼in (47 x 62cm)
£2,500-3,000 *S(NY)*

Ken Kiff (b1935)   British
Sun above Houses and Shadowy Dog
Signed, charcoal and pastel, executed in 1986
53 x 31in (134.7 x 79cm)
£2,600-3,200   *C*

Edward Kienholz (b1927)
American
The Little Eagle Rock Incident
Signed, titled, inscribed and dated 58 on
reverse, oil and trophy head of deer on wood
61¾ x 49 x 20in (156.8 x 124.5 x 50.8cm)
£30,000-35,000   *S(NY)*

Franz Kline (1910-62)
American
Untitled
Signed, ink on paper, executed c1951-53
8½ x 11in (21.6 x 28cm)
£24,000-30,000 *S(NY)*

The modernist American composer John Cage recalled the following story about Franz Kline: Franz Kline was about to have the first showing of his black and white paintings at the Egan Gallery. Realising that his mother had never seen his paintings and that she would surely be interested in doing so, he arranged for her to come to New York for the opening. After she had been in the gallery for some time, she said, 'Franz, I might have known you'd find the easy way.'

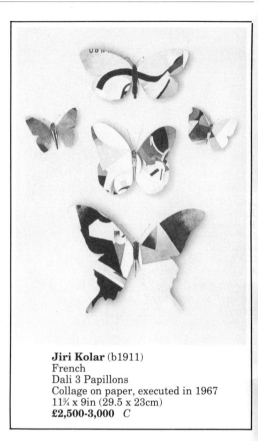

Jiri Kolar (b1911)
French
Dali 3 Papillons
Collage on paper, executed in 1967
11¾ x 9in (29.5 x 23cm)
£2,500-3,000 *C*

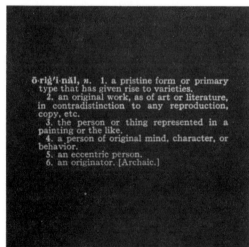

Joseph Kosuth (b1945)
American
Titled (Art as Idea as Idea)
Signed and dated 1967 on the reverse of photostat
47 x 46¾in (119.4 x 118.7cm)
£14,500-16,000 *S(NY)*

The American artist Kosuth was one of the pioneers of Conceptual Art, in which the idea and process of manufacture become 'the art', rather than their ultimate physical product. 'Actual works of art,' claimed Kosuth, 'are little more than historical curiosities.'

Jannis Kounellis (b1936)
Greek
Untitled
Ink on paper, executed in 1961-62
27 x 39in (68.6 x 99cm)
£10,500-11,500 *S(NY)*

Wifredo Lam (1902-82)
Cuban
Sans Titre
Signed and dated 1974 on reverse, oil on canvas
13¾ x 17¾in (35 x 44.8cm)
£11,500-12,500 *S(NY)*

André Lanskoy (1902-76)
Russian/French
Partage de la Nuit
Signed, titled and dated 47-48 on reverse, oil
on canvas
31¾ x 45⅜in (81 x 116cm)
£13,500-15,000 *S*

Michel Larionov (1882-1964)   Russian
Personnage de la Marche Funèbre
Signed, gouache on paper, executed 1919
17½ x 12in (44.5 x 30.5cm)
£7,200-8,200 *S(NY)*

Dirk Larsen (b1951)
British
Family Group
Oil on canvas
34 x 22¾in (86 x 58cm)
£1,000-1,100 *EW*

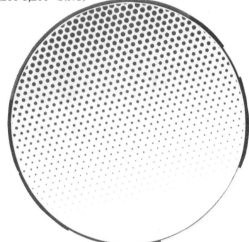

Roy Lichtenstein (b1923)
American
Mirror
Signed and dated 70 on reverse, magna on
canvas
24in (61cm) diam
£45,000-60,000 *S(NY)*

*Mirror belongs to a series of approximately 50
works by Lichtenstein dating from 1969 to
1971 which use the concept of reflection and
perception to explore the respresentative
nature of art. In 1969, Lichtenstein
photographed and sketched several types of
mirrors, including a round magnifying make-
up mirror and an oval bevelled edged mirror.
Lichtenstein commented on 'the interesting
lack of image that identifies a mirror as a
mirror.'*

Arthur Lett-Haines (1894-1978)
British
Escaping Bird
Signed and dated 1931, pencil, coloured
crayon, watercolour, bodycolour and brush
and black ink
18½ x 24in (47 x 61cm)
£1,200-1,800 *C*

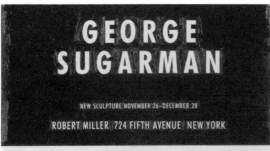

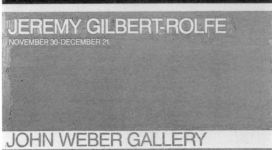

Simon Linke (b1958)
American
George Sugarman, December 85
Signed, inscribed with title and dated on
overlap 1986, oil on canvas
60in (152.5cm) square
£3,000-4,000 *C*

Jean Lurçat (1892-1966)
French
Nature Morte aux Pommes
Signed and dated 27, oil on canvas
10¾ x 16in (27 x 41cm)
£2,000-2,500 *S*

Alfred Manessier
(b1911)
French
Cascade
Signed and dated 59,
oil on canvas
39½ x 32in
(100 x 81cm)
£24,000-30,000 *S*

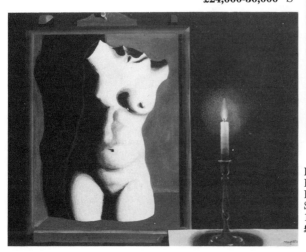

John Mackay (20thC)
The Maze iii
Signed and dated 1988
40 x 46in (101.6 x 117cm)
£2,300-2,800 *CSK*

René Magritte (1898-1967)
Belgian
L'Idée Fixe
Signed, titled on reverse, oil on canvas,
painted in 1966
15 x 18in (38 x 46cm)
£200,000-225,000 *S*

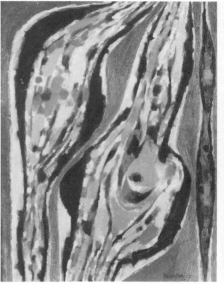

René Magritte (1898-1967)
Belgian
La Coincidence des Lumières
Signed, gouache on paper, executed in 1942
12¼ x 16¼in (30.7 x 48cm)
£90,000-100,000 *C*

Marino Marini (1901-80)
Italian
Groso Acrobatico
Signed and titled on reverse, gouache and collage
15½ x 20½in (39 x 52cm)
£7,200-8,000 S

Georges Mathieu (b1921)
French
Potentille
Signed and dated 64, oil on canvas, painted in 1964
35 x 57¼in (88.8 x 146.3cm)
£18,000-20,000 C

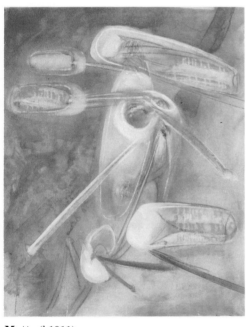

Matta (b1911)
Chilean
L'Etre c'est la Pierre
Signed twice, titled and dated 55 on reverse, oil on canvas
39¼ x 31¼in (100 x 81cm)
£29,000-35,000 S

Joan Miró (1893-1983)
Spanish
Femme et Oiseau
Signed, dated and titled on reverse 18/XI/66, oil and casein tempera on canvas, painted on 18 November 1966
£155,000-175,000 C

Joan Miró (1893-1983)
Spanish
Lithographie pour le centenaire de l'Imprimerie Mourlot
Signed in pencil, lithograph printed in colours, 1953
20 x 25⅜in (50.5 x 65.5cm)
£15,500-18,000 S

Paula Rego (b1935)
South American
Figures and Animal Caricatures
Signed and dated 1984, poster paint and
gouache
15¾ x 14½in (40 x 36.8cm)
£3,700-4,500 *C*

Edward Ruscha (b1937)
American
Mocha Standard
Signed, dated and numbered 57/100,
silkscreen printed in colours
19½ x 37in (49.8 x 93.7cm)
£3,500-4,000 *S(NY)*

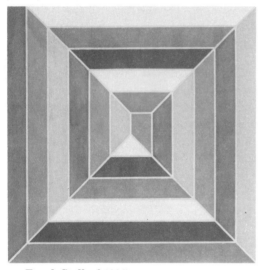

Frank Stella (b1936)
American
Maze
Signed and dated '66 on overlap, acrylic on
canvas
35¾in (91cm) square
£47,000-60,000 *S*

*Stella 'emphasised the flatness of the painting
pattern, abolishing the three dimensional
picture image, and he was uncompromising
in his refusal to permit the introduction of
deep recession behind the picture plain,' notes
the Oxford Companion to 20th Century Art
(see Biblio). His use of stripes and
orthogonals echoed the shape of the picture
itself, his work having obvious affinities with
the so-called 'All-Over' style of painting (a
term first coined to describe the 'drip'
paintings of Jackson Pollock) in which the
whole canvas is treated in a relatively
uniform manner. There are no salient or
individual points of interest or reference and
attention is evenly diffused over the picture
surface.*

Richard Serra (b1939)
American
Almeda Black
Signed, numbered and dated 1981, paintstick
on steel sheet
72in (182.5cm) square
£5,000-6,000 *S*

*Not a missed picture in Miller's Guide, but
simply an all black painting by artist Richard
Serra whose major public sculptures and
installations have created huge controversy in
recent years, exciting high praise from the
critics and often equally strong condemnation
from the general public.*

Rufino Tamayo (b1899)
Mexican
The Sleepwalker
Signed and dated 0-54, oil on canvas
26 x 40in (65.7 x 100.6cm)
£340,000-360,000 *S(NY)*

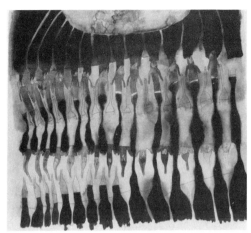

Francisco Toledo (b1940)
Mexican
Fish Sun, 1965
Watercolour, pen and ink
19 x 21in (48 x 53cm)
£2,200-2,600 *P*

Wayne Thiebaud (b1920)
American
Gum Ball Machine
Signed and dated 1970, linoleum cut printed
in colours
24 x 18in (61 x 45.8cm)
£2,400-3,000 *S(NY)*

Victor Vasarely (b1908)
Hungarian
Re-Nab-II-B
Signed, titled and dated 1968, oil on canvas
71in (180cm) square
£16,000-18,000 *S*

Victor Vasarely (1908) Hungarian
Thene-Neg
Signed, titled and dated 1956, oil on canvas
40 x 37in (100 x 93cm)
£12,000-13,000 *S*

Cy Twombly (b1929)
American
Untitled
Signed and dated 1956, oil, crayon and
pencil on canvas
46¼ x 69in (117.5 x 175.3cm)
£1,480,000-1,600,000 *S(NY)*

*Untitled (1956) is a major example
of the gestural paintings of Twombly's
work of the 1950s.*

Joan Miró (1893-1983)
Spanish
Le Couple érotique
Indian ink, pencil and collage on sandpaper,
executed in September 1934
14¼ x 9in (36.5 x 23.2cm)
£39,000-45,000 *C*

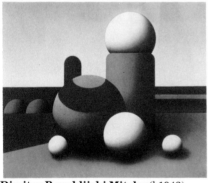

Dimiter Buyukliiski Mitchy (b1943)
Bulgarian
Composition II
Signed with initials, oil on canvas
43¾ x 51¼in (110 x 30cm)
£1,300-1,800 *C*

Henry Moore (1898-1986)
British
Feet on Holiday 1
Signed in pencil, lithograph printed in
colours, 1979
8½ x 10¼in (21.6 x 26cm)
£1,000-1,500 *C*

After Henry Moore (1898-1986)
British
Head of a Man
Screen print on Irish linen, printed Henry
Moore and numbered 37/65
67¾ x 47¼in (172 x 120cm)
£1,400-1,800 *S*

Armando Morales (b1927)
Spanish
Dos Figuras
Signed and dated 81, pastel on buff paper
17 x 23½in (43.2 x 59.7cm)
£7,000-8,000 *S(NY)*

Matt Mullican (b1951)
American
Signs
16 panels, acrylic on cardboard, executed
1980-81
Each panel 24 x 23¾in (61 x 60.5cm)
£3,500-4,000 *C*

Claes Oldenburg (b1929)
American
Urethane Baked Potato
Stencilled with title, signed and dated 1964,
enamel and urethane on stencilled fabric
mounted on wooden board
9 x 11¾in (23 x 28.2cm)
£6,200-7,200 *C*

A.R. Penck (b1939)
Design 2
Signed and titled, gouache on paper,
executed c1982-83
24¾ x 34½in (62.8 x 87.6cm)
£4,000-5,000 *S*

Mimmo Paladino (b1948)
Italian
Untitled
Signed and dated '83, acrylic on canvas,
canvas collage and wood
48 x 35½in (121.5 x 90.5cm)
£54,000-60,000 *S*

Carel Weight (b1908)
The Clouds
Oil on board
30 x 20in (76 x 51cm)
£17,500-18,500 *BRG*

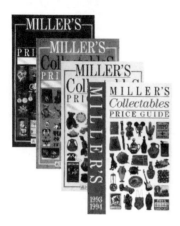
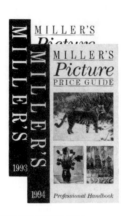
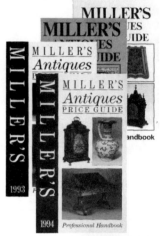
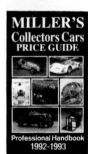

BIBLIOGRAPHY

A Century of British Painters, Richard and Samuel Redgrave, (Phaidon, Oxford), 1981

A Dictionary of Art Quotations, Ian Crofton, (Routledge), 1988.

Anecdotes of Modern Art, Donald Hall and Pat Corrington Wykes, (Oxford University Press), 1990.

Art Detective, Madeleine Marsh, (Pelham Books), 1993.

Art in Paris 1845-1862, Charles Baudelaire, (Phaidon, Oxford), 1981.

British Prints, Ian Mackenzie, (Antique Collectors' Club), 1987.

British Sporting Painting 1650-1850, (Arts Council of Great Britain), 1974.

British Watercolour Artists up to 1920, Huon Mallalieu, (Antique Collectors' Club), 1976.

Dictionary of Sea Painters, E.H.H. Archibald, (Antique Collectors' Club), 1980.

Dictionnaire des Peintres, Sculpteurs, Dessinateurs et Graveurs - 10 vols, E. Benezit, Paris 1976.

Dictionary of Painters and Engravers - 2 vols, Michael Bryan, (George Bell and Sons), 1889.

Dictionary of Subjects and Symbols in Art, James Hall, (John Murray), 1979.

Dictionary of Recent and Living Painters and Engravers, H. Ottley, (Henry G. Bohn), 1866.

Dutch Art and Architecture 1600-1800, Jakob Rosenberg, Seymour Slive and E. H. ter Kuile, (Penguin Books), 1982.

Faber Book of Art Anecdotes, Edward Lucie-Smith, 1992.

French Eighteenth Century Painters, Edmond and Jules de Goncourt, (Phaidon, Oxford), 1981.

How to Buy Pictures, Huon Mallalieu, (Phaidon-Christie's), 1984.

Modern English Painters, John Rothenstein, (Macdonald), 1984.

Painting in Britain 1530 to 1790, Ellis Waterhouse, (Penguin Books), 1978.

Popular 19th Century Painting, Philip Hook and Mark Poltimore, (Antique Collectors' Club), 1986.

The British Portrait 1660-1960, (Antique Collectors' Club), 1990.

The Camden Town Group, Wendy Baron, (Scholar Press), 1979.

The Dictionary of British 18th Century Painters, Ellis Waterhouse, (Antique Collectors' Club), 1981.

The Dictionary of 16th and 17th Century British Painters, Ellis Waterhouse, (Antique Collectors' Club), 1988.

The Dictionary of Victorian Painters, Christopher Wood, (Antique Collectors' Club), 1978.

The English Social History 1066-1945, Christopher Hibbert, (Paladin Books, London), 1988.

The Illustrators, (Chris Beetles Ltd), London, 1992.

The Impressionists at First Hand, Bernard Denvir, (Thames and Hudson), 1987.

The Modern Spirit: American Painting 1908-1935, (Arts Council of Great Britain), 1977.

The Oxford Companion to Twentieth Century Art, Harold Osborne, (Oxford University Press), 1988.

The Oxford Dictionary of Saints, David Hugh Farmer, (Oxford University Press), 1987.

The Popular Antiques Yearbook, Huon Mallalieu, (Phaidon-Christie's), 3 vols. 1985/87/88.

The Thames and Hudson Dictionary of Art Terms, Edward Lucie-Smith, 1988.

20th Century Painters and Sculptors, Frances Spalding, (Antique Collectors' Club), 1990.

Victorian Painters, Jeremy Maas, (Barrie & Jenkins), 1988.

Watercolour Painting in Britain, Martin Hardie, (B.T. Batsford Ltd), 3 vols. 1966/67/68.

Who's Who in the Ancient World, Betty Radice, (Penguin Books), 1984.

Women Artists, An Illustrated History, Nancy G. Heller, (Virago), 1987.

GENERAL CATALOGUING TERMS

For every picture, *Miller's Picture Price Guide* has followed the basic description provided by the auction house or dealer. As all the auction houses stress in their catalogues, while full care is taken to ensure that any statement as to attribution, origin, date, age, provenance and condition is reliable and accurate, all such statements are statements of opinion only and not to be taken as fact.

The conventional cataloguing system used by the auction houses has been maintained.

A work catalogued with the name(s) of an artist, without any qualification, is in their opinion, a work by the artist (where the artist's forename(s) is not known, this is replaced by a series of asterisks, sometimes preceded by any initial).

'Attributed to...' In their opinion probably a work by the artist, but less certainly than in the preceding category.

'Studio of...' 'Workshop of...' In their opinion a work by an unknown hand in the studio of the artist which may or may not have been executed under the artist's direction.

'Circle of...' In their opinion a work by an as yet unidentified but distinct hand, closely associated with the named artist, but not necessarily his pupil.

'Follower of...' 'Style of...' In their opinion a work by a painter working in the artist's style, contemporary or nearly contemporary, but not necessarily his pupil.

'Manner of...' In their opinion, a work in the artist's style, but of a later date.

'After...' In their opinion, a copy of a known work by the artist.

'Signed...'/ 'Dated...'/ 'Inscribed...' In their opinion signature/date/inscription are from the hand of the artist.

'Bears signature, date, or inscription...' In their opinion, signature/date/description have been added by another hand.

Measurements: Dimensions are given height before width.

SELECT GLOSSARY

Acrylic: A synthetic emulsion paint.

Airbrush: A small mechanical paint sprayer permitting fine control and a smooth finish, and similar in appearance to a fountain pen.

Allegory: A work of art conveying an abstract subject, under the guise of another subject.

Aquatint: Etching technique in which a metal plate is sprinkled with resin and then bathed in acid which bites into any uncovered areas. According to the amount of acid used and the density of the particles, darker or lighter shading is obtained.

Bistre: A brown pigment made from charred wood, often used as a wash on pen and ink drawings.

Bodycolour: Opaque pigment.

Cartoon: A full size early design for a painting.

Casein: Protein of milk, the basis of cheese.

Collage: A work of art in which pieces of paper, photographs and other materials are pasted to the surface of the picture.

Conversation piece: A group portrait with the sitters placed informally as in conversation.

Drawing: Representation with line.

Dry-point: The process of making a print by engraving directly on to a copper plate with a steel or diamond point.

Edition: The run of a print published at any one time.

Engraving: The process of cutting a design into a hard surface (metal or wood) so that the lines will retain the ink.

Etching: A technique of printmaking developed in the 16thC, in which a metal plate is covered with an acid-resistant substance and the design scratched on it with a needle revealing the metal beneath. The plate is then immersed in acid, which bites into the lines, which will then hold the ink.

Fête Champêtre: A rustic festival or peasant celebration - also knows as a Kermesse in Dutch and Flemish works.

Fête Galante: Ladies and gentlemen at play, often in a parkland setting.

Fresco: Painting in watercolour laid on wall or ceiling before plaster is dry.

Genre: Art showing scenes from daily life.

Gouache: Opaque watercolour paint.

Grisaille: Painting in grey or greyish monochrome.

Gum arabic: Gum from acacia trees, used in the manufacturer of ink.

Icon: A religious painting on panel usually by a Greek or Russian Orthodox artist, its subject and representation conforming to established traditions.

Impression: An individual copy of a print or engraving.

Lithograph: A print made by drawing with a wax crayon on a porous prepared stone which is then soaked in water. A grease-based ink is applied to the stone which adheres only to the design. Dampened paper is applied to the the stone and is rubbed over with a special press to produce the print.

Medium: The materials used in a painting, i.e. oil, tempera, watercolour, etc.

Mezzotint: The reverse of the usual printing process - the artist begins with a black ground, a metal plate that is completely roughened, and the design is polished or burnished into it, thus the image remains white while the background takes all the ink.

Mixed Media: Art combining different types of material.

Oil: Pigment bound with oil.

Panel Painting: Painting on wood.

Pastel: A dry pigment bound with gum into stick-form and used for drawing.

Pendant: One of a pair of pictures.

Plein-air: A landscape painted outdoors and on the spot.

Plate: The piece of metal etched or engraved with the design used to produce prints.

Print: An image which exists in multiple copies, taken from an engraved plate, woodblock, etc.

Provenance: The record of previous owners and locations of a work of art.

Recto: The front of a picture.

Sanguine: Red chalk containing ferric oxide used in drawing.

Silkscreen: A print-making process using a finely meshed screen, often of silk, and stencils to apply the image to paper.

State: A term applied to prints - to the different stages at which the artist has corrected or changed a plate - and the prints produced from these various 'states', which are numbered first state, second state, third state, etc.

Still Life: A composition of inanimate objects.

Tempera: A medium for pigment mostly made up of egg yolk and water, commonly used before the invention of oil painting.

Tondo: A circular painting.

Topographical painting: A landscape in which the predominant concern is geographical accuracy rather than imaginative content.

Triptych: A set of three pictures, usually in oils, with hinges allowing the outer panels to be folded over the central one - often used as an altarpiece.

Vanitas: An elaborate still life including various elements such as a skull, symbolising the transience of earthly life.

Verso: The back of a picture.

Wash: A thin transparent tint applied over the surface of a work.

Watercolour: Transparent, water soluble paint, usually applied on paper.

Woodcut: Print made from a design cut into a block of wood.

DIRECTORY OF GALLERIES

This directory is in no way complete. If you wish to be included in next year's directory or if you have a change of address or telephone number, please could you inform us by July 1st 1994. Entries will be repeated in subsequent editions unless we are requested otherwise. Finally we would advise readers to make contact by telephone before a visit, therefore avoiding a wasted journey, which nowadays is both time consuming and expensive.

London

Abbey Mills Gallery, Merton Abbey Mills, Riverside Craft Village, Meranton Way, SW19
Tel: 081 542 5035

Ackerman & Johnson Ltd, Lowndes Lodge Gallery, 27 Lowndes Street, SW1
Tel: 071 235 6464

L'Acquaforte, 49a Ledbury Road, W11
Tel: 071 221 3388

John Adams Fine Art Ltd, 200 Ebury Street, SW1.
Tel: 071 730 8999

Alberti Gallery, 114 Albert Street, Camden Town, NW1
Tel: 071 629 1052

Alpine Gallery, 74 South Audley Street, W1
Tel: 071 491 2948

Alton Gallery, 72 Church Road, Barnes, SW13
Tel: 081 748 0606

Michael Appleby, 7 St James's Chambers, 2-10 Ryder Street, SW1
Tel: 071 839 7635

Argile Gallery, 7 Blenheim Crescent, W11
Tel: 071 792 0888

Art Collection, 3-5 Elyston Street, SW3
Tel: 071 584 4664

Art of Africa, 158 Walton Street, SW3
Tel: 071 584 2326

Art Space Gallery, 84 St. Peter's Street, N1
Tel: 071-359 7002

Bankside Gallery, 48 Hopton Street, SE1
Tel: 071 928 7521

Stephen Bartley Gallery, 62 Old Church Street, SW3
Tel: 071 352 8686

Baumkotter Gallery, 63a Kensington Church Street, W8
Tel: 071 937 5171

Beardsmore Gallery, 22-24 Prince of Wales Road, Kentish Town, NW5
Tel: 071 485 0923

Chris Beetles Ltd, 10 Ryder Street, St James's, SW1
Tel: 071 839 7551

Blason Gallery, 351 Kennington Lane, SE11
Tel: 071 735 5280

Blond Fine Art, Unit 10, Canalside Studios, 2-4 Orsman Road, N1
Tel: 071 739 4383

John Bonham & Murray Feely, 46 Porchester Road, W2
Tel: 071 221 7208

Anna Bornholt Gallery, 3-5 Weighhouse Street, W1
Tel: 071 499 6114

Boundary Gallery, 98 Boundary Road, NW8
Tel: 071 624 1126

Browse & Darby Gallery, 19 Cork Street, W1
Tel: 071 734 7984

Bruton Street Gallery, 28 Bruton Street, W1
Tel: 071 499 9747

Burlington Paintings, 12 Burlington Gardens, W1
Tel: 071 734 9984

Cadogan Contemporary, 108 Draycott Avenue, SW3
Tel: 071 581 5451

Caelt Gallery, 182 Westbourne Grove, W11
Tel: 071 229 9309

Duncan Campbell Fine Art, 15 Thackeray Street, W8
Tel: 071 937 8665

Lucy B. Campbell Gallery, 123 Kensington Church Street, W8
Tel: 071 727 2205

Catto Animation, 41 Heath Street, NW3
Tel: 071 431 2892

Catto Gallery, 49 Ladbroke Grove, W11
Tel: 071 221 7765

Century Gallery, Westley Richards & Sons, 100/102 Fulham Road, Chelsea, SW3
Tel: 071 581 1589

Anna-Mei Chadwick, 64 New King's Road, Parsons Green, SW6
Tel: 071 736 1928

Churzee Studio Gallery, 17 Bellevue Road, Wandsworth Common, SW17
Tel: 081 767 8113

Connaught Brown Gallery, 2 Albemarle Street, W1
Tel: 071 408 0362

Cooling Gallery, 2-4 Cork Street, W1
Tel: 071 409 3500

Cooper Fine Arts Ltd, 768 Fulham Road, SW6
Tel: 071 731 3421

Cox & Co, 37 Duke Street, St. James's, SW1
Tel: 071 930 1987

Curwen Gallery, 4 Windmill Street, W1
Tel: 071 636 1459

Charles Daggett Gallery, 28 Beauchamp Place, SW3
Tel: 071 584 2969

Sara Davenport Gallery, 206 Walton Street, SW3
Tel: 071 225 2224

John Denham Gallery, 50 Mill Lane, West Hampstead, NW6
Tel: 071 794 2635

Colin Denny Ltd, 18 Cale Street, SW3
Tel: 071 584 0240

Vanessa Devereux Gallery, 11 Blenheim Crescent, W11
Tel: 071 221 6836

Sebastian D'Orsai Ltd, 39 Theobalds Road, WC1
Tel: 071 609 1275

Dover Street Gallery, 13 Dover Street, W1
Tel: 071 409 1540

Drian Galleries, 7 Porchester Place, Marble Arch, W2
Tel: 071 723 9473

William Drummond 8 St James Chambers, Ryder St, SW1
Tel: 071 930 9696

Durini Gallery, 150 Walton Street, SW3
Tel: 071 581 1237

Eagle Gallery, 159 Farringdon Road, EC1
Tel: 071 833 2674

Ealing Gallery, 78 St Mary's Road, Ealing, W5
Tel: 081 840 7883

East West, 8 Blenheim Crescent, W11
Tel: 071 229 7981

Eaton Gallery, 34 Duke Street, St James's SW1
Tel: 071 930 5950

Entwistle Gallery, 37 Old Bond Street, W1
Tel: 071 409 3484

Finchley Fine Art Galleries, 983 High Road, North Finchley, N12
Tel: 081 446 4848

Fleur de Lys Gallery, 227a Westbourne Grove, W11
Tel: 071 727 8595

Flowers East, 199 Richmond Road, E8
Tel: 081 985 3333

Frith Street Gallery, 60 Frith Street, W1
Tel: 071 494 1550

Gagliardi Design & Contemporary Art, 507-509 Kings Road, SW10.
Tel: 071 352 3663

Gallery K, 101-103 Heath Street, Hampstead, NW3
Tel: 071 794 4949

The Gallery on Church Street, 12 Church Street, NW8
Tel: 071 723 3389

Jill George Gallery, 38 Lexington Street, W1
Tel: 071 439 7343

Martyn Gregory Gallery, 34 Bury Street, St James's, SW1
Tel: 071 839 3731

Gruzelier Modern & Contemporary Art, 16 Maclise Road, West Kensington, W14
Tel: 071 603 4540

Laurence Hallett
Tel: 071 798 8977

Hamilton Fine Arts, 186 Willifield Way, Hampstead, NW11
Tel: 081 455 7410

Hardware Gallery, 277 Hornsey Road, Islington, N7
Tel: 071 272 9651

Marina Henderson Gallery, 11 Langton Street, SW10
Tel: 071 352 1667

Hicks Gallery, 2 & 4 Leopold Road, Wimbledon, SW19
Tel: 081 944 7171

Hildegard Fritz-Denneville Fine Arts Ltd, 31 New Bond Street, W1
Tel: 071 629 2466

Holland Gallery, 129 Portland Road, W11
Tel: 071 727 7198

Holland & Holland Gallery, 31 Bruton Street, W1
Tel: 071 499 9383

Dennis Hotz Fine Art Ltd, 9 Cork Street, W1
Tel: 071 287 8324

Houldsworth Fine Art, 4-6 Bassett Road, W10
Tel: 081 969 8197

Hyde Park Gallery, 16 Craven Terrace, W2
Tel: 071 402 2904

Malcolm Innes Gallery, 172 Walton Street, SW3
Tel: 071 584 0575/5559

JPL Fine Arts, 26 Davies Street, W1
Tel: 071 493 2630

Gillian Jason Gallery, 42 Inverness Street, NW1
Tel: 071 267 4835

Annely Juda Fine Art, 23 Dering Street, W1
Tel: 071 629 7578

King Street Galleries, 17 King Street, St James's, SW1
Tel: 071 930 3993

Knapp Gallery, Regent's College, Inner Circle, Regent's Park, NW1
Tel: 071 487 7540

Stephen Lacey Gallery, Redcliffe Square, SW10
Tel: 071 370 7785

Lamont Gallery, 65 Roman Road, E2
Tel: 081 981 6332

Lantern Gallery,
27 Holland Street
London W8

Leleco Art Gallery,
5 Britannia Road, SW6
Tel: 071 351 9440

Lisson Gallery,
67 Lisson Street, NW1
Tel: 071 724 2739

Llewellyn Alexander (Fine
Paintings) Ltd, 124-126
The Cut, Waterloo, SE1
Tel: 071 620 1322

Julian Machin, Grove
House, 92 Crawthew
Grove, SE22
Tel: 081 693 3178

Manya Igel Fine Arts Ltd,
21/22 Peters Court,
Porchester Road, W2.
Tel: 071 229 1669

Mathaf Gallery,
24 Motcomb Street, SW1
Tel: 071 235 0010

Mathon Gallery,
Pied Bull Yard, 68-69
Great Russell Street, WC1
Tel: 071 242 4443

Mayor Gallery,
22a Cork Street, W1
Tel: 071 734 3558

Mercury Gallery, 26 Cork
Street, W1
Tel: 071 734 7800

Merrifield Studios,
110 Heath Street, NW3
Tel: 071 794 0343

Roy Miles Gallery,
29 Bruton Street, W1
Tel: 071 495 4747

Mistral Galleries,
10 Dover Street, W1
Tel: 071 499 4701

Montpelier Studio,
4 Montpelier Street, SW7
Tel: 071 584 0667

Moreton Street Gallery,
40 Moreton Street, SW1
Tel: 071 834 7773

Guy Morrison,
91 Jermyn Street, SW1
Tel: 071 839 1454

Narwhal Invit Art Gallery,
55 Linden Gardens, W4
Tel: 081 747 1575

Guy Nevill Fine Paintings,
251a Fulham Road, SW3
Tel: 071 351 4292

New Grafton Gallery, 49
Church Road, Barnes,
SW13
Tel: 081 748 8850

Opus 1 Gallery,
25a Maddox Street, W1
Tel: 071 495 2570

O'Shea Gallery, 89 Lower
Sloane Street, SW1
Tel: 071 730 0081

Park Walk Gallery, 20
Park Walk, Chelsea, SW10
Tel: 071 351 0410

Michael Parkin Fine Art
Ltd, 11 Motcomb Street,
SW1
Tel: 071 235 8144

Indar Pasricha Fine Arts,
22 Connaught Street, W2
Tel: 071 724 9541

Paton Gallery,
2 Langley Court, WC2
Tel: 081 986 3409

W. H. Patterson,
19 Albemarle Street, W1
Tel: 071 629 4119

Piccadilly Gallery,
16 Cork Street, W1
Tel: 071 499 4632

Pike Gallery,
145 St John's Hill, SW11
Tel: 071 223 6741

Polak Gallery, 21 King
Street, St James's, SW1
Tel: 071 839 2871

Primrose Hill Gallery, 81
Regent's Park Road, NW1
Tel: 071 586 3533

Pyms Gallery, 13 Motcomb
Street, Belgravia, SW1
Tel: 071 235 3050

Raab Gallery,
9 Cork Street, W1
Tel: 071 734 6444

Railings Gallery, 5 New
Cavendish Street, W1
Tel: 071 935 1114

Sue Rankin Gallery, 40
Ledbury Road, W11
Tel: 071 229 4923

Anthony Reynolds Gallery,
5 Dering Street, W1
Tel: 071 491 0621

Benjamin Rhodes Gallery,
4 New Burlington Place,
W1
Tel: 071 434 1768

Richmond Gallery,
8 Cork Street, W1
Tel: 071 437 9422

Rogers de Rin, 76 Royal
Hospital Road, SW3
Tel: 071 352 9007

Royal Exchange Art
Gallery, 14 Royal
Exchange, EC3
Tel: 071 283 4400

Salama-Caro Gallery,
5/6 Cork Street, W1
Tel: 071 734 9179

Karston Schubert Ltd,
85 Charlotte Street, W1
Tel: 071 631 0031

Mark Senior,
240 Brompton Road, SW3
Tel: 071 589 5811

John Spink,
14 Darlan Road, SW6
Tel: 071 731 8292

Spink & Son Ltd,
5,6 & 7 King Street, St
James's, SW1
Tel: 071 930 7888

Splinter Gallery,
The Old Conveniences, 227
Goldhawk Road,
Ravenscourt Park,
Hammersmith, W12
Tel: 081 741 3399

Oliver Swann Calleries,
170 Walton Street, SW3
Tel: 071 581 4229

Talent Store Gallery,
11 Eccleston Street, SW1
Tel: 071 730 8117

Tesser Galleries,
106 Heath Street, NW3
Tel: 071 794 7971

Thompson Gallery,
38 Albemarle Street, W1
Tel: 071 499 1314

Todd Gallery,
1-5 Needham Road, W11
Tel: 071 792 1404

The Totteridge Gallery,
61 Totteridge Lane, N20
Tel: 081 446 7896

Tryon & Moorland Gallery,
23/24 Cork Street, W1
Tel: 071 734 6961

20th Century Gallery,
821 Fulham Road, SW6
Tel: 071 731 5888

Ben Uri Art Gallery,
21 Dean Street, W1
Tel: 071 437 2852

Rafael Valls Gallery,
11 Duke Street,
St James's, SW1
Tel: 071 930 1144

Gisela van Beers,
34 Davies Street, W1
Tel: 071 408 0434

Waddington Gallery,
10 Cork Street, W1
Tel: 071 437 8611

Walker-Bagshawe,
73 Walton Street, SW3
Tel: 071 589 4582

Waterman Fine Art Ltd,
74a Jermyn Street, St
James's, SW1
Tel: 071 839 5203

Westbourne Gallery,
331 Portobello Road, W10
Tel: 081 960 1867

Wildenstein Gallery,
147 New Bond Street, W1
Tel: 071 629 0602

Wilkins & Wilkins,
1 Barrett Street, W1
Tel: 071 935 9613

Wiseman Originals, 34
West Square, Lambeth,
SE1
Tel: 071 587 0747

Wolsely Fine Arts plc, 4
Grove Park, SE5
Tel: 071 274 8788

Christopher Wood Gallery,
141 New Bond Street,
Belgravia, W1
Tel: 071 235 9141

Wykeham Galleries, 51
Church Road, Barnes,
SW13
Tel: 081 741 1277

Wyllie Gallery,
44(3) Elvaston Place, SW7
Tel: 071 584 6024

Avon

Adam Gallery, 13 John
Street, Bath
Tel: 0225 480406

Alexander Gallery, 122
Whiteladies Road, Bristol
Tel: 0272 734692

Alma Gallery,
29 Alma Vale Road,
Clifton, Bristol
Tel: 0272 237157

Arnolfini Gallery,
16 Narrow Quay, Bristol
Tel: 0272 299191

Cleveland Bridge Gallery,
8 Cleveland Place East,
Bath
Tel: 0225 447885

David Cross Gallery, 30
Boyces Avenue, Clifton,
Bristol
Tel: 0272 732614

4 Miles Buildings,
off George Street, Bath

Ginger Gallery,
84/86 Hotwell Road, Bristol
Tel: 0272 292527

Kingsley Gallery,
Upper Langridge Farm,
Lansdown, Bath
Tel: 0225 421714

St James Gallery, 9b
Margarets Buildings, Bath
Tel: 0225 319197

Saville Row Gallery,
1 Saville Row, Alfred
Street, Bath
Tel: 0225 334595

Toll House Gallery,
Clevedon Pier Trust Ltd,
The Beach, Clevedon
Tel: 0275 878846

The Patricia Wells Gallery,
Morton House, Lower
Morton, Thornbury, Bristol
Tel: 0454 412288

Bedfordshire

Charterhouse Gallery Ltd,
14 Birds Hill, Heath and
Reach, Leighton Buzzard
Tel: 052523 379

Woburn Fine Arts, 12
Market Place, Woburn
Tel: 0525 290624

Berkshire

Marian & John Alway Fine
Art, Riverside Corner,
Windsor Road, Datchet
Tel: 0753 541163

The Collectors Gallery,
8 Bridge Street,
Caversham Bridge,
Caversham, Nr Reading
Tel: 0734 483663

Emgee Gallery,
60 High Street, Eton
Tel: 0753 856329

Graham Gallery,
Highwoods, Burghfield
Common, Nr Reading
Tel: 0734 832320

Jaspers Fine Arts Ltd, 36
Queen Street, Maidenhead
Tel: 0628 36459

Omell Galleries Ascot,
55 High Street, Ascot.
Tel: 0344 873443

Paravicini, 7 Bridge Street,
Hungerford
Tel: 0488 685173

Buckinghamshire

Christopher Cole (Fine
Paintings) Ltd,1 London
End, Beaconsfield
Tel: 0494 671274

Angela Hone Watercolours,
The Garth, 31 Mill Road,
Marlow
Tel: 0628 484170

Images in Watercolour,
8 The Lagger, Chalfont St
Giles
Tel: 0494 87 5592

David Messum, The
Studio, Lordswood, Marlow
Tel: 0628 486565

Mon Galerie, The Old
Forge, The Broadway, Old
Amersham
Tel: 0494 721705

Penn Barn Gallery, By the
Pond, Elm Road, Penn
Tel: 0494 81 5691

Van Riemsdijk Fine Art,
Seven Gables, Stockwell
Lane, Wavendon
Tel: 0908 582621

Cheshire

Baron Fine Art, 68
Watergate Street, Chester
Tel: 0244 342520

Betley Court Gallery,
Betley, Nr Crewe
Tel: 0270 820652

Harper Fine Paintings,
'Overdale', Woodford Road,
Poynton, Nr Stockport
Tel: 0625 879105

Cleveland

E. & N.R. Charlton Fine
Art, 69 Cambridge Avenue,
Marton, Nr Middlesbrough
Tel: 0642 319642

Cornwall

Art & Antiques,
9 St Nicholas Street,
Bodmin
Tel: 0208 74408

The Broad Street Gallery,
9 Broad Street, Penryn
Tel: 0326 377216

Copperhouse Gallery,
14 Fore Street,
Copperhouse, Hayle
Tel: 0736 752787

David Lay,
The Penzance Auction
House, Alverton, Penzance
Tel: 0736 61414

Penandrea Gallery, 12
Higher Fore Street,
Redruth
Tel: 0209 213134

St Breock Gallery, St
Breock Churchtown,
Wadebridge
Tel: 0208 812543

Tony Sanders Penzance
Gallery, 14 Chapel Street,
Penzance
Tel: 0736 66620

Cumbria

The Gallery,
54 Castlegate, Penrith
Tel: 0768 65538

Peter Haworth, Temple
Bank, Beetham,
Milnthorpe
Tel: 05395 62352

Derbyshire

Ashbourne Fine Art, Agnes
Meadow Farm, Offcote,
Ashbourne
Tel: 0335 344072

Devon

A-B Gallery,
67 Fore Street, Salcombe
Tel: 0548 842764

Birbeck Gallery,
45 Abbey Road, Torquay
Tel: 0803 297144

J Collins & Son
The Studio, 63 & 28 High
Street, Bideford
Tel: 0237 473103

Honiton Galleries,
205 High Street, Honiton
Tel: 0404 42404

New Gallery, Abele Tree
House, 9 Fore Street,
Budleigh Salterton
Tel: 039 544 3768

Beverley J. Pyke,
The Gothic House, Bank
Lane, Totnes
Tel: 0803 864219

Dorset

Alpha Gallery, 21a
Commercial Road,
Swanage
Tel: 0929 423692

Chome Fine Art
2 West Lane, North
Wooton, Sherborne
Tel: 0935 812986

Dorchester Gallery, 10a
High East Street,
Dorchester
Tel: 0305 251144

Hampshire Gallery,
18 Lansdowne Road,
Bournemouth
Tel: 0202 551211

Peter Hedley Gallery,
10 South Street, Wareham
Tel: 0929 551777

York House Gallery,
32 Somerset Road,
Boscombe, Bournemouth
Tel: 0202 391034

East Sussex

Barclay Antiques, 7 Village
Mews, Little Common,
Bexhill-on-Sea
Tel: 0797 222734

Barnes Gallery, 8 Church
Street, Uckfield
Tel: 0825 762066

John Day of Eastbourne
Fine Art, 9 Meads Street,
Eastbourne
Tel: 0323 725634

Old Post House Antiques,
Old Post House, Playden,
Nr Rye
Tel: 079 7280 303

E. Stacey-Marks Ltd, 24
Cornfield Road,
Eastbourne
Tel: 0323 20429

Towner Art Gallery,
High Street, Old Town,
Eastbourne
Tel: 0323 411688

Essex

Barn Gallery, Parvilles
Farm, Hatfield Heath, Nr
Bishop's Stortford
Tel: 0279 731228

Brandler Gallery, 1
Coptfold Road, Brentwood
Tel: 0277 222269

Chappel Galleries,
Colchester Road, Chappel,
Nr Colchester
Tel: 0206 240326

Simon Hilton,
Flemings Hill Farm, Great
Easton, Dunmow
Tel: 0279 850107

Richard Iles Gallery,
10a, 10 & 12 Northgate
Street, Colchester
Tel: 0206 577877

Gloucestershire

Astley House Fine Art,
Astley House, London
Road, Moreton-in-Marsh
Tel: 0608 50601

Gerard Campbell,
Maple House, Market
Place, Lechlade
Tel: 0367 52267

John Davies Fine
Paintings, Church Street,
Stow-on-the-Wold
Tel: 0451 831698/831790

Fosse Gallery, The Square,
Stow-on-the-Wold
Tel: 0451 831319

David Howard, 42 Moorend
Crescent, Cheltenham
Tel: 0242 243379

Kenulf Fine Art Ltd,
5 North Street,
Winchombe, Cheltenham
Tel: 0242 603204

Manor House Gallery,
Manor House, Badgeworth
Road, Cheltenham
Tel: 0452 713953

Heather Newman Gallery,
Milidduwa, Mill Lane,
Cranham
Tel: 0452 812230

Ogle Fine Art, Wellington
Square, Cheltenham
Tel: 0242 231011

Priory Gallery, The Priory,
Station Road, Bishops
Cleeve, Cheltenham
Tel: 0242 673226

Turtle Fine Art, 29 & 30
Suffolk Parade,
Cheltenham
Tel: 0242 241646

Upton Lodge Galleries,
No 6 Long Street, Tetbury
Tel: 0666 503416

Nina Zborowska, Damsels
Mill, Paradise, Painswick
Tel: 0452 812460

Greater Manchester

Corner House, 70 Oxford
Street
Tel: 061 228 7621

The Fulda Gallery,
19 Vine Street, Salford
Tel: 061 792 1962

Hampshire

Alresford Gallery, 36 West
Street, Alresford,
Winchester
Tel: 0962 735286

Bell Fine Art, 67b
Parchment Street,
Winchester
Tel: 0962 860439

Fleet Fine Art Gallery,
1/2 King's Parade, Kings's
Road, Fleet
Tel: 0252 617500

On Line Gallery, 76
Bedford Place,
Southampton
Tel: 0703 330660

J.Morton Lee,
Cedar House, Bacon Lane,
Hayling Island
Tel: 0705 464444

Petersfield Bookshop, 16a
Chapel Street, Petersfield
Tel: 0730 263438

Hereford & Worcester

Coltsfoot Gallery, Hatfield,
Leominster
Tel: 056 882 277

Mark Dilleman Fine Art
15 The Huntings, Church
Close, Broadway
Tel: 0386 852159

Hay Loft Gallery, Berry
Wormington, Broadway
Tel: 0242 621202

Haynes Fine Art, 69 High
Street, Broadway,
Worcester
Tel: 0386 852649

Lismore Gallery, 3 Edith
Walk, Great Malvern
Tel: 0684 568610

Mathon Gallery,
Mathon Court, Nr Malvern
Tel: 0684 892242

John Noott, 14 Cotswold
Court, Broadway
Tel: 0386 852787

Hertfordshire

Countrylife Gallery,
41 Portmill Lane, Hitchin
Tel: 0462 433267

Gallery One Eleven, 111
High Street,
Berkhamstead
Tel: 0442 876333

McCrudden Gallery,
23 Station Road,
Rickmansworth
Tel: 0923 772613

Carole Thomas Fine Arts,
Grange Farm Cottages,
Hexton, Nr Hitchin
Tel: 0582 883337

Humberside

Steven Dews Fine Art,
66-70 Princes Avenue, Hull
Tel: 0482 42424

Isle of Wight

Vectis Fine Arts,
2 Ivy Cottages, Newchurch
Tel: 0983 865463

Kent

Bank Street Gallery, 3-5
Bank Street, Sevenoaks
Tel: 0732 458063

Clare Gallery,
21 High Street, Royal
Tunbridge Wells
Tel: 0892 538717

Graham Clarke Gallery
White Cottage, Green
Lane, Boughton
Monchelsea, Maidstone
Tel: 0622 743938

Graham Gallery, 1 Castle
Street, Tunbridge Wells
Tel: 0892 526695

Mistral Galleries, 12
Market Square,
Westerham

Platform Galleries, 136
Sandgate Road, Folkestone
Tel: 0732 458063

Sundridge Gallery,
9 Church Road, Sundridge,
Nr. Sevenoaks
Tel: 0959 564104

The Weald Gallery, High
Street, Brasted,
Nr.Westerham
Tel: 09595 62672

Lancashire

Neill Gallery, 4 Portland
Street, Southport
Tel: 0704 549858

Studio Arts Gallery, 6
Lower Church Street,
Lancaster
Tel: 0524 68014

Leicestershire

Fine Art of Oakham Ltd,
4 High Street, Oakham,
Rutland
Tel: 0572 755221

Foulds-Field Fine Art,
2 Bidford Court, Bidford
Close, Leicester
Tel: 0533 824364

Goldmark Gallery, Orange
Street, Uppingham,
Rutland
Tel: 0572 821424

The Old House Gallery,
13-15 Market Place,
Oakham
Tel: 0572 755538

Merseyside

Lyver & Boydell Galleries,
15 Castle Street, Liverpool
Tel: 051 236 3256

Middlesex

Hampton Hill Gallery,
203 & 205 High Street,
Hampton Hill
Tel: 081 977 1379

Margaret Melville
Watercolours, 11 Colne
Bridge, Market Square,
Staines
Tel: 0784 455395

W Midlands

Driffold Gallery, The
Smithy, 78 Birmingham
Road, Sutton Coldfield
Tel: 021 355 5433

Graves Gallery, No 3 The
Spencers, Augusta Street,
Hockley, Birmingham
Tel: 021 212 1635

Halcyon Gallery, 50-60 The
Pallasades, Birmingham
Tel: 021 616 1313

Midlands Contemporary
Art, Newhall Court, 59
George Street,
Birmingham
Tel: 021 233 9818

Sport & Country Gallery,
Northwood House, 121
Weston Lane, Bulkington,
Nuneaton
Tel: 0203 314335

Norfolk

Bank House Gallery, 71
Newmarket Road, Norwich
Tel: 0603 633380

Crome Gallery, 34 Elm
Hill, Norwich
Tel: 0603 622827

The Fairhurst Gallery,
13 Bedford Street, Norwich
Tel: 0603 614214

Humbleyard Fine Art,
3 Fish Hill, Holt
Tel: 0263 713362

Staithe Lodge Gallery,
Staithe Lodge, Swafield,
Nr. North Walsham
Tel: 0692 402669

Northamptonshire

Savage Fine Art, Alfred
Street, Northampton
Tel: 0604 20327

North Yorkshire

Sutcliffe Gallery,
5 Royal Parade, Harrogate
Tel: 0423 562976

Nottinghamshire

The Hart Gallery, 23 Main
Street, Linby, Nottingham
Tel: 0602 638707

Anthony Mitchell Fine
Paintings, Sunnymede
House, 11 Albemarle Road,
Woodthorpe, Nottingham
Tel: 0602 623865

Oxfordshire

Bohun Gallery, 15 Reading
Road, Henley-on-Thames
Tel: 0491 576228

The Burford Gallery,
Classica House, High
Street, Bloxham, Nr.
Banbury
Tel: 099 382 2305

H.C. Dickens, High Street,
Bloxham, Nr. Banbury
Tel: 0295 721949

Horseshoe Antiques &
Gallery, 97 High Street,
Burford
Tel: 099 382 3244

The Barry M. Keene
Gallery, 12 Thameside,
Henley-on-Thames
Tel: 0491 577119

The Oxford Gallery,
23 High Street, Oxford,
Tel: 0865 242731

Brian Sinfield Gallery,
Grafton House, 128 High
Street, Burford
Tel: 0993 822603

Wren Gallery, 4 Bear
Court, High Street,
Burford
Tel: 0993 823495

Shropshire

Gallery 6,
6 Church Street, Broseley
Tel: 0952 882860

Haygate Gallery,
40 Haygate Road,
Wellington, Telford
Tel: 0952 248553

Teme Valley Antiques,
1 The Bull Ring, Ludlow
Tel: 0584 874686

Valentyne Dawes Gallery,
Church St, Ludlow
Tel: 0584 874160

Somerset

Julian Armytage,
The Old Rectory, Wayford,
Nr. Crewkerne
Tel: 0460 73449

Martin Dodge Interiors
Ltd, Southgate,Wincanton,
Tel: 0225 462202

Heale Gallery, Curry Rivel
Tel: 0458 251234

Plympton Gallery,
31 West Street, Ilminster
Tel: 0460 54437

Staffordshire

Victoria Des Beaux Arts
Ltd, 11 Newcastle Street,
Burslem, Stoke-on-Trent
Tel: 0782 836490

Wavertree Gallery,
Berkeley Court, Borough
Road, Newcastle-under-
Lyme
Tel: 0782 712686

Suffolk

Equus Art Gallery,
Sun Lane, Newmarket
Tel: 0638 560445

Simon Carter Gallery, 23
Market Hill, Woodbridge
Tel: 0394 382242

Mangate Gallery,
The Old Vicarage, Laxfield,
Nr. Woodbridge
Tel: 0986 798524

John Russell Gallery,
Orwell Court, 13 Orwell
Place, Ipswich
Tel: 0473 212051

Surrey

Alba Gallery,
3 Station Approach, Kew
Gardens, Richmond
Tel: 081 948 2672

Boathouse Gallery, The
Towpath, Manor Road,
Walton-on-Thames
Tel: 0932 242718

Bourne Gallery, 31-33
Lesbourne Road, Reigate
Tel: 0737 241614

Cedar House Gallery
Ripley
Tel: 0483 211221

P. & J. Goldthorpe,
Bicton Croft, Deanery
Road, Godalming
Tel: 0483 414356

Bill Minns
64 Frensham Road, Lower
Bourne, Farnham
Tel: 0252 721621

West Sussex

Susan & Robert Botting,
Felpham, Nr. Bognor Regis
Tel: 0243 584515

Sheila Hinde Fine Art,
Idolsfold House, Nr.
Billingshurst
Tel: 0403 77576

Tyne & Wear

The Dean Gallery, 42 Dean
Street, Newcastle-upon-
Tyne
Tel: 091 232 1208

MacDonald Fine Art, 2
Ashburton Road, Gosforth
Tel: 091 284 4214

Vicarage Cottage Gallery,
Preston Road, North
Shields
Tel: 091 257 0935

Warner Fine Art, 208
Wingrove Road, Fenham,
Newcastle-upon-Tyne
Tel: 091 273 8030

Warwickshire

Colmore Galleries Ltd, 52
High Street, Henley-in-
Arden
Tel: 0564 792938

The Chadwick Gallery, 2
Doctors Lane, Henley-in-
Arden
Tel: 0564 794820

Fine Lines Fine Art Ltd,
The Old Rectory, 31 Sheep
Street, Shipston on Stour
Tel: 0608 662323

Sport & Country Gallery,
Northwood House, 121
Weston Lane, Bulkington,
Nuneaton
Tel: 0203 314335

Wiltshire

Courcoux & Courcoux, 90-
92 Crane Street, Salisbury
Tel: 0722 333471

Lacewing Fine Art Gallery,
124 High Street,
Marlborough
Tel: 0672 514580

Summerleaze Gallery,
East Knoyle, Salisbury
Tel: 0747 830790

Worcestershire

John Noott Galleries, 14
Cotswold Court, Broadway
Tel: 0386 852787

Yorkshire

Kentmere House Gallery,
53 Scarcroft Hill, York
Tel: 0904 656507

James Starkey Fine Art,
Highgate, Beverley
Tel: 0482 881179

The Titus Gallery,
1 Daisy Place, Saltaire,
Shipley
Tel: 0274 581894

Nicholas Treadwell
Gallery, Upper Park Gate,
Little Germany, Bradford
Tel: 0274 306065

Walker Galleries Ltd, 6
Montpelier Gardens,
Harrogate
Tel: 0423 567933

Scotland

Ancrum Gallery, 3
Capelaw Road, Colinton,
Edinburgh
Tel: 083 53340

Laurance Black Ltd, 45
Cumberland Street,
Edinburgh
Tel: 031 557 4545

Bourne Fine Art, 4 Dundas
Street, Edinburgh
Tel: 031 557 4050

Carlton Gallery, 10 Royal
Terrace, Edinburgh
Tel: 031 556 1010

Compass Gallery, 178 West
Regent Street, Glasgow
Tel: 041 221 6370

Flying Colours Gallery,
35 William Street, West
Street, Edinburgh
Tel: 031 225 6776

Gatehouse Gallery,
Rouken Glen Road,
Giffnock, Glasgow
Tel: 041 620 0235

Glasgow Print Studio,
22 King Street, Glasgow
Tel: 041 552 0704

Hanover Fine Arts, 22a
Dundas Street, Edinburgh
Tel: 031 556 2181

William Hardie Gallery,
141 West Regent Street ,
Glasgow
Tel: 041 221 6780

Paul Hayes Gallery,
71 High Street,
Auchterarder, Perthshire
Tel: 0764 662320

Malcolm Innes Gallery,
67 George Street,
Edinburgh
Tel: 031 226 4151

Inverbeg Galleries, Nr
Luss, Loch Lomond
Tel: 0436 86277

Barclay Lennie Fine Art,
203 Bath Street, Glasgow
Tel: 041 226 5413

The McEwan Gallery,
Glengarden, Ballater,
Aberdeenshire
Tel: 03397 55429

Open Eye Gallery, 75/79
Cumberland Street,
Edinburgh
Tel: 031 557 1020

Portfolio Gallery, 43
Candlemaker Row,
Edinburgh
Tel: 031 220 1911

Wales

Philip Davies,
130 Overland Road,
Mumbles, Swansea
Tel: 0792 361766

Rowles Fine Art,
Station House Gallery,
Llansantffraid, Powys
Tel: 0691 828478

Martin Tinney Gallery,
6 Windsor Place, Cardiff
Tel: 0222 641411

Michael Webb Fine Art,
Cefn-Llwyn, Bodorgan,
Anglesey, Gwynedd
Tel: 0407 840336

Betty Williams,
The Gallery, Tyreglwys,
Tredunnock, Usk, Gwent
Tel: 063 349 301

Channel Islands

Coach House Gallery, Les
Islets, St Peters, Guernsey
Tel: 0481 65339

GALLERY HIRE

London

Academia Italiana,
24 Rutland Gate, SW7
Tel: 071 225 3474

Kensington Gallery, 202
Kensington Park Road,
W11
Tel: 071 792 9875

Marsden Fine Art,
21 Dulwich Village, SE21
Tel: 071 836 6252

RESTORERS

London

Bates and Baskcomb,
191 St John's Hill, SW11
Tel: 071 223 1629

John Campbell Master
Frames, 164 Walton
Street, SW3
Tel: 071 584 9268

Chapman Restorations,
10 Theberton Street, N1
Tel: 071 226 5565

The Conservation Studio,
The Studio, 107 Shepherds
Bush Road, W6
Tel: 071 602 0757

Cooper Fine Arts Ltd,
768 Fulham Road, SW6
Tel: 071 731 3421

Deansbrook Gallery,
134 Myddleton Road, N22
Tel: 081 889 8389

Harries Fine Art, 712 High
Road, North Finchley N12
Tel: 081 445 2804

Lamont Gallery,
65 Roman Road, E2
Tel: 081 981 6332

Plowden & Smith Ltd,
190 St Ann's Hill, SW18
Tel: 081 874 4005

Relcy Antiques,
9 Nelson Road, SE10
Tel: 081 858 2812

Woolcock Framing,
8 Huguenot Place,
Wandsworth SW18
Tel: 081 874 2008

Jane Zagel,
31 Pandora Road, NW6
Tel: 071 794 1663

Avon

International Fine Art,
Conservation Studios,
43-45 Park Street, Bristol
Tel: 0272 293480

Pelter/Sands Art Gallery,
43-45 Park Street, Bristol
Tel: 0272 293988

Cambridgeshire

Alan Candy, Old Manor
House, 4 Cambridge
Street, Godmanchester,
Huntingdon
Tel: 0480 453198

Essex

Terry Hilliard, The Barn,
Master Johns, Thoby Lane,
Mountnessing, Brentwood
Tel: 0277 354717

Pearlita Frames Ltd,
30 North Street, Romford
Tel: 0708 760342

Gloucestershire

David Bannister, 26 Kings
Road, Cheltenham
Tel: 0242 514287

Keith Bawden, Mews
Workshop, Montpelier
Retreat, Cheltenham
Tel: 0242 23020

Cleeve Picture Framing,
Coach House Workshops,
Stoke Road, Bishops
Cleeve, Cheltenham
Tel: 0242 672785

Hampshire

Printed Page, 2-3 Bridge
Street, Winchester
Tel: 0962 854072

Middlesex

Hampton Hill Gallery,
203-205 High Street,
Hampton Hill
Tel: 081 977 1379

Northamptonshire

Broadway Fine Art,
61 Park Avenue South,
Abington, Northampton
Tel: 0604 32011

Nottinghamshire

Mark Roberts, 1 West
Workshops, Tan Gallop,
Welbeck, Nr. Worksop
Tel: 0909 484270

Surrey

Boathouse Gallery,
The Towpath, Manor Road,
Walton-on-Thames
Tel: 0932 242718

Limpsfield Watercolours,
High Street, Limpsfield
Tel: 0883 717010

S & S Picture Restoration
Studios, The Rookery,
Frensham, Farnham
Tel: 025 125 3673

Wiltshire

D.M.Beach, 52 High
Street, Salisbury
Tel: 0722 333801

Scotland

Alder Arts, 57 Church
Street, Highland,
Inverness
Tel: 0463 243575

Fiona Butterfield,
Overhall, Kirkfieldbank,
Lanark, Strathclyde
Tel: 0555 66291

FRAMERS

London

John Campbell Master
Frames, 164 Walton
Street, SW3
Tel: 071 584 9268

Chelsea Frameworks, 106
Finborough Road, SW10
Tel: 071 373 0180

Cooper Fine Arts Ltd,
768 Fulham Road, SW6
Tel: 071 731 3421

Court Picture Framers,
8 Bourdon Street, W1
Tel: 071 493 3265

Trevor Cumine, 133
Putney Bridge Road, SW15
Tel: 081 870 1525

Deansbrook Gallery,
134 Myddleton Road, N22
Tel: 081 889 8389

John Jones Frames Ltd,
Unit 4, Finsbury Park
Trading Estate, Morris
Place, N4
Tel: 071 281 5439

Lamont Gallery, 65 Roman
Road, E2
Tel: 081 981 6332

Porcelain & Pictures Ltd,
The Studio, Gastein Road,
W6
Tel: 071 385 7512

Railings Gallery, 65
Roman Road, E2
Tel: 071 935 1114

Woolcock Framing, 8
Huguenot Place,
Wandsworth, SW18
Tel: 081 874 2008

Essex

Pearlita Frames Ltd,
30 North Street, Romford
Tel: 0708 760342

Gloucestershire

Cleeve Picture Framing,
Coach House Workshops,
Stoke Road, Bishops Cleve,
Cheltenham
Tel: 0242 672785

Surrey

Boathouse Gallery,
The Towpath, Manor Road,
Walton-on-Thames
Tel: 0932 242718

Limpsfield Watercolours,
High Street, Limpsfield
Tel: 0883 717010

Scotland

Inverbeg Galleries, Nr
Luss, Loch Lomond
Tel: 0436 86277

LIGHTING

London

Chatsworth Commercial
Lighting, 6 Highbury
Corner, N5
Tel: 071 609 9829

Kent

St John A Burch,
Myrtle House, Headcorn
Road, Grafty Green
Tel: 0622 850381

Surrey

Acorn Lighting Products,
21a Kings Road, Shalford,
Guildford
Tel: 0483 64180

INSURANCE

London

Crowley Colosso Ltd,
Ibex House, Minories, EC3
Tel: 071 782 9782

Miller Art Insurance,
Dawson House 5 Jewry
Street, EC3
Tel: 071 488 2345

J. H. Minet, Minet House,
100 Leman Street, E1
Tel: 071 481 0707

Dorset

Gibbs Hartley Cooper,
Beech House, 28-30
Wimborne Road, Poole
Tel: 0202 660866

Oxfordshire

Penrose Forbes, 29-30
Horsefair, Banbury
Tel: 0295 259892

West Sussex

Bain Clarkson Ltd,
Harlands Road, Haywards
Heath
Tel: 0444 414141

ART
CONSULTANTS

London

Art Image,
1/5 The Garden Market,
Chelsea Harbour, SW10
Tel: 071 352 8181

Arts Direction, 60 Albert
Court, Prince Consort
Road, Knightsbridge, SW7
Tel: 071 823 8800

PHOTOGRAPHERS

London

Prudence Cuming
Associates Ltd, 28/29
Dover Street, W1
Tel: 071 629 6430

Flashlight, Unit 15, 7
Chalcot Road, NW1
Tel: 071 586 4024

PICTURE PLAQUES

London

A C Cooper Ltd, 10 Pollen
St, W1
Tel: 071 629 7585

Picture Plaques,
142 Lambton Road, SW20
Tel: 081 879 7841

Somerset

Berkeley Studio, The Old
Vicarage, Castle Cary
Tel: 0963 50748

SHIPPERS

London

Featherston Shipping,
24 Hampton House, 15-17
Ingate Place, SW8
Tel: 071 720 0422

Hedleys Humpers Ltd,
Units 3 & 4, 97 Victoria
Road, NW10

Middlesex

Burlington Fine Art &
Specialised Forwarding,
Vulcan International
Services Group, Unit 8,
Ascot Road, Clockhouse
Lane, Felthem
Tel: 0784 244152

GLASS

London

Rankins (Glass) Company,
The London Glass Centre,
24-34 Pearson Street, E2
Tel: 071 729 4200

SECURITY

London

Ambassador Security
Group plc, 4 Blake House,
Admirals Way, Docklands,
E14
Tel: 071 538 1327

Simba Security Systems
Ltd, Security House,
Occupation Road,
Walworth, SE17
Tel: 071 703 0485

SERVICES

London

Art Loss Register, The
Hogg Group, 1, Portsoken
Street, E1
Tel: 071 480 4000

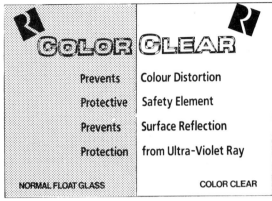

Auctioneers
the South of England

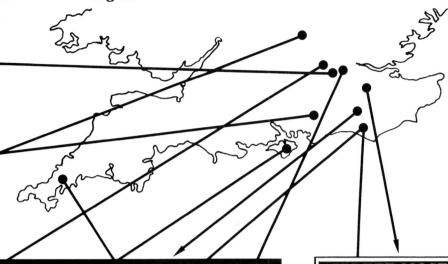

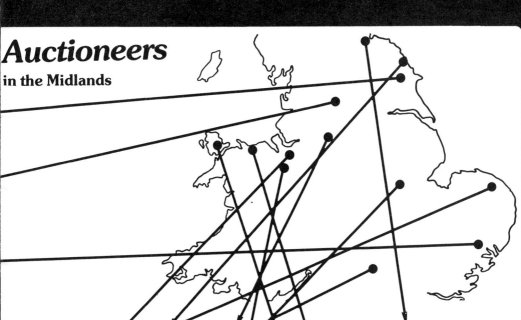

Auctioneers
in the Midlands

H.C.CHAPMAN & SON

Chartered Surveyors   **Established 1903**
MEMBERS OF THE SOCIETY   OF FINE ART AUCTIONEERS

*INDEPENDENT
AUCTIONEERS & VALUERS*

offering

**MONTHLY SALES OF FINE
ART & ANTIQUES**

**SALES EVERY WEEK
OF VICTORIAN AND
LATER HOUSEHOLD
FURNISHINGS &
COLLECTABLES**

**VALUATIONS FOR
INSURANCE,
PROBATE &
FAMILY DIVISION**

H. C. CHAPMAN & SONS
Estate Office & Salerooms: The Auction Mart, North St.
SCARBOROUGH (0723) 372424

F. W. Allen & Son
Established 1924

Regular, General and Specialist
Sales. Professional
valuation service available

Central Salerooms
15 Station Road
Cheadle Hulme, Cheshire
Tel: 061-486 6069
Fax: 061-485 7534

Lithgow Sons & Partners
(Established 1868)
North East Auctioneers

Antique House
Station Road, Stokesley
Middlesbrough
Cleveland TS9 7AB
Tel: 0642 710158
Fax: 0642 712641

MORGAN EVANS & CO LTD.

**GAERWEN, ANGLESEY
NORTH WALES**
*Monthly sales of antique furniture, collectables,
paintings and 'Welsh' fine art (Saleroom 1).
Fortnightly sales of household and general goods
(Saleroom 2).*

Head Office: 30 Church Street, Llangefni
Anglesey. **(0248) 723303**
Saleroom: (0248) 421582. Fax: (0248) 750146

ROGERS JONES CO.

FURNITURE & FINE ART AUCTIONEERS
Probate & Insurance Valuers

Antique Furniture
Collectables and
Paintings every
last Tuesday in the month

Regular Specialist Sales
of 'Welsh' Fine Art

**The Saleroom, 33 Abergele Road,
Colwyn Bay, Clwyd LL29 7RU
Telephone (0492) 532176 24 hrs.
Fax (0492) 533308.**

Wingett's

Fine Art Auctioneers

Auctioneers covering the North West

Valuations for Probate and Insurance

Monthly Antique Auctions

Weekly General Sales

**Head Office and Auction Galleries
29 HOLT STREET, WREXHAM, CLWYD
LL13 8DH TEL: (0978) 353553**

INDEX TO ARTISTS

640

THESAURUS
ART MARKET INFORMATION

The **Thesaurus** Computerised Information Service processes in excess of 2.5 million lots from over 465 auction houses each year throughout the British Isles.

Thesaurus searches daily for items of fine art, antiques and collectables that meet the criteria of each individual subscriber. Whenever lots are matched with clients' instructions, **Thesaurus** sends by post or fax all the details of the forthcoming sales with the full auction lot descriptions. E-Mail facilities are also available.

Once you have received the information, the rest is up to you.

Thesaurus complements the Miller's Price Guides, which have been designed to give readers the opportunity to evaluate items that they may wish to buy, sell or insure. Whether professionals or amateurs, **Thesaurus** subscribers are able to find where items are offered for sale.

This information gives you knowledge and insight, enabling you to participate more effectively in today's increasingly competitive market place.

INFORMATION WORKING FOR YOU
THESAURUS

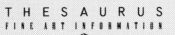

INDEX TO ADVERTISERS